The
Technique
of
PHOTOMICROGRAPHY

POTASSIUM BI-TARTRATE CRYSTALS × 100 (POLARIZED LIGHT)

The Technique of

PHOTOMICROGRAPHY

DOUGLAS F. LAWSON
F.I.B.P., F.R.P.S., F.R.M.S., F.Z.S.

LONDON
GEORGE NEWNES LIMITED
TOWER HOUSE, SOUTHAMPTON STREET,
STRAND, W.C.2

First published 1960

PRINTED AND BOUND IN ENGLAND BY
HAZELL WATSON AND VINEY LTD
AYLESBURY AND SLOUGH

PREFACE

I HAVE written this book with a view to providing some help and inspiration for laboratory workers and amateur and professional photographers who wish to embark upon photomicrography. The photomicrographs illustrated, which range from low- to high-power magnifications and include a variety of subjects, have been obtained by use of numerous techniques, with the exception of electron photomicrography. I have also referred to infrared, ultra-violet, X-ray, fluorescence and interference photomicrography, which are used in industry and research and which play an important part in medical photography.

It is hoped that *The Technique of Photomicrography*, written after many years of work with the microscope in the laboratory, will be of assistance to those already experienced in research, medicine, industry, natural history, etc., and to all scientific branches of Her Majesty's Forces.

No pen, pencil or brush, however skilfully used, can produce the accuracy of a photomicrograph. In order to master the technique of photomicrography the worker must have a knowledge of the optical layout of the microscope and of all methods used to produce a photograph through its lenses.

In my research work I have examined rare and otherwise unobtainable specimens with my microscope and camera, and I wish to thank Dr. J. Farquharson, F.R.I.C., for his permission to reproduce illustrations of some of these uncommon subjects.

I collected and mounted much of the illustrated material while I was engaged in compiling a library of several hundred fixed slides. My keen interest in natural history has contributed to enlarging the collection.

I would particularly like to thank Mr. R. G. W. Ollerenshaw, M.A., M.R.C.S., F.I.B.P., F.R.P.S., for reading the manuscript and checking the drawings, and for his helpful suggestions. To Professor S. Tolansky, D.Sc., F.R.S., and Dr. M. H. F. Wilkins I should like to express my gratitude for their supplying me with photomicrographs of less common subjects.

I am indebted to R. & J. Beck Ltd., Mr. E. J. G. Beeson (A.E.I. Lamp & Lighting Co. Ltd.), Boone Instrument Co., New York, General Electric X-ray Corporation, Milwaukee, Langham Photographic Instruments Ltd., E. Leitz (Instruments) Ltd., Philips Electrical Ltd., Photovolt Corporation, New York, C. Reichert A.G., Vienna, Sylvania Electric Products, Inc., New York, W. Watson & Sons Ltd. and Carl Zeiss, Jena, for the use of illustrations and information; and to the Editor of *Endeavour* (Imperial Chemical Industries Ltd.) and C. Reichert A.G., Vienna, for the use of colour blocks.

I should like to thank my sister Dulcie for her readiness to help at all times, Mr. K. Austin for making several pieces of equipment for me, and Mr. E. Broome for checking the bibliography.

Finally, I wish to express my gratitude to the publishers for their co-operation, which has been enjoyed at all times.

D. F. L.

CONTENTS

LIST OF PLATES

COLOUR PHOTOMICROGRAPHS

I

INTRODUCTION

AT the beginning of the fifteenth century the simple and compound microscopes then in use were known as fleaglasses and flyglasses, probably because fleas and flies were the first subjects to be viewed through them. As photography had not then been invented, sketches were the only means of recording the wonders of nature discovered through the microscope. The first compound microscope was simply an inversion of the telescope and was made by Galileo in 1609; little interest, however, appears to have been aroused. About twenty years later Kepler produced a better form of microscope, which was capable of clear low-power magnifications. It is on record that the capabilities of this instrument were most impressive.

In the middle of the fifteenth century a prominent worker by the name of Cesi used his microscope to study stems, leaves, pollens, spores and many other botanical subjects. It must have been a great inspiration to observe, for instance, the minute spores of the fern or transparent pollen grains. These subjects are today still difficult to study and photograph, and it is quite impossible to see the spores while they are actually being thrown out of the sporangia of the fern.

In the year 1850 photography was in its infancy and the microscope was also a rudimentary instrument, the optical system being far from perfect. Considering the problems of photographic recording with the microscopes of those days, the results obtained were very creditable, particularly since only wet plates were available at that time. The introduction of dry emulsion vastly simplified photomicrography, which is now recognized as constituting a highly specialized branch of photography.

Great advances have been made in the design and construction of microscopes during the past few years and various types of photomicrographic cameras and microscopes are now specially constructed for photomicrography. These special models are to be found in industry, hospitals and research laboratories. In addition, the electron microscope has extended the field of microscopy. Nevertheless, very many microscopes like the one illustrated in Plate 4 (*upper*) are still in use in homes where photomicrography is a hobby; often such a microscope has been handed down from father to son. Many laboratory workers, also, are striving to produce photomicrographic records with the simplest equipment. For these and others about to explore the fascinating subject of photomicrography, this book is written with the hope that they may derive some benefit from its pages.

Photomicrography has become an important branch of applied science in industry, many problems being solved through this medium. A worker taking up photomicrography as a career must acquire a working knowledge of the microscope as well as a knowledge of photography, while the microscopist has only the photographic technicalities to learn. The photographer, on the other hand, has to master the optical system of the microscope and apply his photographic knowledge. Without a sound grasp of both microscopy and photography, good work cannot be produced.

During the past twenty years the properties of the various stains have been greatly improved. Staining a specimen correctly in no way damages any delicate structure in the subject chosen; on the contrary, it will assist in differentiating tissues.

The great progress which has been made in optics offers the photomicrographer special systems, which enable subjects not usually visible through the normal optical system to be seen clearly. With the development of these specially constructed optical accessories, the range of interesting photomicrographic subjects has become unlimited.

It is suggested that those about to take up this work should first devote some time to photographing small subjects which are too large to be photographed through the microscope, preferably immobile subjects such as large mounted specimens of flies, spiders, parasites, corals, small flowering plants, mosses, the delicate underside of leaves and insects' wings. Small moving subjects can then be dealt with, the valuable information gained when photographing 'stills' being used to advantage. Minute moving subjects present many problems to the photomicrographer, subjects such as vorticella being a good example.

Another problem which repeatedly confronts the photomicrographer is that of illumination, which is almost always carried out with artificial light. The proper control of illumination requires much practice and great patience before the many small pitfalls can be avoided.

Ragged, untidy, dirty specimens will not make the best photographic subjects. There are many important opportunities for exhibiting photomicrographs and naturally only those of the highest standard are suitable. Obviously there is scope for judges to deal with work submitted for exhibition purposes in the field of photomicrography. A scientific print should not be retouched or defaced in any way; the true record of the subject should be retained. A bad negative cannot produce a good print and over-enlargement is to be avoided. It should not be forgotten that the camera does not cover up failures caused through insufficient care being taken in the use of the microscope.

Although many colour processes are available today, there does not appear to be any marked progress in colour photomicrography. Obviously, only a few workers are taking advantage of this development, owing perhaps to its high cost.

2

PHOTOMACROGRAPHY

THE fact that in the amateur world little is heard of this branch of photography, which is usually taken to include reproduction from actual size to ×20, suggests that photomacrography is not practised very much. In the professional scientific field, however, photomacrography is used quite extensively and proves invaluable.

An enlarged photograph of a minute object taken with a camera together with a microscope is known as a photomicrograph. An enlarged photograph of a small object taken without the aid of a microscope is called a photomacrograph. A microphotograph would be a minute picture and would require to be viewed through a microscope. It is most unfortunate that the term microphotography is often used in scientific literature when, in actual fact, reference is being made to a photomicrograph. Drawings made from images projected from a microscope are referred to as micrographs.

Photomacrography is less likely to confuse the pictorial worker than is photomicrography, as only one lens and an ordinary camera body are used. Plate 1 illustrates one means of obtaining a photomacrograph; other methods will be described later. Small objects with details barely visible to the naked eye require magnifying up to twenty times or so if they are to become of real value for record or scientific purposes. To obtain such magnifications it is not necessary to use a complex optical system such as that of the microscope. A simple camera lens suffices, and the details of opaque and transparent specimens may be obtained with reflected or transmitted light.

Photomacrography bridges the gap which exists between photomicrography and straightforward photography. Certain features involved in the design of the optical system of a microscope introduce some curvature of the field of view (Fig. 1). Unfortunately, an object lying in a flat plane may produce an image lying in a curved plane. Depending upon the degree of curvature of the image, it may not be possible to focus the central and peripheral zones of the image simultaneously. Therefore,

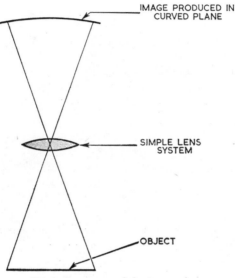

IMAGE PRODUCED IN
CURVED PLANE

SIMPLE LENS
SYSTEM

OBJECT

Fig. I. Curvature of the image plane

when one photographs fairly large objects under the microscope, some difficulty arises in getting the whole field sharp. When one photographs subjects such as that shown in Plate 17, an instantaneous exposure is necessary, which means that the light must be bright and the emulsion–developer combination fast. These factors govern the lens aperture and shutter speed; even so, however, exposures may be surprisingly long. Electronic flash will permit the use of a much smaller aperture and very much shorter exposure, resulting in a far greater depth of field.

A selection of the many subjects which require photomacrography is shown in Plates 17 to 19, and 20 (*upper*).

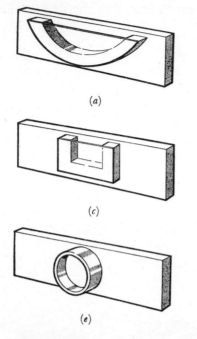
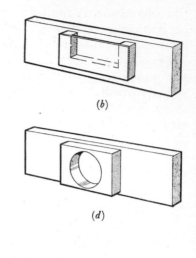

(a)

(b)

(c)

(d)

(e)

Fig. 2. Prepared slides for housing fluids

APPARATUS

In this branch of photography there are limitations as to the
types of camera which can be used successfully. The most suitable
is a plate camera equipped with treble bellows extension and
having simple movements of lens panel and camera back. Both
vertical and horizontal camera arrangements are suitable. The
former is mostly favoured, especially for photographing tadpoles,
static mounted and unmounted specimens, but there are some
subjects, such as pond life, which cannot be recorded except in the
horizontal (Plate 21 (*lower*)) and must be mounted in one
of the first three slides shown in Fig. 2. This diagram shows a
series of slides composed of fused microscope cells. Such slides are
invaluable and can be used with either a vertical or horizontal
camera arrangement. They are not cemented in any way, but are
fused together, and will withstand normal heat and acids. Cameras
such as the bellows type are best fitted with short-focus lenses,
ciné-camera lenses or low-power objectives. If the camera does
not have treble bellows, or even double bellows length, the
requisite extension can be provided by bringing the lens forward
by means of a metal tube, an improvised cardboard roll or even

an extension box built on to the camera (Fig. 3). When possible, it is suggested that the camera lens should be reversed, that is, with the back lens facing the specimen. This position of the lens usually provides the best results since the optical conditions are similar to those for which they were designed. Specially constructed lenses for macro work should not, of course, be reversed. Focusing

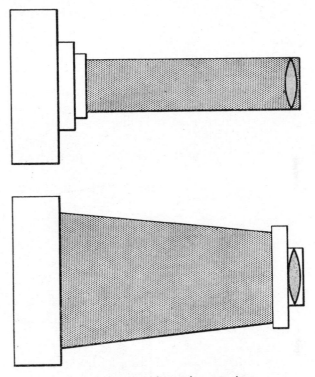

Fig. 3. Bellows and lens tube extensions

is carried out by raising and lowering the camera into its approximate position, after which fine focusing can be carried out in the normal manner. A ground-glass screen for accurate observation of the image is essential. By using a 2- or 3-in. lens it is possible to get within a few inches of the specimen but, of course, the depth of field is decreased accordingly. In view of this, a small aperture is needed to give greater depth; when small moving creatures are photographed, however, a small aperture becomes a handicap, as an instantaneous exposure is demanded.

The subject shown in Plate 17 proved to be very difficult to photograph, because working at such close range automatically created little depth of field, as can be seen by the out-of-focus area. Critical focusing on a certain point was carried out and a fairly large aperture used. Plate 20 (*lower*), however, was static, which enabled a long exposure to be given.

Since the magnification of the negative image is controlled by two factors, lens and camera bellows extension, it can be calculated by the following formula:

magnification $m = l-f/f$, where l is the lens-to-emulsion distance and f the focal length of the lens. Therefore, with a 3 in. lens and 21 in. bellows length, a magnification of $\times 7$ is obtained.

To give additional magnification, an auxiliary lens can be used (see Fig. 4 and Plate 13). If the lens is uncorrected, difficulty will be experienced in filling the whole negative area without some detail falling away at the edges. Aplanatic magnifiers are, however, available. These are triplet lenses cemented

Fig. 4. Simple auxiliary pocket lens

together, giving a large flat field with excellent definition, and are superior to the single-lens magnifier.

Another method of giving extra magnification is the use of a converging spectacle lens of the meniscus type. A meniscus lens should be fitted in front of the existing lens, and a range of these lenses, which can be purchased quite cheaply from an optician, should, therefore, be to hand. The existing filterholder, or an improvised holder, can be used to house the lenses.

Reflex cameras, fitted with interchangeable lenses, are suited to this work, but the lenses must be fitted to a somewhat long tube to give greater magnification. The subject can be viewed in the reflex mirror right up to the time of exposure. With this type of camera particular care should be taken to ensure rigidity when the shutter is operated. When it is held in the hand, there is a tendency to move the camera as the shutter is being released and this must be avoided.

Twin-lens reflex cameras are not altogether suitable for this work, because two of everything must be procured, which entails additional expense. When using taking-lens and finder-lens as one apparatus, focusing is carried out in the usual way. To obtain an idea of the field covered with a Rolleiflex camera, the supplementary lens attachment can be fitted over the finder-lens, which is very effective in correcting the new field of view.

For miniature cameras such as the Leica, Exakta and Contax, there are interchangeable lenses and many other accessories for close-up photography. Spacing rings to extend the lens take the place of bellows and are very satisfactory. Some miniature cameras require an optical device for near focusing, while with others no difficulty is experienced, as the focusing mount of the lens remains the same and normal fine adjustment can be carried out. The greatest difficulty when using a miniature for photomacrography arises from the lack of a focusing screen, which makes it difficult to examine the whole of the image before the picture is taken.

The Aristophot II is ideal for this branch of photography, enabling translucent and opaque specimens to be photographed with the utmost precision and ease. Fairly large specimens, up to $3\frac{3}{4}$ in. in diameter, can be mounted and covered with the Summar or Milar series of lenses. The interchangeable stage, having insets with different apertures, can be selected to suit the particular object-field diameter. The specially designed lamphouse carries a stage for inserting the illuminating lenses and the specimen stage is adjusted vertically by rack and pinion. After the bellows length has been adjusted as required, focusing takes place by movement of the object stage. With objectives of short focal length, fine focusing is carried out by rack-and-pinion movement of the lens carrier. Final focusing can be adjusted by inspection of the image on the ground-glass screen. This particular macro-camera can also be equipped for use with transmitted and polarized light, and photographs may be taken with either the bellows camera or a Leica.

When the photomacrographic arrangement is used in incident light, the specimen is placed on the base plate of the Aristophot and illuminated by the ring illuminator. Adjustment is made vertically along the auxiliary bar attached to the base. The subject can be illuminated from all sides, or a cast shadow can easily be arranged by disengaging any one or more of the lamps. The ring illuminator consists of four lamps which can be adjusted and inclined at will. Alternatively, the 6-volt 5-amp lamp can be used.

ILLUMINATION

The recording of fine detail demands a great deal of skill in both vertical and oblique lighting and is of great importance. The lighting can either make or mar a picture. As the area to be photographed is small, it is more difficult to record detail; the light, therefore, must be arranged to make the best possible picture.

The shadows should help to tell the story when a vertical plan view is taken. Shadows of legs and body may be used to reveal an insect, which is normally camouflaged against the leaf upon which it rests. In a case such as this, therefore, the shadows need to be both dark and sharp.

There is no hard-and-fast rule as to the form of lighting to be used, but the 500-watt Photoflood lamps fitted into reflectors have many advantages. Lamps of lesser wattage can be used to good advantage, but the exposure time must be increased accordingly. Good results can be obtained by using one light in a reflector, together with a strong white sheet or card, which acts as a second reflector and lightens the shadows. Results free from shadow can be obtained by photographing the object on a piece of sheet glass acting as either an easel or a table-top. Various coloured backgrounds can be placed some distance from the glass, and these can be arranged to be out of focus, to leave the object standing out sharply against an evenly illuminated and shadow-free background.

With a working distance of only a few inches, it is essential to use a lens hood to prevent stray light from entering the lens. With small transparent specimens mounted on microscope slides, it is advisable to use a small microscope lamp or a × 3 or × 6 pocket lens, acting as a condenser. The slide may be placed about 6 in. above or in front of a sheet of white paper and the light-spot concentrated on the paper immediately beneath the slide. Great care must be taken to prevent glare or reflection from the glass cell and slide. On occasions it may not be possible to remove a specimen from its natural surroundings to the indoor equipment; in such instances there is no alternative but to make the best use of existing light. Shadows are accentuated in photomacrography and, in view of this, a diffused light is desirable. When insects are in a hibernating state, which usually means that they are in a dark corner, a pocket torch can safely be used, provided a sufficiently long exposure is given.

FILTERS

Care should be taken in the choice of filters (Plate 25). Money is always well spent on a set, and in the absence of a complete set one or two main colours are invaluable. When photographing insects and mounted stained specimens, a filter is almost always necessary to emphasize the part which is required. This re-introduces the problem of exposure, as the light absorbed by the filter necessitates an increase in exposure. Consideration must be given to the various colours of the subject in order to make it stand out from its background. Many specimens are double- or treble-stained, and in such cases it may be required to differentiate one particular tissue from the rest.

Let it be imagined that the section has been stained both green and red. If a red filter is used, red-stained tissues will become light in tone and the green-stained dark. Conversely, if a green filter is used, the green becomes light and the red dark. The point to remember is that a filter will lighten its own colour and at the same time darken the complementary colour to a degree. Filters can be either used between the light-source and the subject, if a lens system is employed, or placed at the back of the lens. In the former case the filter does not interfere with the sharpness of the image, but bad filters anywhere near the lens (back or front) can play havoc with sharpness.

SENSITIVE MATERIAL

As has already been implied, photomacrography is a scientific tool and the emulsion chosen will make or mar the final record, as in photomicrography. A first-class negative, which will produce a good print without any retouching, is absolutely essential. Retouching and print finishing is such a fine art today that the ultimate print can be a complete transformation of the original specimen; a scientific print, however, must be a true recording without any after-work, otherwise it ceases to be of value.

A hard-and-fast rule cannot be laid down as to the type of emulsion to be used, but certain recommendations can be made. Soft Gradation Panchromatic and P.1200 plates, or similar panchromatic films, are equally good, and on many occasions an orthochromatic plate can be put to good use. When a range of emulsions which give the best results has been found, it is advisable to use it exclusively. Some workers switch from one to another, which results in a poor standard of work. The O.250 emulsion gives both speed and a reasonably balanced colour rendering, which are often very necessary requirements in this field of photography. When photographing moving subjects, one is sometimes forced to use a panchromatic emulsion to eliminate possible movement. Panchromatic material, of course, does not resolve as many lines per millimetre as some orthochromatic emulsions; it is, therefore, a case of image movement as against resolution. Many emulsions have been used in the illustrations of this book, each emulsion having its own particular use. If a fast panchromatic emulsion is used, this may cause some trouble with large grain size.

Mention will be made later of fine-grain processing. Speed and grain are closely related and should always be treated as a joint problem before the exposure is made; afterwards it is too late to rectify any errors. Fine-grain developers, such as D.76, should be used and the developing technique standardized. By these methods enlargements can be obtained, but if the original negative does not contain sufficient detail no amount of enlarging will make any improvement—in fact the reverse would be the case.

PHOTOMACROGRAPHS BY PROJECTION

When the macro apparatus is not to hand, certain subjects can be projected through the enlarger on to either a negative or a piece of bromide paper. These reproductions in macro form can be very satisfactory. This method can be used only with transparent objects which are mounted on a microscope slide with a cover slip, thus sandwiching the specimen.

The method used is as follows. A piece of black card is cut to the overall size of the enlarger negative carrier. In the centre of the card is cut an aperture allowing the slide to be placed over it. The specimen slide is then fastened to the card and put in the negative carrier in the normal way (Fig. 5). When focusing and adjusting the size of the image one should substitute a piece of white card for the plate, while the specimen is in the negative carrier. It is advisable to put some sort of block on the enlarger-table top, thus making sure that when the plate is put into position in the dark it is in the correct place, the positioning of the image having first of all been done with safe light on. The enlarger lens is then stopped down appropriately and the exposure is made in the same way as for a bromide print. The exposure can be found with an exposure meter. When greater degrees of enlargement are required, it is advisable to use a short-focus lens, and in this case the bellows length is reduced considerably.

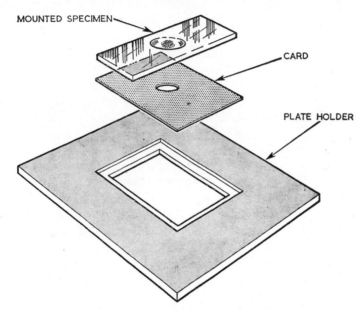

Fig. 5. Negative carrier as used for projection

Fig. 6 illustrates another method of illumination, designed by the author. (A microscope can also be used with this.) Its main purpose is to enable translucent subject-matter to be photographed when lying or mounted on transparent material. Precipitation bands which are formed in a thin ($\frac{1}{4}$-in.) layer of agar gel are seen in Plate 23. Owing to the faintness of many of the bands and the closeness of the bands to each other, difficulties arise in attempting to obtain good photographic definition and resolution. There is no limit to the number of subjects which can be photographed with this apparatus (Plate 16). The aperture surrounding the specimen can easily be reduced by spacing rings which eliminate stray light.

To achieve a permanent record of the scientific information

contained on a gel plate it is essential that a true reproduction
of the band patterns, which can be very complex, be obtained
(Plate 23). Free-hand drawings of the patterns are not entirely

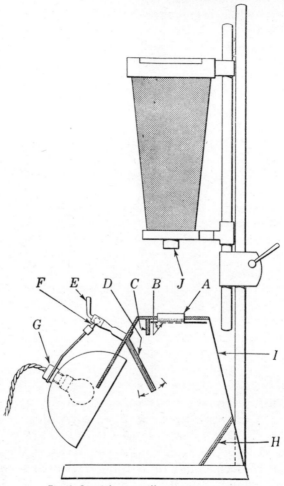

Fig. 6. Special macro illuminating set-up

A, Petri dish (specimen); B, glass support; C, baffle plate; D, adjustable baffle plate
and white reflector; E, ball joint lock; F, ball joint; G, 500-watt Photoflood; H,
reflector; I, body painted dead black; J, $4\frac{1}{2}$ in. focal length lens
(Manufactured by Shandon Scientific Co. Ltd.)

satisfactory; they are tedious to carry out and subject to observa-
tional error and unconscious psychological bias. Unconsciously
the eye can see what does not exist and overlook what does.

The camera, therefore, is the best available tool for recording the bands formed in Ouchterlony plates. The arrangement of the apparatus can be followed from Fig. 6. *A* is the specimen or Petri dish which rests on a glass plate *B*. The top of the housing has an aperture in the centre sufficiently large to allow the specimen to fit in, and at the same time prevent light from passing around it and entering the lens. *C*, acting as a baffle plate, prevents the edge of the Petri dish or mounted specimen from receiving an uneven amount of light. *D*, an adjustable baffle plate and reflector, throws an even scattering of light through the underside of the Petri dish or specimen. *E*, the ball-joint lock, locks the lamp adjustment ball joint and arm. *G*, a 500-watt Photoflood light, can be easily adjusted to illuminate in all directions. The light is directed on to a black velvet base, and some light is reflected from this and the white surface of *D* and reflector *H*. These surfaces reflect diffuse light which passes through the gelatine at oblique angles, thus clearly illuminating the precipitation bands. Direct light rays do not pass through the specimen. The inside of the housing, *I*, is painted dead black and is heat resisting. Lens *J* is used at all times at $f/22$. Filters can be used to enhance the illumination. It has been found that no material other than black velvet reflects such an even amount of soft light.

With this arrangement, various magnifications can be obtained. In addition to this, enlarged images can be made from clearly defined bands and other subjects which lie almost touching. A $4\frac{1}{2}$-in. focal length lens was used, but any reasonable focal length may be used to give any desired degree of magnification attainable with the available bellows extension.

Plate 23 illustrates the use of the special illumination described above. The highly illuminated lines stand out clearly against the black background, but in actual fact the lines are the same density as the medium in which they are formed. This means of illumination is very similar to dark-ground illumination, also described in this book. These two illustrations were chosen from a number and represent the various line formations.

3

THE MICROSCOPE

IN this chapter the construction and component parts of the microscope are surveyed briefly. Each component part will be dealt with in detail separately.

The eyepiece is the uppermost part of the microscope (Plate 3) and fits into the head of the draw tube. When photographs are to be taken through the eyepiece a metal collar, forming a light-tight trap, is placed around it, thus preventing stray light from passing into the camera and fogging the plate. The draw tube is a smooth sliding fit in the body tube in which it is firmly retained without any slackness. The body tube, carrying the draw tube, is operated by a rack and pinion, which provides the coarse focusing adjustment. This is supplemented by a fine focusing control to provide the necessary adjustment, thus allowing a greater degree of accuracy when focusing high-power objectives.

At the base of the body is the objective, which is fitted by means of a thread. In some instruments there is only a single objective, but a revolving nosepiece is frequently fitted to house two, three, four and sometimes five objectives. The main support of the microscope is known as the limb, and this is connected to the foot by means of a hinged joint, thus allowing the instrument to be used in a vertical or horizontal position. The stage, on which the specimen slide is carried, is positioned approximately in the centre of the microscope and runs at right angles to the axis of the body tube. A mechanical stage is often fitted, and this allows the specimen slide to be moved as desired in any direction. Directly beneath the stage is placed the substage, which is also on a rack and pinion, allowing the substage condenser free movement up or down. Slightly below the condenser are the iris diaphragm and filterholder and directly beneath them is the tailpiece housing the mirror. The mirror mounting allows either the concave or plane side of the mirror to be used.

The microscope should be kept in good condition, so that the body tube always moves smoothly and freely in both directions without any play being evident on either the coarse or fine adjustments. The function of the coarse adjustment is to move the body tube in line with the optical axis until the object is clearly seen, the alignment being maintained by means of a sliding dovetail which fits into the upper section of the limb.

The fine adjustment is of the greatest importance. It should work with precision without any play and be sensitive to the slightest touch. Fine adjustments vary according to the particular make of instrument, but all respond to the same firm and delicate touch. Both coarse and fine adjustments are operated by a milled head, the former being the larger. In many of the latest models the milled head of the fine-focusing control is graduated to a high degree of precision, commonly 1/500th of a millimetre, corresponding to the up and down movement of the body. The fine adjustment plays a far more important part when working with a 2-mm. or $\frac{1}{12}$-in. objective. The focal depth of these objectives is very limited, so that absolute precision and stability are required in the whole of the focusing mechanism.

The draw tube is sleeved into the body tube. It is sometimes actuated by rackwork; this is not essential, but it is often of great assistance. Many draw tubes are held only by friction. In either case, however, they may be withdrawn to suit the particular objective in use. The draw tube is graduated and is usually used at 160 mm., though some objectives require 170 mm. All draw tubes are well marked in heavy numerals, with an engraved line around the circumference. It is imperative that the tube length be adjusted to that recommended by the makers of the objective, if the utmost resolution is to be attained. In addition, adjustment of the draw tube allows for correction when one works with cover glasses of varying thicknesses. A wide draw tube (50-mm.) is recommended, to avoid any possibility of internal reflections; if the draw tube should be narrow, the interior may be lined with black paper or velvet to prevent reflection from stray light within the tube.

The mechanical tube-length and optical tube-length will be referred to later on.

The limb is quite a simple part of the microscope. It carries the optical parts and allows them to be operated in vertical or horizontal positions. The upper end of the limb carries the body tube and the lower portion supports the stage, substage and bracket holding the mirror. Both limb and body tube are, of course, machine made. Their accuracy is as nearly perfect as possible, thus guaranteeing parallelism between the mechanical and optical axes.

The foot is attached to the lower part of the limb by means of a hinged joint, which allows easy movement from the vertical to the horizontal and vice versa. The hinged joint sometimes carries a locking nut, the necessity for which is a question of personal taste. When deciding upon a microscope for photomicrography, one should take special care to ensure that the foot stands absolutely firm and flat. It should be sufficiently heavy to allow the instrument to operate without having to be clamped down and should also give adequate support when in the horizontal position.

The stage can be either round or square and has a central circular aperture which allows the light to pass from source to objective, between which is placed the specimen. The stage should be firm, as pressure is often put upon it when placing Petri dishes and other relatively large objects in position. Vibration must be avoided, as this can completely spoil photographs taken with high-power objectives. All stages should be fitted with two clips, which hold the slide firmly in position. Modern microscopes have a mechanical stage which allows the object to be moved smoothly in all directions while one searches for a particular field. Should a microscope not have this particular fitting, an attachable mechanical stage can be purchased which will fit almost any microscope.

The built-in mechanical stage is far better, as there is less likelihood of its being displaced from its true right angle to the optical axis. Should the stage develop this fault, it will be impossible to bring the two outer edges of a flat field into focus simultaneously. If the slide is slightly tilted, owing perhaps to a minute piece of foreign matter under it, the same effect will be evident, and the higher the degree of magnification the more evident the fault becomes. The mechanical stage is of great value in searching for a particular field in high-power photomicrography. The slightest movement of the slide is amplified many times on the ground-glass or viewing screen; the operator must, therefore, exercise great care when manipulating the stage.

Another indispensable use of the mechanical stage is in searching for actively moving microscopic organisms. When they have been found, the difficulty is to hold them in the field of focus long enough to photograph them. As can be seen, this difficulty has been overcome by the mechanical stage, used with the observation eyepiece, which enables the object to be seen right up to the time of exposure. When using a ciné-camera on moving objects, the mechanical stage allows the operator to keep the subject in view by means of free movements at right angles one to the other. The stage is operated by independently milled heads, easily accessible and responsive to the touch of thumb and forefinger, which allows approximately 2 in. of the 3-in. microscope slide to be examined.

The centring mechanical stage is the most useful of all stages. Like many others, it allows the specimen to be revolved and is, therefore, helpful when positioning the image on the ground-glass screen in readiness for photographing. It is particularly useful when examining crystals under polarized light. There are mechanical stages on the market which have been especially designed for attachment to any make of microscope, whether fixed- or rotating-stage. Attachable mechanical stages can also be procured from Golder & Co. These stages give 40 mm. lateral movement, and a forward slide movement of 30 mm. is obtained by the use of an accurate skew-cut rack and spiral-cut pinion which reduces possible backlash. The scales are divided into millimetres as with other stages.

The electrically heated warm stage is a great asset when a subject has to be maintained at a certain temperature. The warm stage can be purchased from several well-known makers of microscopes. The maximum temperature of some is 1,800°C, while others reach only 50°C; nearly all are thermostatically controlled. This piece of valuable equipment is most compact, being approximately 3 × 3 in. and $\frac{3}{4}$ in. in depth. It has the normal clips which hold fast the microscope slide. An American development in warm stages now enables the melting or other critical temperatures of minute quantities of material to be observed both accurately and easily. These methods are now being used in the examination of fibres and the analysis of drugs, amino acids and other materials. High-temperature microscopy has also been applied to metals, oxides, ceramics and minerals. The warm-stage technique has also been used to study organic chromatograms on cotton threads and paper, and in most cases a camera may be used to record the various changes as they take place.

The cold stage is an invaluable piece of apparatus in many fields of research, although some subjects do not lend themselves to this treatment; great care is necessary in the interpretation of the results. The development of these stages is rapidly advancing, and at present it is possible to conduct a controlled study within the range -100 to $+100°$ C. The melting-points of waxes and resins, etc. may readily be obtained by the cold-stage technique.

The substage is also of very great importance to the photomicrographer. What has already been said about the other parts can be applied to it. It is essential to have a substage condenser for medium- and high-power work using transmitted light. Good results, however, can be obtained without a substage condenser when operating with low power. Plates 33(d), and 36(c) were recorded without a substage condenser. The substage houses the condenser, iris diaphragm and sometimes a filterholder, these having free movement in the direction of the optical axis to ensure accurate adjustments and focusing. The substage condenser should be free from any lateral movement, so as to prevent the optical system from being out of alignment or the light rays from being off the optical axis after leaving the condenser. The iris must also be in true alignment, as this controls the angle of light passing through the condenser.

When high-power work is to be done, the use of the centring type of substage condenser is recommended. It is then possible to alter the position of the condenser at right angles to the optical axis, thus ensuring perfect alignment. Although this is mentioned, it is felt that the centring type of substage condenser is not an essential piece of apparatus and that with care it can certainly be omitted. The authors photomicrographs in this book, apart from those taken with phase-contrast illumination, were taken without the aid of a centring substage.

Directly beneath the substage condenser is an iris diaphragm. This should be used in conjunction with the light-source and the condenser in use. This enables the amount of light passing through the condenser to be regulated at will. Many microscopes are fitted with a filterholder below the iris. It is easily accessible and swings in and out of the light path through the instrument, but this addition is not an essential piece of the equipment. Sometimes the lamphouses make provision for the filters. The mirror has already been mentioned.

Plate 28(*b*) was taken with the inclusion of a blue filter and Plate 25(*a*) with a green. Filterholders capable of holding more than one filter are sometimes necessary. Two filters were used when making photomicrographs illustrated in Plates 33(*b*) and 49(*a*).

MAINTENANCE AND CARE

If looked after at all times, the microscope should never be in need of repair; in order to get the best from the instrument it is necessary to keep all movable and optical parts in perfect adjustment.

The microscope is a precision-made instrument which calls for a great deal of skill in handling and a thorough knowledge of its application to scientific work. Great care is put into the making of a microscope, and if equal care is put into its maintenance and use, the instrument should be as good as new after many years of regular use. Unfair wear and tear is detrimental to the instrument. If the slides show signs of play, coarse and fine adjustments soon fail to respond to the touch.

To maintain unimpaired efficiency, care should be taken to keep the instrument away from damp, as this is harmful to the optical parts as well as the movable parts. Always wipe off any stray water which may have been spilt on the mechanical stage, which should move as freely as any other part of the instrument. To enable this particular part of the microscope to respond to sensitive adjustments, it must be kept free from dust and foreign matter of all descriptions. Dust will cause the moving parts to wear far more quickly than will constant use. Surplus grease should be removed from the microscope because this is often the cause of many layers of dust clinging to movable parts, the combination of grease and dust having an abrasive effect. When not in use, the microscope should be placed in its case. If the instrument is set up and cannot be moved, then a cover should be placed over it.

After using oil for immersion purposes the stage should be thoroughly cleaned. A *little* xylol on a soft rag will quickly remove

surplus oil, but if immersion oil is allowed to dry on the microscope, it becomes very difficult to remove and in doing so damage
may be caused. The slides of the mechanical stage should work
freely and smoothly. When the movable parts show signs of jerki-
ness it is time to attend to the lubrication: the slides should be
lightly smeared with the correct lubricant, after which the stage
should be worked backwards and forwards and from side to side,
to enable the grease to work well under the slides. It is recommended that the apparatus be taken to pieces only by an expert.

To enable the coarse and fine adjustment to work smoothly
without side shake or slackness, careful usage and maintenance is
necessary. The bearings must not be stiff; this is as bad as excessive oiling or greasing. If there is any slackness or play, it will be
particularly evident when working at high magnifications. These
fine bearings must also be kept free from dust, as this can cause
damage if allowed to enter into the closely fitting joints.

On occasions it has been known for the rack-and-pinion
adjustments to become loose, thereby allowing the tube to slide
slowly downwards towards the mounted specimen. This movement, of course, quickly throws the focusing out and can have
some effect on the photograph. A badly adjusted instrument is
practically useless. Minor adjustments must be undertaken with
great care and a careful tightening up of the one adjusting screw;
too much tension is as bad for the instrument as not enough.
Before adjusting the rack and pinion, remove both slide and
objective from the microscope in case the adjusting screw is
turned the wrong way, which would allow the tube to fall quickly.
If an objective is left on the instrument the lower objective lens
may be damaged. All movable parts of the microscope should be
under proper control, the movement ceasing immediately the
milled head is released.

The revolving nosepiece rarely causes any trouble, as very
little dust can work its way into the movable parts. Should a little
oil be needed, the revolving nosepiece is easily removed by the
centre screw, thus allowing the interior to be lubricated.

The optical system needs careful handling and should not be
touched unless absolutely necessary. Some workers prefer to leave
the objectives attached to the nosepiece when not in use, and also
the eyepiece. Cases are, however, provided for housing both
objective and eyepiece.

Care should also be taken of the lenses when in use. Many are made from soft material and, being highly polished, are very easily scratched or damaged by careless usage.

It is advisable, before focusing on the specimen, to lower the tube towards the subject by the coarse adjustment until the lower lens of the objective is just clear of the cover glass. This operation is carried out by bending down and getting level with the slide and lower lens of the objective and then watching the objective to prevent it from colliding with the slide. Before focusing, bring the tube away from the specimen, thus making sure that the lower objective lens does not in any way come into contact with the cover glass. It is advisable always to work away from the subject with the tube. Often objectives become damaged because the operator has looked down the tube when focusing towards the specimen, and has passed through the point of focus without realizing this until the objective comes to rest on the slide. This must, of course, be avoided.

These optical glasses quickly become tarnished by contact with chemicals. Many chemicals give off vapours which also cause oxidation on the lens. The optical glasses should be protected against this and should be properly cleaned before they are stored away. As has been pointed out, some optical parts are very soft and easily scratched; this will not happen if a lens tissue, soft cambric or soft fabric is used. On no account should a pocket handkerchief be used to clean the optical system. The back lens of an objective should be cleaned with a soft camel-hair brush. Avoid finger marks on the polished surfaces and never take the lens to pieces. Should the front lens need cleaning, it is advisable to use a lens tissue which has been slightly moistened with alcohol or a *little* xylol. If too much is used it may loosen the lens.

Eyepieces should be kept stored in their cases, unless of course they are used to prevent dust from falling down the tube on to the back lens of the objective. In such cases a cover should be placed over the eyepiece.

An oil-immersion objective cannot be used unless it is put into immersion oil, and this results in its getting dirty; therefore, the lens should be cleaned immediately after use. If left to dry, the oil becomes difficult to remove, thus creating a greater risk of damage to the delicate front lens.

When the substage is being racked down, care should be taken to prevent it from falling out on to the table when clear of the pinion teeth. If this is likely to occur, a folded selvyt cloth or

similar material should be placed below the stage. Some microscopes have been made to overcome this fault, the V-grooves
being sprung together with the pinion. Mention was made earlier
of the objective lens coming into contact with the cover glass.
Equal care should be taken to prevent the top lens of the condenser
being forced up against the underside of the slide. If this is allowed
to take place when oil immersion is used, a triple damaging effect
is possible, i.e. to the objective lens, specimen and condenser lens.

The care of the microscope and its optical parts has now been
discussed briefly, and it is felt that a few words about the glass
slides would not be amiss. It is well known that absolute cleanliness
is essential if the manipulation of the microscope is to be successful.
Used slides can be cleaned and re-used time and time again if they
are soaked and boiled in a weak solution of sulphuric acid and
bichromate. A quick rinse in running water will remove all traces
of acid and the slides can then be polished with a soft cloth and a
little alcohol. It is not advisable to re-use cover glasses, as these
are fragile and lead to a large number of breakages; it is quicker
and more efficient to purchase new covers.

At all times it should be remembered that the microscope is a
precision-made instrument.

4

OBJECTIVES AND EYEPIECES

THE most important part of the microscope is the optical system. This consists of the following:

(*a*) the objective—a combination of lenses, which magnifies the object;

(*b*) the eyepiece or ocular—a combination of lenses situated in the top of the draw tube;

(*c*) the substage condensers—a series of detachable lenses used for controlling the illumination of the specimen;

(*d*) collecting lens or lenses used between substage condenser and light-source.

The sole purpose of the objective is to produce a magnified image of the specimen under examination. This image is further magnified by the eyepiece, which projects it either for viewing with the eye or into a position where it may be recorded on a photographic emulsion.

When an objective is being selected, one of the main considerations is the magnification of which it is capable. Other characteristics to be considered are: its working distance, focal length, numerical aperture, depth of field and diameter of field, and faults peculiar to some optical systems. The earliest objectives were of simple construction, with lenses of short focal length and of one type of glass. In time the objectives were improved and were made of two types of glass; today some are made of three or even four.

The quality and resolution of the final image cannot be better than that produced by the objective; its actual magnification, however, depends upon a number of other factors. These are: the magnification (or power) of the eyepiece; the tube-length employed on the microscope; and the bellows extension provided between the eyepiece and the photographic emulsion. Each objective is corrected for a particular tube-length. Most manufacturers use a length of 160 mm. This is by no means standard, however, and care should be taken to ensure that the microscope body-tube extension is correctly set for each objective. If a cover glass is used, of thickness other than that for which the objective is corrected, the tube-length must be amended accordingly; here the manufacturer's literature may be of help. In the absence of precise information, the body tube may be adjusted while the image is inspected for optimum clarity and contrast. As the thickness of the cover glass is decreased, the optimum tube-length for any given objective is increased. Care should also be taken that the figures engraved on the side of the body tube allow for the presence (or absence) of any multiple-objective holder which may be fitted.

When a microscope is bought there is, as a rule, a set of two

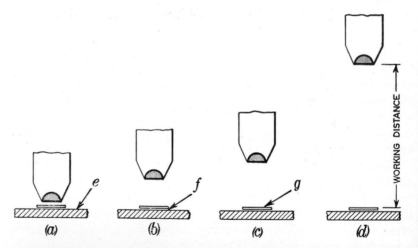

Fig. 7. Comparison in working distances of various apochromatic objectives
(a) 4 mm. = 0·18 mm.; (b) 16 mm. = 5·0 mm.; (c) 25 mm. = 14·0 mm.; (d) 3 in. = 92·0 mm.; (e) microscope slide; (f) specimen; (g) cover glass

or three objectives, which usually cover the range from low to high power. These leave some gaps in the degree of magnification which can be attained, and it is desirable that further objectives be obtained to cover as wide a range of magnification as possible. Plates 27(a), 29(d) and 40(b) were all taken with the same eyepiece, but the objectives used ranged from 25 mm. to 4 mm.; the magnifications are recorded.

The working distance of an objective is the distance between the cover glass (focusing on the specimen) and the lower surface of the bottom lens of the objective (Fig. 7). This must not be confused with the focal length of an objective, which is measured from the lower focal plane of the lens. Low-power lenses have the greater working distance, and the greater the magnification the less the working distance becomes. In other words, the magnification increases as the working distance and focal length of an objective decrease.

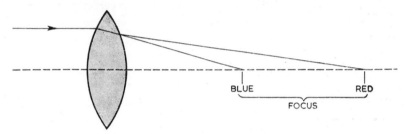

BLUE   RED

FOCUS

Fig. 8. Chromatic aberration

TYPES OF OBJECTIVE

There are three general types of objective in use in photomicrography today: achromatic, semi-apochromatic and apochromatic. The choice of objective depends upon the use for which it is required, the difference between the various types being the degree of correction for chromatic and spherical aberrations and, of course, flatness of field.

Chromatic aberration is the inability of a lens to bring light of all colours to a common focus. The total angle of refraction of a beam of light passing through a simple lens depends partly upon the wave-length (i.e. the colour) of the light. This is the effect often demonstrated by projecting a narrow parallel beam of white light through a prism, when the emerging beam of light is separated into all the colours of the spectrum. The chromatic aberration of a simple lens is illustrated in Fig. 8.

Spherical aberration arises when rays passing through the central and outer parts of a lens system are not brought into focus at the same distance from the lens. This defect is illustrated diagrammatically in Fig. 9. It clearly becomes more serious as the effective diameter (or aperture) of the lens is increased.

These and other faults are minimized in all good objectives by the use of glasses of varying refractive indices, together with a suitable design and arrangement of the individual component lenses.

Achromatic objectives are corrected for spherical aberration for one colour only, usually yellow-green; for chromatic aberration these objectives are corrected for two colours of the spectrum (Fig. 8). In view of this there is always some part of the spectrum which is not covered by such a lens system. Achromatic objectives

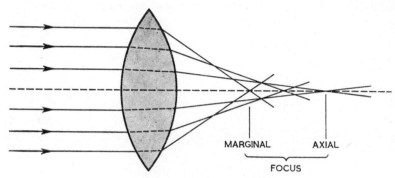

Fig. 9. Spherical aberration

can be used successfully only when the specimen is stained to the colour for which the objective has been corrected. In the case of an unstained specimen a suitable filter can be used in the light train.

The semi-apochromatic objective is more highly corrected than the achromatic type, and this is usually achieved by the incorporation of a fluorite lens in the system. These objectives are not manufactured in as wide a range of focal lengths as are achromatic and apochromatic objectives. W. Watson & Sons, Ltd. manufacture 16-mm., 8-mm., 4-mm. and 2-mm. semi-apochromatic objectives. They claim that although these objectives have no fluorite components, they are equal in performance to those with fluorite. The fact that these are termed fluorite objectives is somewhat confusing. In spite of the introduction of the fluorite lens into the semi-apochromatic objective, it is still not on a par with the fully apochromatic objective. The working distances of the Watson parachromatic objectives are almost double those of the corresponding apochromatic objectives. They are as follows: 2 mm.–0·23 mm.; 4 mm.–1 mm.; 8 mm.–1·5 mm.; and 16 mm.–7 mm.

Apochromatic objectives are strongly recommended for use in photomicrography, since they are corrected for spherical aberration in two colours; for chromatic aberration they are corrected for the three colours, red, green and blue. Such objectives should always be used when photographing treble-stained specimens and for all colour work. For photomicrography these objectives are undoubtedly the best, giving finer structure and a more perfect colour correction. Furthermore, an eyepiece giving a higher magnification can be used without introducing deterioration of the image near the edge of the field. With the exception of the 2-mm., these objectives give a greater numerical aperture than achromatic objectives.

The recently introduced Leitz flat-field objectives are a boon to the photomicrographer. It has always been very difficult to obtain a wide area of view having a marginal sharpness on a par with the central. These objectives are, therefore, an outstanding advance in the development of microscope equipment. They are available in a range of focal lengths and the surfaces of the lenses are coated to minimize internal reflections, glare and resulting lack of contrast in the image. The ×40, 4·63-mm. N.A. 0·65 objective and the ×100, 2·43-mm. N.A. 1·32 oil-immersion objective also have a spring-loaded front mount which provides a measure of protection to both the lens and the specimen.

The Leitz flat-field objectives of ×4 and ×10 magnification are not provided with spring mounts. Whenever either of the high-powered objectives is used in a multiple-objective holder with other lenses, extra care must be exercised when changing objectives, since the flat-field objectives are about 8 mm. longer than ordinary objectives. In any case, whenever working with medium- or high-power objectives, unless they are absolutely parfocal (i.e. adjusted so that their lower lenses come into exactly the same position as they are interchanged), one should always rack the body tube up, interchange the objective and then rack down until the objective is almost in contact with the specimen. The eye may then be applied to the eyepiece and the objective racked up until the image appears. Thus there is no danger of pushing the objective against the specimen or cover glass when it is swung into place, or of ramming the objective down into the specimen when attempting to focus the image. Leitz periplanatic 170-mm. eyepieces are recommended for use with these objectives.

Carl Zeiss, Jena, however, have recently completed a number of flat-field achromatic objectives termed Planachromats. The individual magnifications are ×2·5, ×10, ×16 and ×40 (oil immersion). When used with a Zeiss flat-field eyepiece, they produce a flat image of the whole of the observed area.

No flat-field objectives were used for any of the illustrations in this book, although they have been used by the author.

The ultra-violet reflecting objectives have lower numerical apertures and a higher obstruction ratio than conventional objectives. Several makers have produced an objective with a N.A. of 0·65 and an obstruction ratio of 0·35; such objectives can be used only with special ultra-violet microscope equipment.

Apropos of objectives, the following may be of interest. L. V. Foster, of Bausch and Lomb Optical Co., states in *Analytical Chemistry*, **21**, 433, that Bausch and Lomb apochromatic objectives are so well corrected for chromatic and spherical aberrations that they give excellent images in ultra-violet illumination, and that the use of a P 25 image tube ensures their being in focus from 5,461 Å to 3,659 Å. B. K. Johnson developed (*Proc. Phys. Soc. Lond.* (1939), 1034–9) in 1939 a 25-mm. objective, using lithium fluorite and fused quartz. He claims that this objective was sufficiently well corrected for chromatic and spherical aberrations over a range from 2,550 Å to 4,000 Å to enable the inventor to focus in visible light and photograph in ultra-violet without re-adjusting the focus.

Objectives are manufactured in many focal lengths, the most common of which are:

4 in.	100 mm.
3 in.	75 mm.
2 in.	50 mm.
1 in.	25 mm.
$\frac{2}{3}$ in.	16 mm.
$\frac{1}{3}$ in.	8 mm.
$\frac{1}{6}$ in.	4 mm.
$\frac{1}{12}$ in.	2 mm.

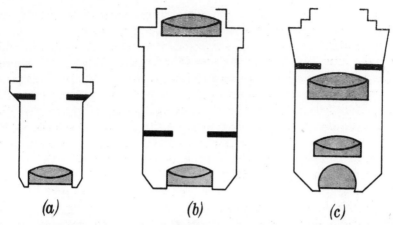

Fig. 10. Optical construction in low- and medium-power objectives
(a) 3 in. objective; (b) 25 mm. Holos., 0·30 N.A.; (c) 8 mm. apochromatic, 0·55 N.A.

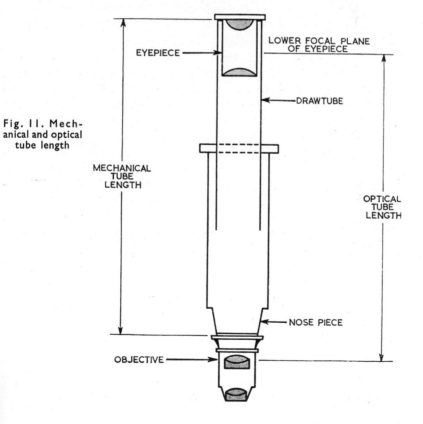

Fig. 11. Mech-
anical and optical
tube length

Some manufacturers list their 2-in., 3-in. and 4-in. systems as macrolenses, while others refer to them as objectives.

The differences between these objectives having been pointed out, the function of the various focal lengths can now be discussed. When high magnifications are required, both objective and eyepiece should be used. In addition, some considerable increase in magnification can be obtained by the use of the bellows extension, and even by further enlargement through the enlarger. Care must be taken, however, to ensure that the image is not overmagnified. An objective can resolve only a certain amount of detail, and a good rule is to limit the magnification to 1,000 × the numerical aperture of the objective. This rule should be broken only if the final image is to be projected for viewing at a distance. If a pocket camera or one of the Macca type is used the magnification will depend solely upon the optical combination of the objective and eyepiece in use.

No doubt, the chapter dealing with photomacrography has caused the dividing-line between photomacrography and photomicrography to be questioned. It is obvious that these two applications of photography do encroach upon each other. Some photographic lenses of short focal length will give a magnification of approximately twenty diameters, whereas some objectives of long focal length will not give magnifications as high as this. For low magnifications anastigmatic lenses are very useful, because of their greater degree of correction for field curvature and their wider field of view. In low-power photomicrography one of the most important considerations is the flatness of the field; this decreases as the N.A. of the objective increases. Should an objective of low power fail to give a sharp image of both the centre and the edges at the same time, a small aperture should be introduced. This may be done either by means of an iris diaphragm or a disc of black paper with a small aperture placed over the back lens of the objective. The use of a small aperture ensures a greater depth of field but, of course, also increases the exposure time. Low-power objectives can be used successfully without an eyepiece, preferably in conjunction with a wide draw tube. Greater skill in handling the microscope and optical system is necessary when working at low magnifications.

It is extremely difficult—perhaps impossible—to state with accuracy where the series of low-power objectives ends and the high-power objectives take over, since many medium-power

PLATE I. UNA CAMERA AND LENS ADAPTER

Quarter-plate Una camera in working position (*upper*) with special lens-holder which replaces the camera lens and is threaded to take low-power objectives.   This fitting allows subjects which are too small for normal photography and too large for photomicrography to be photographed.   The camera shutter, iris and focusing are handled in the normal manner.

A 3-in. objective fitted to the lens-holder is reproduced actual size (*lower*).

PLATE 2.   LINHOF CAMERA WITH LEITZ MICROSCOPE

The author is shown using a Linhof camera with a Leitz microscope, Linhof tripod, and Baker intensity lamp.   The camera is swung into the vertical by means of a swivel ball-top fitted to the tripod.   Camera bellows give extra magnification but must, of course, have extra support if fully extended.

COMPONENT PARTS OF MICROSCOPE

A. Light-trap ring.
B. Coarse adjustment.
C. Fine adjustment.
D. Limb.
E. Stage adjustment (lateral).
F. Stage adjustment (forward movement).
G. Mechanical-stage attachment nut.
H. Joint.
I. Foot.
J. Eyepiece.
K. Draw-tube.
L. Body-tube.
M. Revolving nosepiece.
N. Objectives.
O. Stage.
P. Slide-holder.
Q. Substage.
R. Iris (substage).
S. Filter.
T. Tailpiece carrying mirror.
U. Reversible mirror.

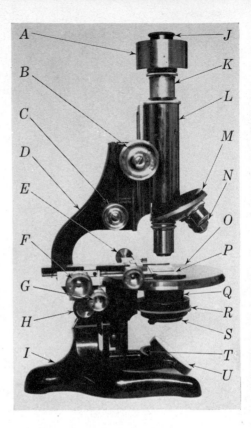

(left) SIMPLE ARRANGEMENT FOR TRANSMITTED ILLUMINATION

Watson quarter- and half-plate micro camera as frequently used by the author. The metal baseboard of the camera is firmly secured by the frame fixed to the top of the box. The hole in the box and camera baseboard are always in alignment. A Beck intensity lamp can be seen in the specially constructed housing, permitting direct vertical illumination. The box must be made of strong material and be absolutely firm so that the microscope and camera are rigid.

PLATE 3

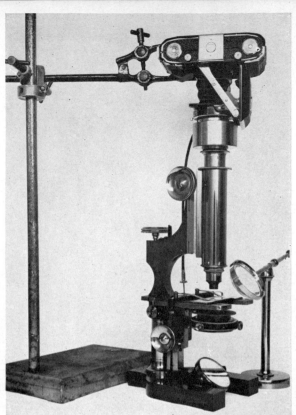

SIMPLE PHOTOMICRO-
GRAPHIC SET-UP

Zeiss Ikon camera in use with Watson microscope (see page 162).

(*right*) ADVANCED
APPARATUS

The Watson Holophot research microscope with vertical camera and illumination combination (see page 163).

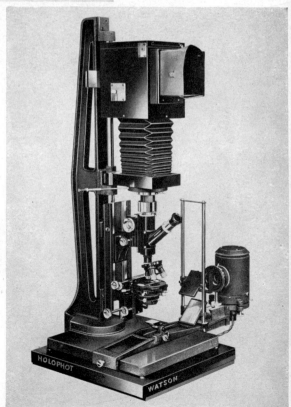

PLATE 4

PLATE 5. LEITZ WETZLAR PANPHOT

The Leitz Panphot research model with built-in xenon illumination (see page 165).

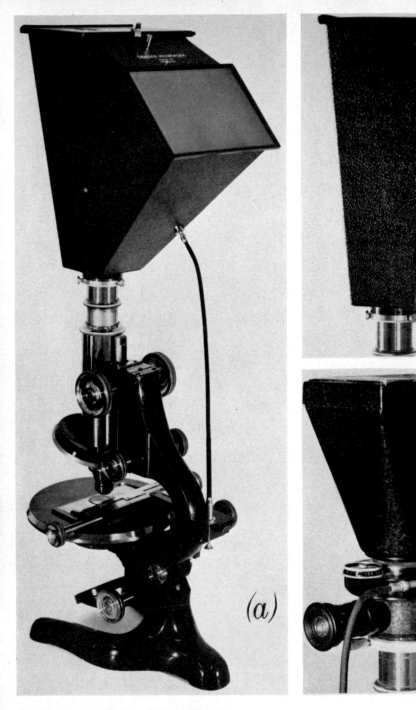

PLATE 6. CAMERA ATTACHMENTS

(a) The Golder Microflex camera fits over the eyepiece and takes $2\frac{1}{4} \times 3\frac{1}{4}$-in. plates or cut film. It has a free-moving reflex shutter. The image is clearly seen on a very fine ground-glass screen up to the time of exposure (see page 161).

(b) E.C.2. camera attachment also takes $2\frac{1}{4} \times 3\frac{1}{4}$-in. plates or cut film. The viewing screen is situated on the top of the attachment (see page 162).

(c) The Leitz Macca $\frac{1}{2} \times$ camera attachment takes $6 \times 4\frac{1}{2}$-cm. plates. The Leitz Makam $1 \times$ also fits the microscope. With both cameras the subject can be seen before, during and after the exposure. Shutter speeds: T.B. 1/125, 1/50, 1/10, 1/5, 1/2 and 1 second (see page 161).

EYEPIECE AND LENS OF BOX CAMERA

The camera lens must not touch the eyepiece for fear of vibration. The light-protective ring should be used at all times to prevent stray light from reaching the photographic image, as this would cause slight fog through the space between the camera lens and eyepiece.

AKER PHASE-CONTRAST OUTFIT

The phase illustrations in this book were all produced by using this outfit (which fits any microscope) in conjunction with a Leitz microscope. *Left to right:* phase contrast substage apparatus; × 10 PH, 16 mm., N.A. 0·25 objective; viewing and centring microscope; × 40, mm., N.A. 0·73 objective.

PLATE 7

PLATE 8.   BAKER INTENSITY LAMP AND STEREO-PHOTOMICROGRAPHIC TILTING STAGE

(a) The Baker intensity lamp used with the microscope in the horizontal and a box camera.   A camera with a fixed lens and focused on infinity produces good photomicrographs (see page 160).

(b) This stage (shown approximately actual size, with a 3-in. slide) gives a tilt of 7° on either side.   It is operated by a thumb-screw on

PHOTOMICROGRAPHIC EXPOSURE METER

This meter has been made to take various eyepieces, which fit tightly to the photo-cell by means of a collar with a quick release. The overall size is $4\frac{1}{2} \times 5 \times 3$ in. (see Figs. 52 and 53).

(a)

(b)

(a) POLARIZING ATTACHMENTS

The polarizer on the left takes the place of the substage condenser, and the analyser on the right fits on to the objective and nosepiece.

(b) POLARIZER AND ANALYSER IN POSITION (see Fig. 63)

PLATE 9

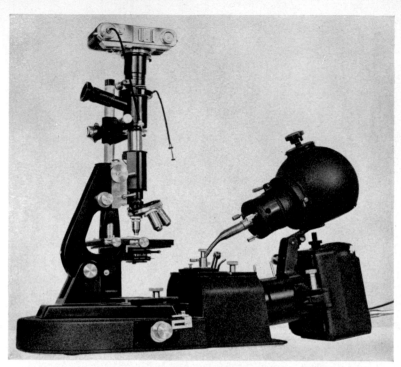

THE REICHERT FLUORESCENCE MICROSCOPE AND
CAMERA (see page 149)

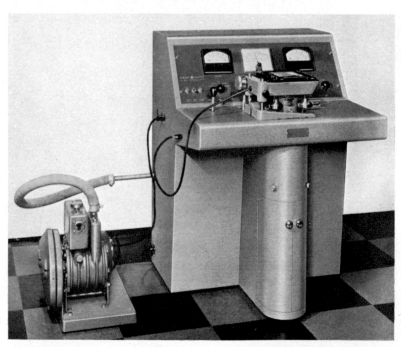

THE GENERAL ELECTRIC X-RAY MICROSCOPE AND CAMERA
(see page 153 and Fig. 90)

PLATE 10

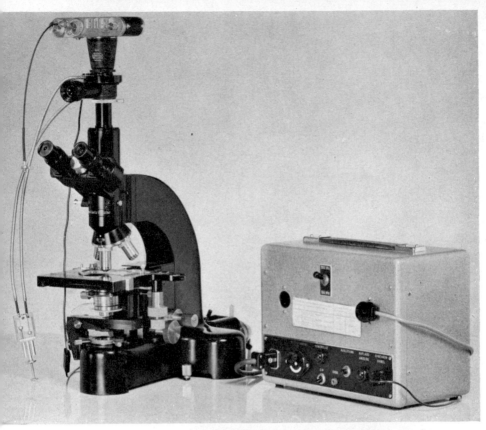

PLATE 11. ORTHOLUX MICROFLASH

(above) Microflash apparatus fitted to Leitz Ortholux research microscope.

(right) Microflash attached to substage of Leitz Ortholux microscope (see page 184). The small flash container is fixed immediately under the substage condenser, which is accurately adjusted to the optical path of the microscope by means of set screws.

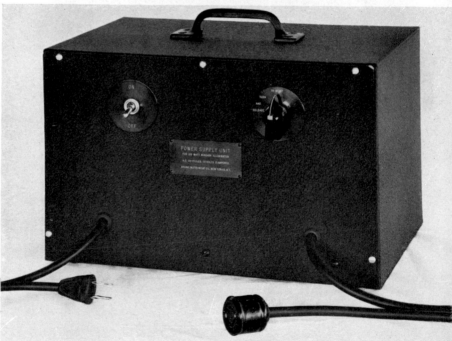

PLATE 12. 'MIKRARK' ZIRCONIUM-ARC LAMP (*upper*) AND POWER
SUPPLY UNIT (*lower*)

The power supply unit contains apparatus for rectification, starting current, and running current. It operates on a.c. or d.c. (see page 83).

CROMETER AND SCALE LINE

The micrometer is used to determine the precise magnification obtainable with any
rticular arrangement. It normally consists of a finely divided scale engraved on glass.
t is placed on the object stage and its image focused on the screen, the magnification
ay be calculated by dividing the length of the image by the actual length of the observable
rt of the scale. The inset scale here is × 20.

UXILIARY POCKET LENS IN USE

An auxiliary lens may be used either for viewing a minute object or, as illustrated, to
e greater magnification and detail, as seen in the shadow area, not visible to the
ed eye. The fine chain on either side of the lens is × 2.

PLATE 13

PLATE 14.
INTENSITY LAMP

The image of a 6-volt, 30-watt intensity lamp as seen on the ground glass when the source is correctly centred and critical illumination is ensured. Here the lamp filaments are magnified × 14.

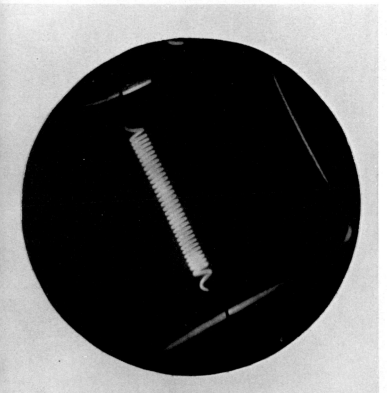

The filaments of a 12-volt, 24-watt intensity lamp. This type of lamp is used by the author in the apparatus shown in Fig. 31, and is seen here × 14 (see page 158).

PLATE 15.   MONO-CYCLOHEXYLAMINE CRYSTALS, × 10 (total × 40)

Mono-cyclohexylamine poured on to slide and allowed to crystallize overnight. This subject could almost be classified as a pictorial.   A successful 20 × 16-in. print has been made for exhibition purposes.

Microscope: Leitz.   Camera: Watson.   Objective: 1 in.   Eyepiece: 45 mm. × 6. Substage: lower condenser only.   Tube length: 163 mm.   Bellows length: 4 in.   Emulsion: Ilford Special Rapid.   Filter: diffuser only.   Illumination: transmitted.   Exposure: 2 sec.

PLATE 16. SODIUM AZIDE CRYSTALS, × 5 (total × 25)

These sodium azide crystals were grown in a Petri dish under normal conditions; the overall thickness of the thin film was approximately 1/64 in. To obtain this rare photomicrograph the microscope was positioned on special macro illuminating apparatus (Fig. 6).   The effect is very similar to that produced by dark-ground illumination but, in addition, a three-dimensional effect has resulted.

objectives intervene. Medium-power objectives are dry objectives, having a shorter working distance than the low-power objectives (Figs. 7 and 10). As a comparison, the 2-in. and 1-in. have a working distance of 45 mm. and 14 mm. respectively, whereas the working distance of 16-mm. and 8-mm. objectives is 5 mm. and 0·56 mm. respectively. Thus, it can be seen that the higher the power of the objective the smaller the working distance.

The Mechanical Tube-length.—This (Fig. 11) is measured from the top of the draw tube of the microscope (where the eyepiece fits) to the bottom of the threaded portion of the nosepiece into which the objective screws. The draw tube is adjustable within the body tube and it is engraved with numbers from 150 to 200. The intersection of these graduations with the top of the body tube indicates the mechanical tube-length. Most manufacturers compute their lenses for a tube-length of 160, 170 or 180 mm. A heavy line is commonly engraved at the appropriate position.

The Optical Tube-length.—This (Fig. 11) is the distance from the upper focal plane of the objective to the lower focal plane of the eyepiece, and is controlled by the focal length of the objective in use. For objectives with a focal length of 4 mm. and less, the optical tube-length is usually 180 mm. Typical optical tube-lengths are given below:

Focal Length of Objective in mm.	Magnification of Objective	Optical Tube-length in mm.
40	×3	130
24	×6·5	145
16	×10	160
8	×20	170
4	×40	180
2	×90	180

Some objectives are manufactured to work with a cover glass and a mechanical tube-length of 160 mm., and others are corrected to work at 170 mm. Great care should always be taken to ensure that the objective is used at the correct tube-length. With an apochromatic objective a compensating eyepiece should always be used. When it is said (in a catalogue, for instance) that a certain objective is corrected for use with a cover glass, it simply means that the particular lens has been computed to work with a cover glass of a certain thickness. This is not so with some objectives; the introduction of a cover glass between the specimen and the objective will then interfere with the optical system. Therefore, the necessary corrections should be carried out by adjusting the tube-length. On occasion it is possible to use an objective without an eyepiece; this enables a wider field to be covered but, unfortunately, a lower magnification is introduced. Some schools of thought seem to think that this is not good practice, but no harm can possibly be done to the objective by removing the eyepiece. It is, however, a makeshift method, and should be used only when a suitable combination of objective and eyepiece is not available. Should the quality of the photomicrograph

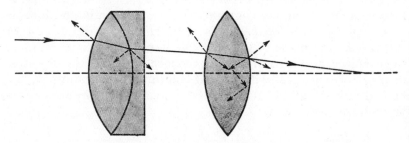

Fig. 12. Lens flare, shown by dotted lines

be poor, due to the removal of the eyepiece, it is not advisable to work without it, the final result being the governing factor.

The 2-mm. objective is known as a high-power oil-immersion objective. Its working distance is, however, approximately 0·12 mm. As the focal length of an objective is reduced, so the number of component lenses is increased, thus enabling the necessary optical corrections already mentioned to be made.

As the number of component lenses in an objective is increased, so also is the number of air/glass interfaces. A certain amount of reflection and scatter occurs at each interface, causing lens flare. The lenses in the latest types of objectives are surface treated to minimize this lens flare and enhance the brilliance and contrast of the image (Fig. 12). Scattered light may also arise from a dirty lens, scratches on the lens surface, or even a bright metal patch within a lens mount.

REFRACTIVE INDEX

Most immersion objectives are used with a thin layer of oil between the lens and the cover glass, although water is sometimes used. Suitably refined cedarwood oil has been found to be very satisfactory for this purpose, because its refractive index is approximately the same as that of the cover glass and it does not dry out quickly. A ray of white light passing through a substage condenser, oil, slide, specimen, cover glass and oil, to the objective, suffers little refraction at each glass–oil interface, as all these media have approximately the same refractive index (Fig. 13).

A very useful system, whereby the refractive index of unknown crystals may be measured, is that known as the Becke method.

Place a drop or two of liquid of a known refractive index on a slide, and into this place the material of unknown refractive index. Focus on the unknown quantity with an 8-mm. or 4-mm. objective, slightly raising the objective to render the image a little out of focus. At this stage a clear white line will be seen on two sides of the unknown material, at opposite ends to each other. This is known as the Becke line. If, when raising the objective, the Becke line moves away from the unknown medium and merges into the liquid, the latter has the higher refractive index. If the Becke line moves into the unknown quantity, then the position is reversed. A range of liquids of varying refractive indices may then be employed until a precise match is obtained.

The refractive index is inversely proportional to the velocity of light within a crystal. Isotropic crystals have, therefore, only one refractive index for light of a given wave-length. Uniaxial crystals have two refractive indices and biaxial crystals have three. These indices may be determined in a manner similar to that described above; the actual technique, however, is very specialized and beyond the scope of this book. Details of the technique, which requires polarizing and analysing equipment, are given in pages 53–59 of *The Thin-section Mineralogy of Ceramic Materials*, by G. R. Rigby, published by the British Ceramic Research Association (1953).

Oil immersion.—Refraction (i.e. a change in angle) occurs whenever a ray of light passes through an interface between media of differing refractive indices. Immersion oil, possessing a similar refractive index to that of glass, minimizes the refraction of the light rays emerging from the top of the cover glass, thus

increasing the amount of light gathered by the lower lens of the
objective. It will be seen from Fig. 13 that the ray B is refracted
away from the lens on leaving the cover glass, but that the equivalent ray A passes through the oil and continues at the same angle.
Ray B_1 does not enter the front lens but A_1 passes through the
lens. Ray B_2 strikes the front lens after being refracted by the
cover glass but ray A_2 continues in a straight uninterrupted line,
penetrating the lens nearer to its axis. In this way an oil-immersion
objective provides greater brilliance and resolution, and a more
complete image of the object.

The use of oil sandwiched between objective and specimen,
and between specimen and substage condenser, also minimizes
possible ill effects when using the tilting stage for stereo work.

One disadvantage of an oil-immersion lens, compared with a
dry lens, is that the former has a shorter focal length, restricting
the working distance. More expensive oil-immersion objectives
(see Fig. 14) may also have an iris diaphragm situated immediately
above the back lens. This enables the effective numerical aperture
of the lens to be varied from its maximum down to 0·2. The
intermediate positions corresponding to 0·5 and 1·0 are usually
marked on the body of the lens. An objective of this type was used
to record the bacteria seen in Plate 70.

Objectives are designated either by their focal length or by a
more or less arbitrary number given them by the manufacturer.
The focal length of an objective is the distance between the lower
focal plane of the objective and the specimen, when an image is
formed at the correct distance behind the lens. This enables the
approximate magnification of the lens to be calculated from the
relationship:

$$\text{Magnification of objective} = \frac{\text{Appropriate tube-length}}{\text{Focal length of objective}}$$

Thus, for a 16-mm. focal length objective used with a tube-length
of 160 mm., the magnification $= \frac{160}{16} = \times 10$ (diameters).

Numerical Aperture.—The larger the diameter of the front lens
of an objective of given focal length, the larger the cone of light
which it can admit from a given point on a specimen (Fig. 15).
Similarly, a change in the refractive index of the medium between
the objective and the specimen will result in a differing amount of
light being accepted by the objective. A point source of light may
be considered to emit a continuous series of spherical wave-fronts

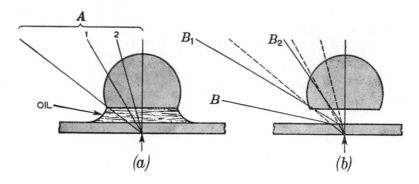

Fig. 13. Use of immersion fluid

(a) rays unrefracted when immersion fluid is used; (b) rays refracted when air is used between cover glass and front lens

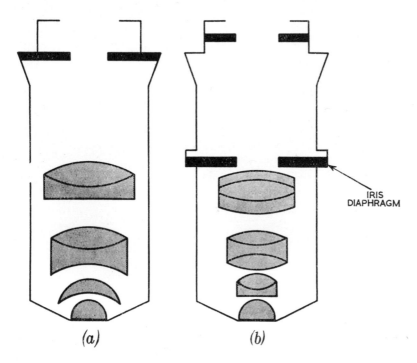

Fig. 14. Optical construction in high-power oil-immersion objectives

(a) $\frac{1}{12}$th objective, 170 mm. tube length, 1·30 N.A., 0·2 mm. diameter of field; (b) 2 mm. objective, 160 mm. tube length, iris stops 1·37 N.A., 1·0 N.A., 0·5 N.A., 0·2 N.A., 0·1 mm. diameter of field

which expand away from it into the surrounding space. In order to express the fraction of a wave-front admitted by an objective, we use a quantity called the numerical aperture. This is commonly

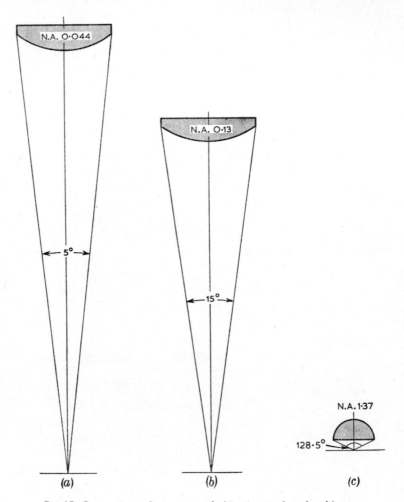

Fig. 15. Comparison of apertures of objectives and angle of beam

(a) Watson 4 in.; (b) 40 mm. 1½ in. Watson parachromatic; (c) 2 mm. Watson apochromatic

abbreviated to N.A. and is the product of the refractive index of the medium and the sine of half the angle of the cone of light admitted by the objective. Hence, from Fig. 15a, if n is the refractive index of the medium between the objective and the cover slide and u is half the apical angle of the cone of light:

$$\text{Numerical Aperture} = n \sin u.$$

This is an extremely important quantity in microscopy, because it is a measure of the resolving power of the lens and also because it may be shown that the intensity of illumination of an image varies with the square of the N.A., other things being equal.

The aperture of a camera lens is described by the f number, which is expressed as the ratio of the focal length of the lens to its effective diameter (f/D). Similarly, the diameter of an objective

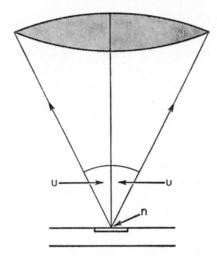

Fig. 15a. Numerical aperture

is related to its N.A. It may at first be difficult to grasp the concept of the N.A.; it is most important, however, that the relationship between the N.A. of an objective and its performance be clearly understood. It should be noted that the N.A. of an objective increases with the decreasing diameter of the front lens; the f number of a camera lens decreases as the aperture increases. Of two objectives of the same focal length but of different numerical aperture, the one with the higher N.A. is the better lens, since it is capable of resolving finer detail. However, it should be noted that the degree of penetration, flatness of field and working distance decrease as the N.A. increases.

TABLE 1. REFRACTIVE INDICES OF VARIOUS SUBSTANCES

Subject	Refractive Index
Air	1·000
Alcohol (methyl)	1·323
Distilled water	1·334
Sea water	1·343
Egg-albumin solution	1·350
Alcohol (absolute)	1·367
Chloroform	1·450
Glycerine jelly	1·450
Turpentine	1·470
Olive oil	1·470
Castor oil	1·480
Euparal	1·483
Diaphane	1·483
Xylene	1·497
Toluene	1·498
Benzene	1·504
Cedarwood oil	1·510
Detel	1·510
Gum dammar	1·520
Canada balsam in xylene	1·524
Oil of cloves	1·530
Canada balsam, solid	1 535
Clarite	1·540
Permount	1·540
Monobromonaphthalene	1·549
Styrax	1·582
Hydrax	1·710
Naphrax	1·7+
Methylene iodide	1·743
Pleurax	1·770
Crown glass	1·46–1·53
Flint glass	1·53–1·65
Calcite	1·57
Dense flint glass	1·65–1·92
Fluorite, approx. average	1·434
Quartz, approx. average	1·567

While it is possible to arrive by several methods at an approximate value for the N.A. of a lens, an accurate value can be obtained only with an instrument such as the Abbe apertometer. This is suitable for both dry- and oil-immersion objectives.

RESOLVING POWER

The maximum useful magnification which may be attained with a microscope is that at which all the detail resolved by the objective becomes visible to the eye of the observer. This depends ultimately upon the resolving power of the objective (Plate 36(d)), which is a function of the numerical aperture of the objective and the wave-length of the light used. Unfortunately, the precise calculation of the resolving power of an objective is not a simple matter, since it is influenced by interference effects.

Light is propagated by a wave motion, and when the whole of the specimen is self-luminous the light from any particular point on the surface of the specimen is independent of that emitted from a neighbouring point, so that interference effects are minimized. In these circumstances, and dependent upon the optical perfection of the objective, the maximum resolvable distance between two self-luminous points may be shown to be

$$\frac{0{\cdot}61\lambda}{\text{N.A.}}$$

where λ is the wave-length of the light used. This ratio is commonly quoted as the resolving power of the lens and is denoted by r. When the subject is not self-luminous, different points upon its surface may receive some illumination from the same point on the external source of light. Under these conditions interference effects may occur. In an extreme case a wave crest may be superimposed upon a trough, with the result that the two cancel out and no light is seen.

Much controversy surrounds the precise manner in which the resolving power of a lens should be calculated when it is used to examine a non-luminous subject by added light; for practical purposes, however, it is usually sufficient to assume that the resolving power of an objective under these conditions is given by

$$r = \frac{\lambda}{\text{N.A.}}$$

Thus, the resolving power increases with a decrease in the wave-length of the light and decreases with a decrease in the numerical aperture of the objective.

If we take as an example monochromatic green light of wavelength 5.5×10^{-5} cm. and an objective of numerical aperture 1.4, then, under the most favourable conditions, the maximum attainable resolution is given by

$$r = \frac{0.61 \times 5.5 \times 10^{-5}}{1.4} = 2.39 \times 10^{-5} \text{ cm.}$$

or approximately 2.4×10^{-5} cm.

TABLE 2. COMPARISONS IN RESOLVING POWER OF VARIOUS OBJECTIVES

Focal Length			Primary Mag. at 160 mm. t.l.	N.A.	Lines/mm. Resolved	Useful Magnification
Low Power	{2 in.	50 mm.	×2·75	0·15	435	50
	1 in.	25 mm.	×6	0·21–30	588	150
Medium Power	{$\frac{2}{3}$ in.	16 mm.	×10	0·30	820	200
	$\frac{1}{3}$ in.	8 mm.	×20	0·65	1,333	350
High Power	{$\frac{1}{6}$ in.	4 mm.	×50	0·75	2,222	550
	$\frac{1}{12}$ in. (water immersion)	2 mm.	×100	1·2–35	3,570	1,000
	$\frac{1}{12}$ in. (oil immersion)	2 mm.	×100	1·37	4,166	1,900

At a receiving distance of 25 cm. the average eye cannot resolve a spacing of less than some 1×10^{-2} cm. If the detail resolved by the objective is to be discernible to the eye of an observer, it must be magnified to exceed 1×10^{-2} cm. This condition is satisfied if the magnification is 1,000 times, when, for the example quoted above, the distance becomes 2.4×10^{-2} cm. It is this reasoning which leads to the commonly quoted rule that the maximum useful magnification which may be attained with an objective used in the visible region of the spectrum is of the order of $1,000 \times$ its N.A.

The resolving power of an objective is sometimes expressed as the reciprocal of the ratio given above, when it becomes a certain number of lines/mm. or lines/in. It cannot be emphasized too strongly that the whole question of resolving power is a very controversial one; and the observer must take care that, in the examination of very minute detail, diffraction phenomena do not invalidate the true interpretation of the shape of the subject (Plate 62). Similarly, it is most important that the N.A. of the condenser be properly matched to that of the objective. This aspect is dealt with in the next chapter.

The upper limit of useful magnification which may be attained in a microscope employing visible light is, therefore, in the region of 1,500 diameters. (Over 2,000 can be obtained by incor-

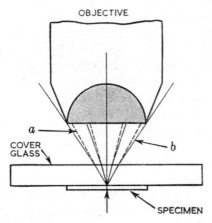

Fig. 16. Inferior image caused by rays *b* compared with rays *a*

porating a × 25 eyepiece; the author has never found it necessary to introduce such high power.) This magnification is increased a little for ultra-violet microscopy (see section on reflecting microscopy in Chapter 9), but the relative opacity of glass to ultra-violet radiations means that the components of the objective must be constructed from quartz and other materials of suitable physical properties, which involves considerable difficulty and expense. If higher magnifications are required, electron-microscope technique must be used.

CORRECTION COLLAR

The introduction of a cover glass of incorrect thickness between the specimen and the objective can unbalance the optical system and result in spherical aberration, as shown in Fig. 16. This defect becomes more serious with objectives of smaller focal length. It gives a curved appearance to the field of view and causes difficulty in obtaining sharp focusing near the edges of the field. This, of course, is due to the oblique rays of light being refracted at a greater angle than those nearer the centre of the objective.

To overcome this problem, most manufacturers compute the objectives to work with a certain fixed cover-glass thickness; some objectives, however, are provided with a correction collar which can be adjusted to suit cover glasses of various thicknesses. These correction collars are usually confined to objectives of $\frac{1}{6}$- and $\frac{1}{12}$-in. focal length. Cover glasses are available in three standard thickness ranges: size 1—nominally 0·12–0·18 mm.; size 2—nominally 0·25 mm.; and size 3—nominally 0·50 mm. When an objective has been corrected for a cover-glass thickness, the correction is usually for 0·12–0·25 mm., refractive index 1·524.

Low-power objectives are less sensitive to variations in the thickness of the cover glass over the specimen. Eight-mm. and 16-mm. objectives are moderately sensitive to variations in thickness of the cover glass, but high-power dry objectives with a numerical aperture of 0·85–0·95 are extremely sensitive to changes from the recommended cover-glass thickness. However, there may be a variation of $\pm 0·03$ mm. or so between cover glasses from the same batch; and for high-power work with dry objectives the correction of the objective should be checked. There is, however, a very useful cover-glass thickness gauge made by Zeiss, which is a precision micrometer reading in millimetres. The maximum thickness it can measure is 10 mm., and the thickness of a slide may be determined to $\pm 0·005$ mm. If such a micrometer is not to hand, the following method may be used to measure the thickness of a cover glass. With an objective of magnification $\times 40$, carefully focus on the top surface of the specimen, i.e. at a position slightly below the lower surface of the cover glass, depending upon the thickness of mounting medium between specimen and cover glass. After carefully focusing with the fine adjustment, note the position of the graduated fine-adjustment control. Then focus carefully upon the upper surface of the cover glass and again note the position of the fine-adjustment control. The product of the displacement of the objective (measured with the graduated fine-focusing control) and the refractive index of the cover-glass material will then indicate the thickness of the cover glass. The actual precision of the observation will naturally depend upon the proximity of the upper surface of the specimen to the cover slip.

In the absence of an objective-spacing collar, the tube-length should be increased to compensate for a decrease in cover-glass thickness. Oil-immersion objectives are insensitive to minor variations in cover-glass thickness, since the oil and cover glass form a more or less optically homogeneous medium.

If there is any doubt as to the precise thickness of a cover glass it can quite easily be measured with an ordinary micrometer.

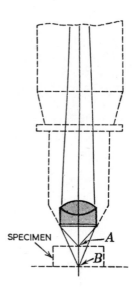

Fig. 17. Depth of field

When focusing on A all else is out of focus. Focusing on B causes difficulties due to the necessity of penetrating the specimen. Depth of field (μ): 0·5 (2 mm.); 1–2 (4 mm.); 3 (16 mm.)

DEPTH OF FIELD

The depth of field is outside the microscope, while depth of focus is within. When a low-power objective is focused upon a particular plane in the subject, there is a certain latitude above and below this position in which neighbouring planes will be in focus (Plate 26 (*upper right*)). The depth embraced by these planes represents the depth of field of the arrangement in use. In general, the depth of field decreases with the square of the focal length for objectives of equal numerical aperture. Hence, when photographing thick transparent specimens (Fig. 17) or opaque specimens with an irregular surface, it is necessary to achieve a compromise between resolution (which requires a large N.A.) and depth of field (Plate 26 (*upper left*)). A simple expedient when a wide range of objectives is not available is to select an objective which has a N.A. larger than that required and decrease its effective N.A. by means of a piece of black paper with a central hole of suitable size placed over the back lens of the objective.

In visual microscopy a limited depth of field is usually less important than adequate resolution, because the observer can rack the microscope body tube up and down to obtain a complete picture of the subject. In an extreme case, when sufficient depth of field cannot be obtained without sacrificing resolution, a series of photomicrographs can be taken at different levels. Such photographs, however, are rather difficult to interpret.

If the subject is a moving one (e.g. a daphnia), a further complication is introduced by the necessity of using a short exposure. In such a case an intense illumination combined with a fast photographic emulsion will be required if the aperture of the objective is to be restricted.

NOSEPIECE

Almost all early microscopes were equipped for only one objective. In some models this screwed directly into the base of the tube; in others it was fastened to an independent slide which was held in position by a spring-loaded ball catch.

Today the rotating nosepiece is almost standard equipment, and is made to carry two, three, four or even five objectives. These rotating objective-carriers are made so that they ensure the accurate alignment of each objective as it is turned into position. They are also dust-proof. The changeover action is quite simple and is carried out by rotating the nosepiece until the required objective is directly beneath the body tube, where it snaps firmly into position and is ready for use. Some objective mounts are so constructed that the lenses may be interchanged without disturbing the focusing of the microscope. A set of such objectives is said to be parfocal.

CRITICAL FOCUSING

Plate 30 shows three photomicrographs of the same field in the same subject. The variations have been made by focusing on three different planes as shown in the diagrams. Each photomicrograph appears to be of a different specimen. The centre picture illustrates critical focusing, while the top picture shows the effect of focusing at a point nearer to the objective lens. The

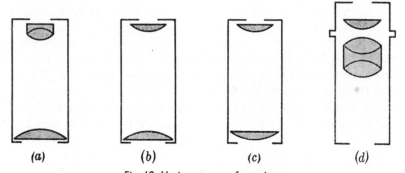

Fig. 18. Various types of eyepiece
(a) achromatized Ramsden; (b) Ramsden; (c) Huyghens'; (d) compensating

lower picture is completely the reverse, white areas becoming black and vice versa. Unfortunately, if any one of these pictures were shown on its own, it could be accepted as a true likeness of the specimen. This series of photomicrographs shows that at all times critical focusing must be the aim. The specimen illustrated is a section of a fungus found in water, at a magnification of ×800.

EYEPIECES

The principal function of an eyepiece is to magnify the image provided by the objective and to project the image into a position in which it can be photographed. In addition, some degree of correction is often introduced into the eyepiece to remedy aberrations in the image provided by the objective. The construction of typical eyepieces is illustrated in Fig. 18.

Huyghens' (c. 1690) eyepieces (Fig. 19) are probably the most widely used. They consist of a pair of plano-convex lenses arranged one above the other with a circular diaphragm between them. The lower lens is called the field lens; its purpose is to collect rays of light from the objective from as wide an angle as possible and focus them near the plane of the diaphragm. The small upper eye-lens is then used to magnify this image within a cone of rays which can be accepted by an eye.

The Ramsden (1783) eyepiece (Fig. 19) also contains two plano-convex lenses but, unlike the Huyghenian eyepiece, the convex faces are opposed. When a field diaphragm is fitted to an eyepiece of this type it is placed below the field lens. These eyepieces are mainly used for measuring and counting purposes, when the appropriate graticule is placed on the field diaphragm.

Compensating eyepieces are rather more complicated in construction and are specially designed for use with apochromatic objectives, though they may also be used with advantage in conjunction with high-power achromatic objectives. These eyepieces are known as orthoscopic. Table 3 shows various fields of view projected by compensating eyepieces.

Holoscopic eyepieces may be used with both achromatic and apochromatic objectives, but they are not generally used for

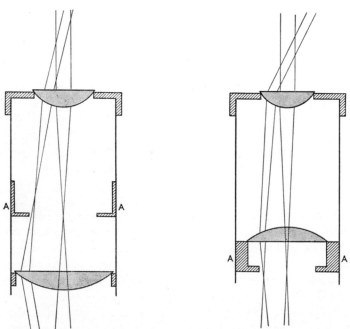

Fig. 19. Path rays in Ramsden and Huyghens' eyepieces

The image plane within a Huyghenian eyepiece lies between the field-lens and eyelens (A) in the plane of the diaphragm

The image plane within a Ramsden eyepiece lies under the field-lens (A) in the plane of the diaphragm

photomicrography. The separation between the two lenses is variable and provides a measure of compensation.

The Zeiss Homal eyepiece is specially computed for photomicrography; it gives a wide flat field.

The projection eyepiece (Fig. 20) is also specially corrected to give a flat field for photomicrography. This type of eyepiece is obtainable only in a limited range, ×6 and ×10, and is produced by a number of firms. The eyepiece shown is of the Huyghenian

TABLE 3. FIELDS OF VIEW*

Apochromatic Objectives		Field of view (in.)				
Focal Length (mm.)	Numerical Aperture	Compensating Eyepieces				
		× 6	× 8	× 11	× 17	× 25
40	0·11	0·25	0·18	0·18	0·11	0·09
16	0·35	0·075	0·06	0·06	0·035	0·03
8	0·65	0·04	0·03	0·03	0·017	0·014
4	0·95	0·02	0·015	0·015	0·01	0·007
¹3	1·2	0·015	0·01	0·01	0·009	0·005
¹2	1·3	0·009	0·007	0·007	0·004	0·003
Fluorite Objectives						
¹3·75	0·95	0·02	0·014	0·014	0·009	0·007

* R. & J. Beck Ltd.   ¹ Oil immersion.

type, with the eye lens fitted into a separate adjustable ring to assist in giving a greater degree of correction when focusing. This eyepiece and the Ramsden type are often made with some correc-

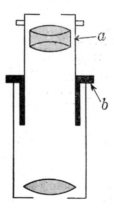

Fig. 20. Achromatized projection eyepiece

a is sleeved into *b* allowing free movement

tion for chromatic aberration. There is no standard method of identification of eyepieces in use by all manufacturers. Plates 29(*a*), 33(*d*) and 36(*a*) illustrate the use of eyepieces of various magnifications.

The field produced by the periplanatic type of eyepiece is even more flat than those already mentioned. This eyepiece is usually

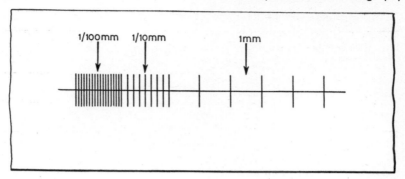

Fig. 21. Stage micrometer

used with the small Macca micro-camera attachment. It is made
in a limited range of sizes, ×10 and ×12 being the most useful.

The viewing eyepiece is used in conjunction with photomicrographic cameras, and is extremely useful when photographing
living organisms which can be followed and focused upon right
up to the instant of exposure. The viewing eyepiece usually has
the same magnification as the normal ocular and is constructed
to intercept only some 20 per cent of the incident light. This
permits the bulk of the light to be transmitted on to the photographic plate.

The latest type of wide-field eyepiece is that made by Leitz.
This eyepiece is specially designed to operate with their flat-field
objectives, but can, however, be used with a wide range of
objectives. This type is particularly valuable to photomicrographers because the lenses are coated to reduce reflections. These
eyepieces are at present obtainable in magnifications of ×10,
×16, ×20 and ×25; they cover an angle of view from 44° to 53°.
A micrometer eyepiece of the same design has also been manufactured, but this is available only in a magnification of ×25.

MAGNIFICATION

The magnification of the final recorded image in a photomicrograph depends upon the following factors: the focal length
of the objective; the power of the eyepiece (if used); the tube-
length of the microscope; the distance between the eyepiece and
the photographic plate (usually protected from stray light by a
bellows and hereafter referred to as the bellows extension); any
enlargement given to the final print made from the negative.

The important considerations affecting the choice of tube-length and the available resolution have already been discussed. The novice is often tempted to over-magnify an image, thus producing a measure of empty magnification: this is an error which must be avoided. Wherever the precise magnification is required, it is necessary to employ a stage micrometer. This consists of a microscope slide bearing a finely divided graticule such as that shown in Fig. 21. The divisions are usually either 0·1 mm. or 0·01 mm., and direct measurement of the size of the image of these divisions provides the only accurate means of determining the magnification with any particular combination.

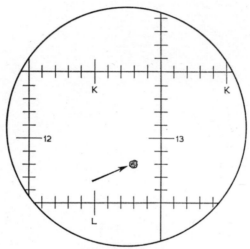

Fig. 22. Slide field finder

For any given set of equipment it is convenient to compile a table giving the combination of objective, eyepiece and bellows extension corresponding to each required standard magnification. Tables 4 and 5 will be of assistance for general work.

Most of the illustrations in this book have been enlarged several times to give a higher degree of magnification than that of the original negative. When a negative has been enlarged it is indicated by giving the total magnification.

FIELD FINDER

The Lovins Micro-slide Field Finder is a simple precision device which enables quick and accurate relocation of fields. The specimen is mounted in the normal manner and rests above a precision

TABLE 4. APPROXIMATE MAGNIFICATIONS

Objective Focal Length		Eyepiece	Camera Extension (cm.)					
			10	20	30	40	50	60
			Diameters					
75 mm.	3 in.	× 4	—	—	12	16	20	24
75 mm.	3 in.	× 6	—	—	15	20	25	30
75 mm.	3 in.	× 8	—	14	21	28	35	42
75 mm.	3 in.	× 10	—	16	24	32	40	48
50 mm.	2 in.	× 4	6	12	18	24	30	36
50 mm.	2 in.	× 6	8	16	24	32	40	48
50 mm.	2 in.	× 8	10	20	30	40	50	60
50 mm.	2 in.	× 10	12	24	36	48	60	72
25 mm.	1 in.	× 4	10	20	30	40	50	60
25 mm.	1 in.	× 6	15	30	45	60	75	90
25 mm.	1 in.	× 8	20	40	60	80	100	120
25 mm.	1 in.	× 10	23	46	69	92	115	138
16 mm.	$\frac{2}{3}$ in.	× 4	16	32	48	62	78	94
16 mm.	$\frac{2}{3}$ in.	× 6	22	44	66	88	110	132
16 mm.	$\frac{2}{3}$ in.	× 8	28	58	88	118	148	178
16 mm.	$\frac{2}{3}$ in.	× 10	34	68	102	136	170	204
8 mm.	$\frac{1}{3}$ in.	× 4	35	70	105	140	175	210
8 mm.	$\frac{1}{3}$ in.	× 6	50	100	150	200	250	300
8 mm.	$\frac{1}{3}$ in.	× 8	66	132	198	264	330	396
8 mm.	$\frac{1}{3}$ in.	× 10	77	154	231	308	385	462
4 mm.	$\frac{1}{6}$ in.	× 4	80	160	230	300	370	440
4 mm.	$\frac{1}{6}$ in.	× 6	97	194	291	388	485	582
4 mm.	$\frac{1}{6}$ in.	× 8	132	264	396	528	660	790
4 mm.	$\frac{1}{6}$ in.	× 10	175	350	525	700	875	1,050
2 mm.	$\frac{1}{12}$ in.	× 4	150	300	450	600	750	900
2 mm.	$\frac{1}{12}$ in.	× 6	208	416	624	832	1,040	1,248
2 mm.	$\frac{1}{12}$ in.	× 8	270	540	810	1,080	1,350	1,620
2 mm.	$\frac{1}{12}$ in.	× 10	334	668	1,002	1,336	1,670	2,004

Measurements were taken from the top of the eyepiece mount to the ground glass screen.

TABLE 5. OBJECTIVES AND COMPENSATING EYEPIECES*

Apochromatic Objectives			Magnification with Eyepieces				
Focal Length (mm.)	Numerical Aperture	Initial Magnification	42 mm. ×6	30 mm. ×8	22 mm. ×11	15 mm. ×17	10 mm. ×25
40	0·11	3	17	27	32	55	85
16	0·35	10	55	80	100	160	255
8	0·65	20	115	170	205	345	545
4	0·95	40	215	320	390	650	1,020
3	1·2	55	300	440	525	900	1,400
2	1·3	90	500	720	875	1,450	2,250
Fluorite							
[1]3·75	0·95	45	240	350	425	700	1,110
[2]3·75	0·95	45	240	350	425	700	1,110

* R. & J. Beck Ltd.   [1] Oil immersion.   [2] Water immersion.

grid of rectangular co-ordinates engraved on a slide 5 × 1 in. Large areas of subjects above the normal size, as well as minute areas, can be relocated with accuracy by means of the finely graduated lines, numerals and letters. Fig. 22 illustrates an area as seen through the microscope. The grid lines are graduated in numbered and lettered divisions of 1 mm., thus eliminating the need for any additional marks on a slide for further reference. This microscope-slide is very suitable for high-power photomicrography, as an area selected for a photograph can be arranged to lie between the graduations. A slide with a larger scale would, perhaps, be more suitable for low-power work. There is, however, another field-locating device invented by T. Maltwood, who presented a paper on the subject to the Microscopical Society in early 1858. The manufacturer of the slide was Becks, and, although its production was discontinued some years ago, several are still in use. C. N. England, of the School of Medicine, Leeds, recently put forward a prototype of a modified version. The original Maltwood slide has some 9,375 separate divisions, whereas England's has 1,875 squares—a much simpler method. The area is graduated on the top from 1 to 75 and on the side from A to Z, each square being divided into five panels. For reference purposes it should read as indicated in Fig. 23, Q6.3 and S5. When an area which happens to fall over the grid lines is being recorded, the lines appear quite sharp at low power, but at high power some confusion arises due to their width and the degree to which they are out of focus. Similar slides are manufactured by Curley Troy, N.Y., and are of particular interest to the histologist, biologist, pathologist, bacteriologist and botanist. A small label on a slide can be used to record the necessary evidence for re-location of any required area; this will not disturb the normal filing of the slides. Figs. 22 and 23 illustrate a section of

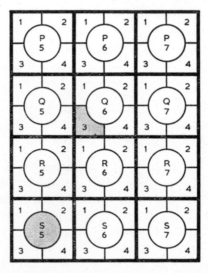

Fig. 23. Modified Maltwood micro-slide field finder

the grid with an object at the positions 12·8, K.7 and Q6.3, S5.

The 3 × 1-in. slide is usually thicker than the standard 1·1-mm. This increased thickness may affect the accuracy of measurements when a scale is projected on to the ground-glass screen.

Often it is necessary to count the number of objects in a particular field, e.g. dust particles, bacteria in milk, red and white blood cells, yeast and spores of numerous fungi. To do this properly it is advisable to employ an eyepiece fitted with a suitable graticule.

The Whipple Disc is a very useful graticule and easy to insert. It is divided into four squares, each further divided into 25 smaller squares. The sides of the larger squares are calibrated to coincide with the stage micrometer for the particular optical system in use. A graticule of this type may be used in one of three ways: the image can be projected on to a white card or viewed through the eyepiece in the normal manner; or a photomicrograph can be taken to include the calibrated squares on the negative. This eyepiece is manufactured by the American Optical Co. of Buffalo, N.Y. Another similar measuring and counting eyepiece of the Huyghens' type is made by B. J. Howard of the United States Microanalytical Laboratory.

5

THE CONDENSER

THE condenser is a very important part of the optical system, its function being to collect the light from the source and concentrate it, in the form of a cone, through the specimen and into the objective.

The substage condenser is used in two ways, to give either a solid or a hollow cone of light. The width of the cone is controlled to some extent by the use of an auxiliary condenser, but mainly by an iris diaphragm fitted immediately beneath the condenser lens system. The hollow-cone method provides dark-field illumination because the central rays of light are blocked by means of a stop situated beneath the lower condenser lens, leaving only the converging marginal rays to intersect at the specimen. In this way no light passes directly from the condenser to the objective and the only light accepted by the latter is that which is deflected in one way or another by the specimen itself.

If the condenser is to be used only for visual work at moderate powers, an Abbe type is quite suitable. But for critical work and particularly for high-power photomicrography a condenser of equal quality to the objective in use is necessary. The Abbe type condenser consists of either two or three lenses which are only slightly corrected. With high-power objectives an Abbe condenser not only fails to make the whole of the N.A. of the objective available but also reduces the contrast of the image by the introduction of glare (Fig. 24). The two-lens Abbe condenser has a

N.A. of 1·00, and the three-lens type has a N.A. of 1·03, but the correction is so poor that these figures are reduced to an effective (aplanatic) N.A. of about 0·5, both dry and immersed. It should be noted that, in the absence of oil between condenser and slide, the N.A. of a condenser cannot exceed 1·0. It is not advisable to use the simple Abbe condenser with apochromatic objectives.

For precision work, where critical illumination is required and where objectives of N.A. greater than 0·7 are used, the use

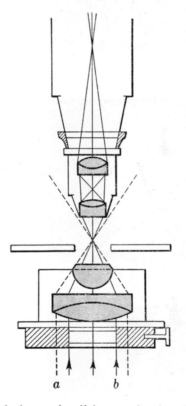

Fig. 24. Lens glare

a, the flood of light caused by too large an aperture in the substage iris; *b*, controlled illumination

of an achromatic, aplanatic or holoscopic oil-immersion condenser is necessary. Fig. 25 illustrates the nature of the illumination provided by different types of condenser. Swift and Son make a dry apochromatic condenser of N.A. 0·95 which is considered by many to be one of the best on the market.

An achromatic condenser can be used both dry and with oil and is fully corrected for use with objectives of the highest power. These condensers, as a rule, have a N.A. of 0·95–1·0 when used

58   The Technique of Photomicrography

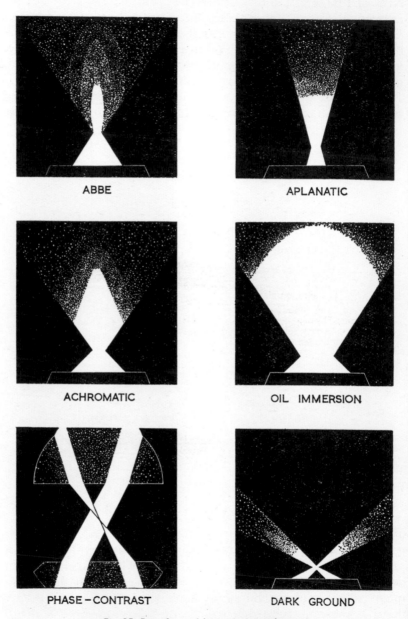

Fig. 25. Rays formed by various condensers

dry; this is increased to 1·40 when oil is used. The Watson holoscopic N.A. 1·40 condenser has a higher numerical aperture. Condensers are made with various focal lengths, but the top lens can usually be removed to increase the focal length for work at low powers. A typical condenser may have a focal length of 1·2 mm.; this will be nearer to 5·5 mm. when the front lens is removed. By way of contrast the Zeiss Achromatic Condenser of N.A. 1·00 has a focal length of 12 mm. The effect of removing the top lens is illustrated in Fig. 26.

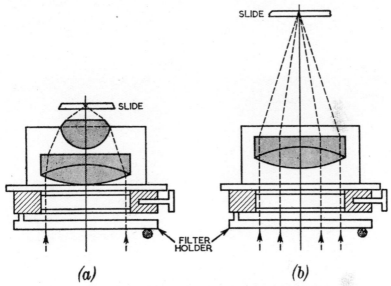

Fig. 26. The effect of removing the top lens from a condenser
(a) Top lens in place; (b) top lens removed

The Leitz achromatic condenser of N.A. 1·30 has a small back lens and is particularly suitable for critical photomicrography when used in conjunction with an objective of N.A. 1·30. This condenser is therefore particularly suitable for the photomicrography of bacteria, pollen grains, fungi spores and similar subjects.

The Watson Universal achromatic condenser N.A. 1·00 is widely used for photomicrography and the triple back lens system provides exceptionally fine corrections. Recently Watson and Son have computed a long-focus condenser increasing the focal length from 10 to 14 mm.; with the top lens removed, the focal length is increased to 28 mm. This condenser will provide a large image of

the light-source in the plane of the object, being particularly
suited for photomicrography. The Leitz aplanatic-achromatic
condenser with top lens removed is N.A. 0·65, the bottom lens
has a N.A. of 0·30 to 0·25, giving an even cone of light, well
suited for photomicrography.

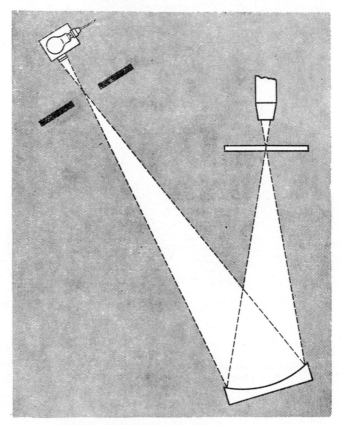

Fig. 27. Use of the concave side of the mirror

When working at fairly low magnifications, a relatively large
area of the specimen requires illumination. In these cases difficulty
may be experienced in achieving even illumination over the whole
of the field, due to the short focal length of the substage condenser.
In such cases, removal of the front lens usually permits adequate
illumination to be obtained. For the very lowest magnifications
it is rarely necessary to use the condenser at all. Plates 45(c) and
63((a), (d) and (f)) were taken in this way. In the absence of the

condenser, the concave face of the mirror may be used (Fig. 27);
whenever the condenser is in place, the plane mirror must be
used (Fig. 28).

The condenser must be accurately centred so that its optical
axis coincides with that of the rest of the microscope, and it must
also be accurately focused so that the light is concentrated
accurately upon the field which is to be viewed or photographed.
The centring is usually adjustable by means of two screws which
work against the body of the condenser, which is itself spring-
loaded against the movement of the screws to eliminate backlash.
To centre a condenser, open the condenser iris diaphragm and
verify that the lamp and mirror are correctly adjusted to project

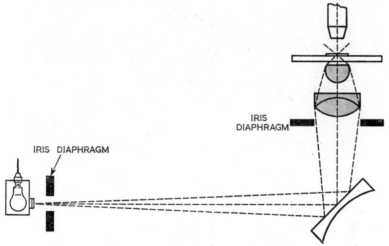

IRIS
DIAPHRAGM

IRIS   DIAPHRAGM

Fig. 28. Use of the flat side of the mirror

a parallel beam of light into the base of the condenser. Close the
iris diaphragm, remove the eyepiece and observe the back lens
of the objective. A small spot of light will be visible on this back
lens, and when this is centred by means of the centring screws, the
condenser is properly aligned. The iris diaphragm should then
be opened until the back lens of the objective is just filled with
light.

To focus the condenser it is only necessary to establish that an
image of the light-source is projected into focus in precisely the
same plane as the subject. If the light-source is equipped with an
iris diaphragm, this may be closed to provide a small aperture
which can be focused by the condenser. If no iris diaphragm is

available, a piece of black card having a small hole cut in it may be placed in front of the light. In either case, the condenser should be racked gently up and down until an image of the light is focused accurately in the plane of the specimen. The stop in front of the light may then be removed.

In medium- and high-power work it is most important that any condenser which is used dry be correctly matched to the thickness of the glass slide. If this is not done, considerable loss of contrast will occur in the final image. Some condensers are provided with a means of varying the matching slide-thickness, in a similar way

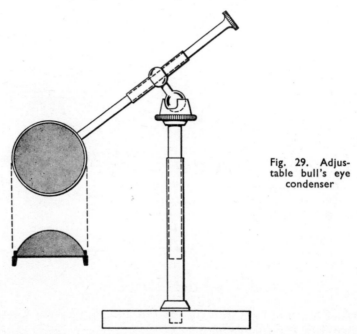

Fig. 29. Adjus-
table bull's eye
condenser

to that provided for objectives and cover slides. In an extreme case, when the condenser focal length is so short that it cannot be racked high enough to bring the light-source into focus, owing to the front lens of the condenser coming into contact with the lower face of the slide, the lamp may be moved a little nearer the condenser. This expedient must be used with caution, however, since it upsets the correction of the condenser and may decrease its effective numerical aperture.

Having both centred and focused the condenser, it is also necessary to ensure that the cone of light emitted by the condenser is not greater than that which can be accepted by the objective. If the condenser iris diaphragm is too wide, the path of the light will be as shown in Fig. 24 and excessive glare and loss of fine detail and contrast will result. If the eyepiece is removed, the condenser iris may be adjusted until the back lens of the objective is just filled with light. If, in subsequent focusing, the diameter of the illuminated field is found to be considerably greater than the diagonal of the area to be recorded, the condenser iris may be closed a little more so that only the area required is illuminated. At very high magnifications, diffraction phenomena may appear if the condenser iris is made very small (Plate 62). At no time should the condenser iris be used to regulate the intensity of the light. This must be done at the source, by suitable stops or filters.

The whole art of photomicrography depends upon an intelligent appreciation and application of the principles of microscopy, but it must be emphasized that, when the initial adjustments described above have been made, a final delicate adjustment here and there will usually improve the final image.

An auxiliary condenser, usually of the bull's-eye type, in a suitable holder (Fig. 29), is a very useful accessory, particularly for the photomicrographer. It is used between the lamp and the substage condenser in transmitted-light work, and is also useful for focusing the light directly on to opaque specimens for work by oblique light. It may be used with the plane side towards the specimen if daylight illumination is being employed, but with a small lamp the plane side should face the light-source. If an iris diaphragm is combined with the auxiliary condenser, a considerable measure of control can be exercised over the illumination incident upon condenser or specimen. In general, the lower lens of the condenser should be just filled with light, but the degree of divergence of this beam should be carefully controlled to obtain the maximum efficiency from the condenser. A critical examination of the image produced by the whole system is the only way to ensure that all the adjustments are correct.

6

ILLUMINATION

EVERY photographer appreciates the importance of illumination in conventional photography; in photomicrography, however, satisfactory illumination is often much more difficult to achieve. This is mainly due to the small size of the subject and the frequent necessity to emphasize particular features, many of which may not be clearly distinguished from the rest of the subject-matter in the field of view. The range of lamps and associated equipment available is now almost unlimited, and from these the photomicrographer must select the particular systems which provide suitable conditions for his own work.

A few years ago the lamps available to the photomicrographer could be counted on the fingers of one hand. Today there are a great many. Briefly, the means of artificial illumination has passed through the following phases: paraffin, incandescent gas, acetylene, alcohol, carbon arc, Pointolite lamp, tungsten lamp, coiled-filament gas-filled lamp, ribbon-filament lamp, high-pressure mercury-discharge lamp, electronic-flash tubes, electronic-flash tubes combined with continuous arc (xenon), the zirconium concentrated-arc lamp and the high-pressure xenon lamp.

It is almost impossible to achieve perfect efficiency in the handling of all the modern types of lamp, and the operator should standardize the lighting equipment best suited to his particular work.

There are two basic types of lighting—daylight and artificial.

There are many methods of artificial illumination and the type chosen must depend, not only upon the subject, but also upon the type of microscopy involved. This may be transmitted-light, dark-field, phase-contrast, polarized-light, ultra-violet, etc.

In general, it is essential that the light-source have the following characteristics in order that a high standard of work may be attained. It should be small and highly directional, and the intrinsic brightness must be steady and capable of being controlled. The radiations should have a continuous spectrum, with a suitable colour temperature, and this should remain unchanged throughout the life of the lamp.

The subject-matter can be divided into two main categories—transparent or opaque. Some specimens, however, may combine both these characteristics in the same field as shown in Plates 33(d) and 40(c). Transparent specimens are usually photographed by transmitted light which is projected through the specimen by the substage condenser. If the structure is transparent and has approximately the same refractive index as the medium in which it is mounted, phase-contrast and interference microscopy may be required to make the subject visible. Dark-ground illumination is used when the refractive index of the subject differs from that of the surrounding medium.

The mirror has both plane and concave surfaces, the latter being used only when working with low-power objectives (Figs. 27 and 28). The concave side gives a greater concentration of light than the plane side and it may be used to illuminate the specimen without using a condenser. Whenever an objective of less than 1 in. focal length is required, it is usually necessary to employ a substage condenser. Whenever this is done, only the plane side of the mirror must be used.

LIGHT-SOURCES

The days when oil-lamps, gas and acetylene were used to form the light-source for the photomicrographer are past. The disadvantages of these light-sources included uneven illumination, inconsistent light-power, the inconvenience of trimming the wicks and adjusting the burners, refilling with carbide and oil, and coping with the jumping flame produced by the acetylene lamp.

An efficient and popular modern type of illumination is the Pointolite, which consists of a small glass bulb containing a tungsten filament and either one or two small tungsten balls (Fig. 30).

This type of lamp requires special starting equipment and is available for a.c. or d.c. supplies. It is made in a wide range of candle-powers, from 10 to 1,000. The filament is first used to ionize the gas within the bulb and preheat the tungsten spheres. Within a few seconds the filament is switched off and the light is given out by the tungsten spheres. This is a very steady and intense light concentrated in a very small area (hence the name of the lamp). The spectrum is continuous and the lamp has a colour temperature of about 3,200° K (see page 189). The d.c. lamp has only one sphere, but the a.c. type (shown in Fig. 30) has two. For photomicrography with the latter type, the bulb should be arranged so that the two tungsten spheres are along the optical axis. In this way one sphere alone acts as the source of light. Ordinarily, the Pointolite lamp is only suitable for use in the vertical position, with the cap down. The approximate colour temperatures of various light-sources are given below:

	° K
Candle flame	2,000
60-watt tungsten lamp	2,500
Very warm fluorescent tube	2,800
100/150-watt tungsten lamp	3,000
500-watt tungsten lamp	3,000
Pointolite lamp	3,200
Clear flashbulb	3,400
500-watt Photoflood lamp	3,450
Warm fluorescent tube	3,500
Small flashbulb	3,900
Daylight blue fluorescent tube	4,200
Electronic flash	5,000
Winter sunlight	5,000
Noon sunlight with cloud	5,400
Haze sunlight	5,800
Blue flashbulb	6,000
North sunlight	15,000

The coiled-filament low-wattage bulb of the type shown in Plate 14 is a very efficient and convenient light-source for microscopy and can often be used for photomicrography, but the illumination is not quite as intense as that provided by some of the other light-sources, with the result that rather longer exposures may be required. The lamps used are usually 24- or 30-watt at either 6 or 12 volts. The heat dissipated by these lamps is so low that they rarely require a heat-absorbing filter. A wide range of automobile-type bulbs is available, and the pre-focus caps commonly fitted to these lamps greatly facilitate their use. They may very conveniently be run from a.c. mains via a small transformer, and if this is also combined with a variable resistance or a variably tapped secondary winding the intensity of the illumination is readily controlled. It should, however, be noted that such a control also affects the colour temperature of the light, and if work involving colour rendering is being conducted, such lamps

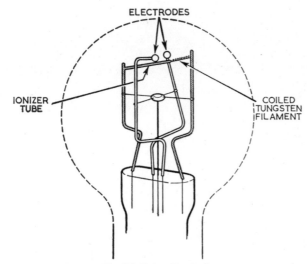

Fig. 30. Pointolite bulb

should be run at full power. The specially designed filament of the 6-volt 30-watt gas-filled lamp fitted to the Baker phase-contrast microscope is shown in Plate 14.

The ribbon-filament lamp consists of a single ribbon of tungsten connected between the electrodes within the bulb. The element is of low resistance, and a typical bulb requires nearly 20 amperes at 6 volts. A small area of the incandescent filament is selected for use and this provides an intense and evenly illuminated source of light.

The carbon-arc lamp is also very popular as an intense source of light of near-daylight quality. Either a.c. or d.c. arcs may be used. The former possess the advantage that a transformer may be used to supply the low voltage (of the order of 40–60 volts) usually required, but the d.c. arc is much quieter in operation and gives a more steadily sustained light. In either case, one carbon lies along the optical axis of the microscope and the other lies at right angles to it. The arc length is usually adjusted to $\frac{3}{16}$–$\frac{1}{4}$ in., and the crater of the carbon rod in line with the axis is used as the light-source. A clockwork mechanism is commonly provided to feed the carbons together as they are used up, and the positions of the carbons must be periodically checked to make sure

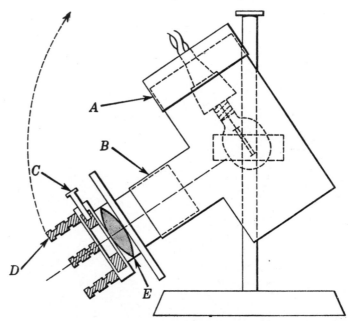

Fig. 31. Beck intensity lamp

that the second electrode has not advanced enough to block the light from the first. All arc lamps dissipate so much heat that a water bath or special heat-absorbing glass filter must be placed in front of the lamp to prevent damage to the lenses in the microscope.

EQUIPMENT AND TECHNIQUES

Lighting equipment can vary from the home-made lamphouse, which simply houses the bulb, to the most up-to-date illuminating bench. Probably the lamphouse in most general amateur use is the home-made one, which houses the normal household electric-light bulb. For general purposes this is quite satisfactory and gives a bright uniform light, though unfortunately a great deal of heat is

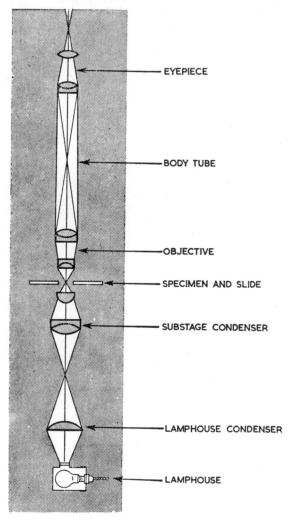

Fig. 32. Path of light from source to eyepiece

produced. Such bulbs are, as a rule, housed in a strong wooden and metal home-made lamphouse, having an iris diaphragm and recess for housing the filters and diffuse glass. These must be some inches away from the light-source on account of the intense heat.

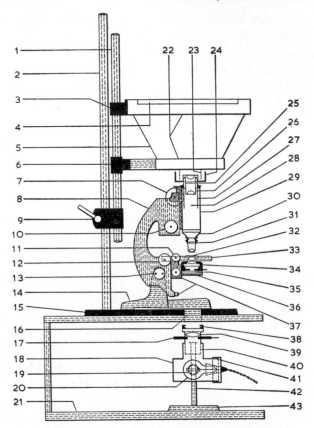

Fig. 33. Vertical photomicrographic apparatus

1. Camera height adjustment bar
2. Camera support
3. Height adjustment
4. Plate holder and ground glass screen
5. Bellows (treble length)
6. Height adjustment
7. Coarse adjustment
8. Limb
9. Main height adjustment clamp
10. Fine adjustment
11. Stage adjustment (lateral)
12. Stage adjustment (forward movement)
13. Joint (hinged)
14. Foot
15. Metal base board
16. Aperture in base board and cabinet
17. Lamphouse iris diaphragm
18. Lamphouse body
19. Height and tilt adjustment screw
20. Coiled filament bulb
21. Cabinet
22. Camera
23. Lens mount
24. Light protective ring
25. Primary image
26. Eyepiece
27. Draw-tube
28. Optical axis
29. Body tube
30. Nosepiece
31. Objective
32. Specimen
33. Stage
34. Substage condenser
35. Substage iris diaphragm
36. Filter carrier
37. Substage focusing adjustment and mirror attachment
38. Filter carrier
39. Lamphouse condenser
40. Focusing sleeve
41. Bulb adjustment sleeve
42. Height bar
43. Foot

It is most important that the iris diaphragm should cut out all unwanted light, leaving only a beam sufficient to illuminate the whole subject. In addition to this the illuminant should be uniform; an opal bulb is ideal. There must be some means whereby the bulb can be centralized, to enable the worker to align it correctly.

Fig. 31 shows the Beck intensity lamp, a good all-purpose lamphouse which was used to illuminate Plates 32, 39 and 63(*b*). The source of light is a closely coiled filament, the lamphouse being fitted with condensing lenses with focusing adjustments. There is the choice of a simple lens *E*, or a corrected combination, either achromatic or aplanatic, and an iris diaphragm can be fitted to the lamphouse. The iris is, of course, essential to the efficient working of the illuminant. The lamphouse is mounted on a firm base and has height- and tilt-adjustments. *A* illustrates the means of centralizing the bulb with the lens; *B* the adjustment sleeve used for focusing purposes; *C* the iris diaphragm adjustment; *D* the housing for both filters and ground-glass diffusers; *E* the lamphouse condenser. This type of lamp can run off a.c. or d.c. With a.c. a transformer is employed, which can also be used to regulate the intensity of the illumination. These lamps are extremely versatile.

In photomicrography too much attention cannot be given to the question of illumination. As in all fields of photography, the lighting can make or mar a picture. Practically any type of light, however, can be used with success.

The lighting set-up is one of the most important factors if good results are to be obtained. As illustrated in Fig. 28, a mirror can throw the light up through the microscope and substage condensers. The camera set-up can also be used without the mirror (Fig. 32). In this case the light is placed beneath the microscope, the light rays passing through the lamphouse condenser and into the substage condenser without being reflected in any way (Plate 3 and Fig. 33). When this form of lighting is used the microscope must be standing on a box, table or bench, in which is a hole through which the light passes. In both cases the condenser collects the light and passes it on to the slide which holds the specimen. It then travels through the objective, up the body tube and out through the eyepiece, finally spreading out on to plate or film. It is most essential that the light should travel absolutely vertically from the time it leaves the mirror or lamphouse, according to set-up.

The quality of all photomicrographs depends upon the projected image and correct negative treatment. At times, when working at low powers, it is very difficult to illuminate the whole area required to be photographed, and to get even illumination (Plates 31(b) and 63(d)) extra care should be taken in placing the light-source at the correct distance from the specimen. Should the lighting set-up used not fill the substage condenser, it may be improved by introducing a piece of finely ground glass, or an auxiliary condenser, between the source and substage condenser, to widen the beam of light. The ground glass must be evenly ground, otherwise the light transmitted will cause uneven illumination of the subject-matter.

At the beginning of this chapter mention was made of illumination by daylight. The value of this method is limited, not only by the difficulty of focusing an image of the source on the subject, but also by the fact that the light may change within a few minutes of making an exposure, thereby causing some difficulty in estimating the correct exposure for further endeavours. With the present-day optical systems and the photographic emulsion in use there is very little latitude in exposure, and this necessitates consistent, even illumination.

The Aristophot II is fitted with a special lamphouse neatly placed between the twin columns of the stand and designed to operate directly with the Ortholux microscope (Plate 11). This unique lamphouse houses two Philips high-pressure mercury lamps (CS 150-watt, ideal for work in the ultra-violet), thus enabling photomicrographs to be taken with transmitted or combined incident and transmitted illumination.

When photographing opaque objects through the microscope, oblique reflected light is usually used (Fig. 34 and Plate 53(a) to (f)). It is sometimes considered that the axially aligned set-up forms the only means of illumination in photomicrography, but this is not so, and it is hoped that the following brief description of methods of oblique lighting will support this. In actual fact there are several of these methods and they are very exacting. The lamp or mirror is placed in a position similar to that in Fig. 34 and the light is concentrated on to the specimen by means of the small condenser in the lamphouse. With the aid of the attached focusing device and iris diaphragm, the amount of light illuminating the specimen may be controlled. This type of photomicrograph is far more difficult to produce than those illuminated by transmitted light, as it becomes very difficult to illuminate the subject when using a 4- or 8-mm. objective, owing to the limited working distance of the objective (Fig. 7). The making of low-power photomicrographs is also quite difficult, because although the working distance is greater, the depth of field may not be very much.

If the subject is too large, preventing the whole from being covered with the longest focal-length objective, photomacrography may solve the problem. If one is about to photograph a live specimen in water, a viewing eyepiece is necessary, leaving both hands free to move the slide and adjust the focus, and the exposure may be made with the elbow placed on a static push-switch, or with a foot-switch similar to that fitted to an enlarger. Oblique

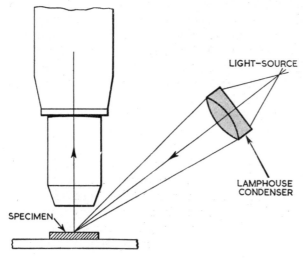

Fig. 34. Oblique illumination

lighting, as a rule, causes hard shadows, which are not always required. On the other hand, there are times when such shadows are necessary to give some sort of perspective to the subject-matter. The use of a white card placed on the opposite side to the source will help in creating a somewhat softer shadow. In addition, the exposure time will be reduced; as a rule, this is rather long for oblique lighting.

When the working distance of an objective is limited, the parabolic reflector, a small silvered parabolic mirror (Fig. 35), is a most useful accessory. In use it is placed near the objective

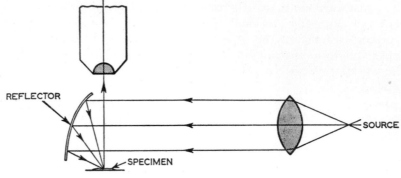

Fig. 35. Side silver reflector

and slightly above the stage. The beam of light from the source is focused via the polished side on to the specimen. Strangely enough, this means of illumination is particularly useful for revealing fine structural detail and the optical system does not suffer from glare due to stray light from the beam. As can be seen from Fig. 35, only objectives of long focal length can be used with this type of unidirectional illumination. It gives good results in working with opaque subjects and is often a great improvement on the ordinary oblique method.

This latter very old method of illumination, which is rarely used today, consists of a piece of curved metal, having the inner surface highly polished. The reflector is fixed to the objective, but it is not recommended for use with objectives of higher power than 16 mm. Direct lighting is used to throw a parallel beam of light on to the reflecting surface. This must be done with lamphouse iris diaphragm at full aperture. The reflector produces a brilliant flat beam covering a wide angle and illuminating a large area. By using this type of reflected light the hardness of shadows is reduced. When adjusting this reflector to suit a particular objective, great care should be taken to get the correct focus, otherwise the final result will be unevenly illuminated. It would perhaps be an improvement if these reflectors were made to give a variable angle of light and thus increase the chances of obtaining a more satisfactory result.

Another old method of oblique illumination is to direct the light from two sides, as compared with the previous type, which uses only one. A concave silver reflector is used to give top lighting and is known as the Lieberkühn illuminator (Fig. 36). The illuminator must be used with a matching objective to ensure the correct working distance. This form of illumination can be used only for comparatively small specimens, since the light is incident on the surface at an angle very near the normal which produces very little relief in the image. The light may be either direct from the lamphouse or reflected by means of the flat side of the mirror and projected upwards through the slide on to the reflectors. In this case the specimen must be mounted to allow the light rays to pass on either side.

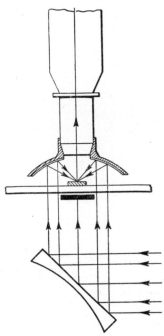

Fig. 36. Lieberkühn illuminator

It is suggested that an opaque disc be placed immediately below the specimen to ensure that there is no reflection of light from the outer fringe of the object. Some correction may be necessary when focusing because the reflector is automatically brought nearer to, or taken farther away from, the specimen, and this upsets the focusing of the light-source. Correct light-focusing is carried out by simply projecting the rays of light from the reflector on to the approximate centre of the field about to be photographed. This reflector, like the previous one, reflects light from a silvered surface, thus giving high brilliance. The great advantage with a parabolic reflector is that an opaque object is illuminated from all sides, preventing the shadows from being as hard as with a single-side reflector or direct from a lamp.

Incident-light Illuminators.—The incident-light method of illuminating the surface of a specimen is of great value and is widely adopted today in the examination of flat surfaces at both low and high magnification. It is used in the study of metals, ceramics, fibres and minerals, and in the pharmaceutical field it is used to examine the surface of tablets (Plate 50).

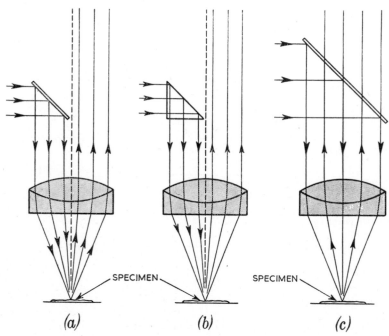

Fig. 37. Vertical illuminators
(*a*) mirror; (*b*) prism; (*c*) glass slip

These illuminators produce an axial beam of light. When this is reflected from a plane polished surface, any pits or scratches upon the surface of the specimen will appear dark. Vertical illuminators are readily interchangeable and fit between the body tube and the objective. The light enters the illuminator at right angles to the optical axis of the instrument.

The mirror type of incident-light illuminator shown in Fig. 37(*a*) contains a small metal mirror at an angle of approximately

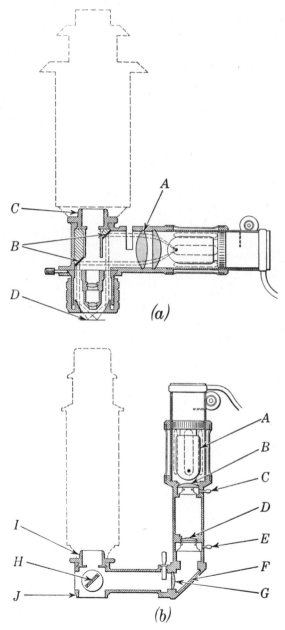

Fig. 38. Beck-Chapman Opaque Illuminator (*a*); Wrighton-Beck Metallurgical
Illuminator (*b*)

45° to the optical axis. This directs the light beam through the objective and on to the surface of the specimen. A total internally reflecting prism may be used in place of the mirror as shown in Fig. 37(*b*). Both these types of illuminator suffer from the disadvantage that the light incident upon the specimen is not perfectly parallel to the optical axis of the microscope, but a more serious objection to their use is the fact that the obstruction which they produce reduces the numerical aperture and the resolving power of the objective by 50 per cent. These limitations are avoided when a thin cover glass is used at 45° to the optical axis, just behind the objective (Fig. 37 (*c*)). This acts as a reflector to illuminate the specimen via the objective and then transmits a proportion of the light reflected back from the specimen. The Beck illuminator is of this type and enables the full numerical aperture of the objective to be achieved, together with truly axial illumination.

To enable a greater depth of focus to be obtained when operating with low-power incident-light objectives, a detachable iris diaphragm, known as the Davis Shutter, is now available.

The Beck-Chapman Opaque Illuminator is entirely portable and easily attached to the base of the body tube after first removing the objective. The image is viewed and photographed in the normal manner. There are many subjects for which this apparatus can be usefully employed. The construction of the illuminator is shown in Fig. 38(*a*) in which it can be seen that the condensers at *A* transmit the light from a 6-volt 15-watt bulb. Only the marginal rays *B* are utilized, and these are focused as an annulus of light on to the surface of the specimen *D*. A central circular stop removes any light which would suffer direct reflection back into the objective from a flat surface. In this way a dark-field effect is produced. The general result is of reversal of contrast as compared with normal vertical illumination. *C* replaces the objective.

The Wrighton-Beck Metallurgical Illuminator shown in Fig. 38(*b*) can be attached to any microscope *I* for work by vertical illumination. The light from *A* is controlled by a diaphragm *C* set behind a condenser with one ground surface *B*. The illuminator screws into the microscope between body tube and condenser. At a lower point within the tube is a further condenser *D* and iris diaphragm *E*; the image of the lens is formed at the same distance from the reflector *H* as the image formed by the eyepiece to ensure critical illumination. Lens *G* assists in forming an image of the light after being redirected by mirror *F* close to the back

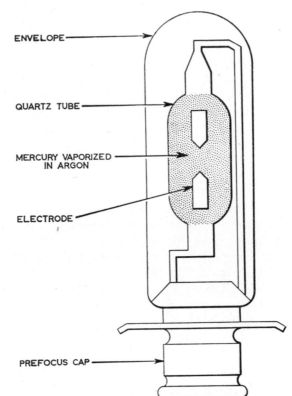

ENVELOPE

QUARTZ TUBE

MERCURY VAPORIZED
IN ARGON

ELECTRODE

PREFOCUS CAP

Fig. 39. Mercury com-
pact-source lamp

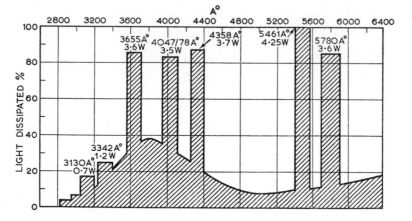

Fig. 40. Continuous spectrum, ME/D 150-watt lamp

lens of the objective at $\mathcal{J}$. Most work in reflected light is conducted without a cover glass over the specimen, and it is important
that high-power objectives are suitably compensated. A metallurgical microscope and camera is shown in Plate 5.

The Beck aplanatic ring illuminator is a valuable accessory,
but unfortunately it is going out of date. Its operation is very
similar to that of the other types. The light is reflected into the ring
illuminator, the centre rays being stopped by means of a light-
obscuring patch beneath the specimen. Having passed through
the slide on either side of the specimen, the light rays strike the
illuminator, pass through the thick glass ring, strike the silvered
back-edge, are then reflected to the surface and again refracted
at the front edge. As explained, the light is refracted, then
reflected and again refracted, which ensures a much better form
of illumination than that of the Lieberkühn illuminator (Fig. 36),
and many others which have only the surface to reflect light. The
Beck aplanatic ring illuminator can also be corrected for spherical
aberration and is one of the best of its type. The light is delivered
at an angle corresponding to a N.A. of between 0·75 and 0·95.
These ring illuminators are very useful for emphasizing the relief
of irregular surfaces in which the degree of irregularity in the
subject is small.

In addition to these few special illuminators, which have been
mentioned briefly, many improved light-sources are available.
Some of these are referred to below.

RECENT DEVELOPMENTS

Mercury Compact Source.—This is a very-high-pressure discharge
lamp, made by Philips Electrical Ltd. and known as the ME/D
150-watt lamp (Fig. 39). The ME/D 250-watt is a much later
model of higher power; many features, however, are similar to
those of the ME/D 150-watt.

The lamp was designed, developed and became the light-source
for the Leitz fluorescence-microscope equipment. The lamp uses
mercury vaporized in argon and does not require any special
means of cooling. The discharge tube is of quartz and the envelope
of a special hard glass which is transparent to ultra-violet. A
special pre-focus cap is fitted to facilitate the maintenance of
correct alignment. Unlike some high-pressure discharge lamps,
the ME/D 150-watt has a continuous spectrum throughout the
visible and ultra-violet regions, and the mercury lines (Fig. 40).

ATE 17.   MALE COCKCHAFER WITH OUTSTRETCHED ANTENNAE, × 12

n unusual subject, as this nocturnal creature, *Melolontha melolontha*, is rarely seen with its
:nnae out.

*:amera: Sanderson, treble bellows, f/7·7 anastigmat lens, 4 in. focal length.   Exposure: 1/25
nd at f/16.   H.P.3. D 76.*

PLATE 18.   PENICILLIUM GLAUCUM, × 25

The method used for photographing Plates 18 and 19 was as follows: a Watson micro camera wit[h] long bellows length and 3 in. lens produced the initial magnification; further enlargement w[as] through the enlarger.   The subject was illuminated by two tubular lamps, 50-volt and 63 mm. [in] length.   These were placed very close to the subject, giving modelling and even illumination.

TE 19.   PENICILLIUM NOTATUM, × 25

e purpose in photographing this and the previous subject was primarily to make possible the identi-
on and count of fungi cultured on agar in small Petri dishes.   These dishes were left in selected places
rious factories, and thus an estimation of the foreign airborne fungi was made.

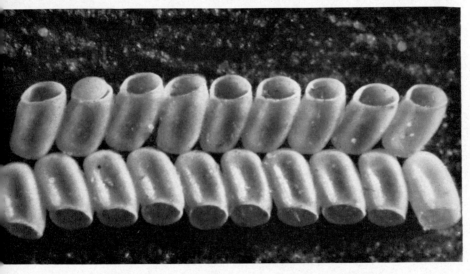

(*upper*) LARVAE OF ICHNEUMON FLY, *Apanteles glomeratus* × 6

Found in pupa of Large Cabbage White Butterfly, the outer shell of which is shown. Two Photofloods were used, at 4 ft. and 2 ft., producing a slight shadow.

Exposure: 1/25 second at f/16. P.1200. D. 76.

(*lower*) EGGS OF MOTH, *Brachyplatys pacificus*, × 25

The eggs and part of the fern leaf on which they were found were mounted on a microscope slide and photographed with the aid of the lens-holder shown in Plate I. The light-source was a Beck microscope lamp, approximately 6 in. from the specimen, and a white card was used to prevent the shadows from becoming too hard.

Objective: 2 in. Exposure: 3 seconds. P.1200, processed in Johnson's fine-grain developer.

PLATE 20

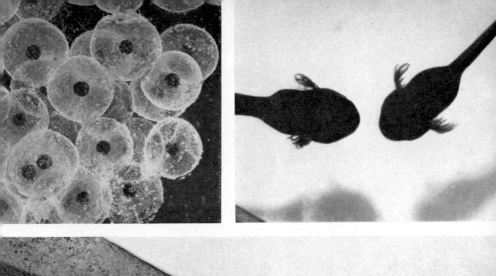

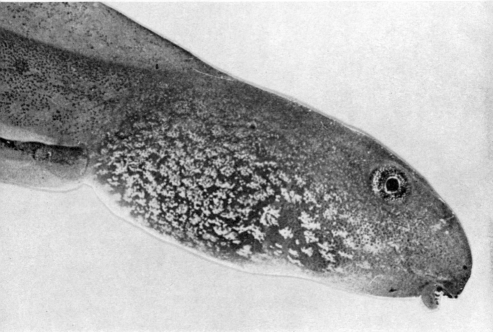

LATE 21. FROG SPAWN AND TADPOLES

The frog spawn was photographed with the camera in the vertical.   Normal lighting was used, ith a reflector.   A dark card was placed around the subject to avoid reflections.

Magnification: × 4.   Exposure: 2 seconds.   P.1200, processed in M.Q.

The tadpoles (*upper right*) have just swum free from the spawn and were photographed in a × ½ in. glass cell holding 1 in. of water.   A 500-watt Photoflood was used and the camera mounted the vertical.

Magnification: × 8.   Exposure: 1/25 second at f/8.   H.P.3, processed in M.Q.

The more developed tadpole was photographed in a 3 × 1-in. glass cell holding 2 in. of water d a 500-watt Photoflood was used to give frontal lighting.   The camera was in the horizontal ith treble bellows length.

Magnification: × 20.   Exposure: ⅕ second at f/16.   H.P.3.

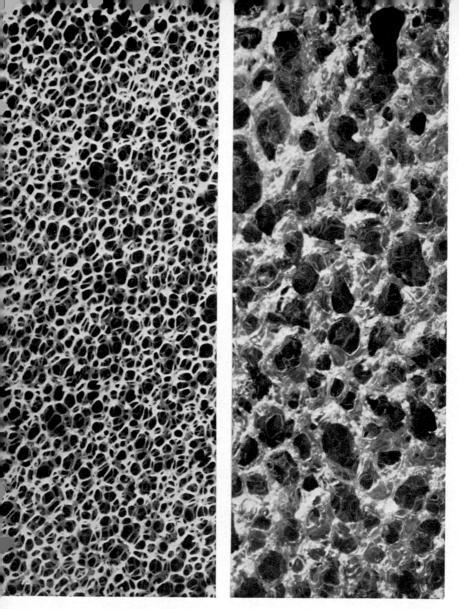

PLATE 22.   FOAMED PLASTICS, × 5 (total × 15)

Foamed polyurethane (*left*) and low-density foamed polyurethane.   The purpose of
these photomicrographs was to enable the manufacturer to assess the size of mesh,
defects (if any) and general structure (see Fig. 48 for set-up).

Microscope: Leitz body tube.   Camera: Watson.   Objective: 4 in.   Eyepiece: × 1·25.
Tube length: 180 mm.   Bellows length: 3 in.   Emulsion: 0.250.   Illumination: oblique.
Exposure: 2 seconds.

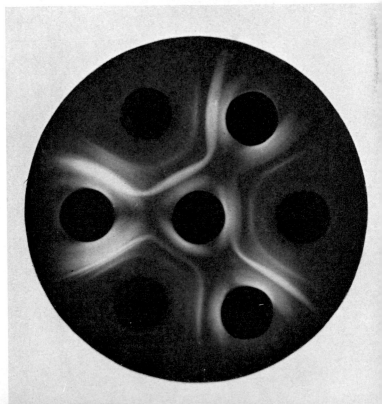

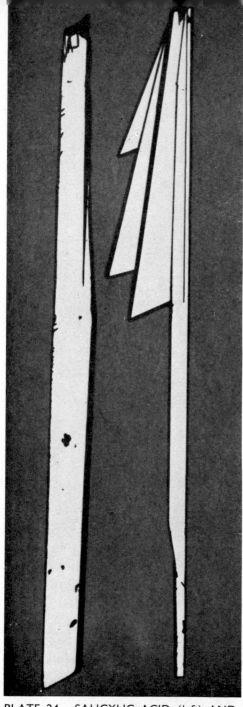
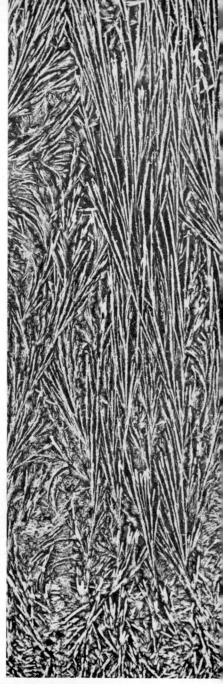

PLATE 24. SALICYLIC ACID (*left*) AND D.76 DEVELOPER CRYSTALS

The substage condenser was used with the top lens removed, the specimen being quite large. The crystals on left were grown on a tablet and carefully removed to the slide.

Magnification: × 25 (total × 100). Microscope: Leitz. Camera: Watson. Objective: 1 in. Eyepiece: × 2. Substage: less bull's eye. Tube length: 170mm. Bellows length: 8 in. Emulsion: N.40. Filter: nil. Illumination: dark ground. Exposure: ½ second.

The D.76 crystals were allowed to form on an emulsion which was exposed to strong light, fully developed in D.76, and allowed to dry without further attention. When dry the crystals were photographed with an objective which replaced the camera lens.

Magnification: × 25. Camera: ¼-plate. Objective: 2 in. Eyepiece: nil. Bellows length: treble. Emulsion: B.20. Filter: nil. Illumination: daylight. Exposure: 2 seconds.

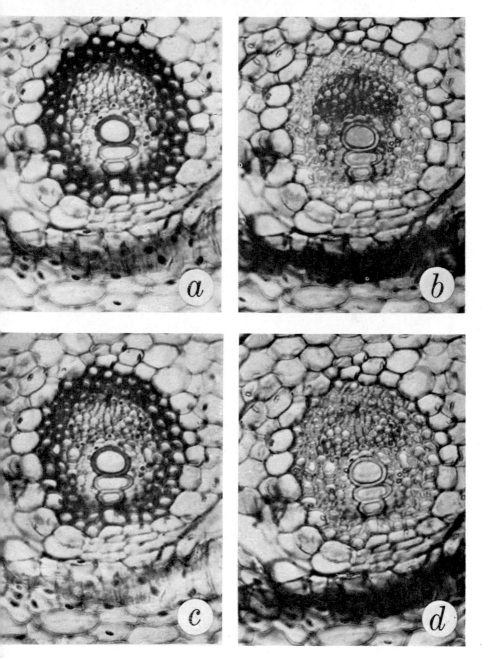

PLATE 25. TRANSVERSE SECTION OF GRASS BUD, × 360

The subject of this series of photomicrographs is a young bud of cocksfoot grass, *Dactylis* *omerata*. The specimen was stained red and blue, and the plate illustrates the use of iters to control a subject of intense colour. A green filter, Wratten B2, was used for *a*); a red filter, Wratten A, for (*b*); yellow and green filters, Wratten G and B2, for (*c*); id an orange filter, Wratten E, for (*d*).

EGGS AND LARVAE OF SEVEN-SPOT LADYBIRD,

Coccinella septempunctata

Great care was exercised to prevent undue heat reaching the fertile eggs. Oblique lighting was used.

Magnification: × 25 (total × 130). *Microscope: Leitz. Camera: Watson. Objective: 1 in. Eyepiece:* × 2. *Tube length: 170 mm. Bellows length: 8 in. Emulsion: soft gradation pan. Filter: pale yellow. Illumination: reflected. Exposure: 1 second.*

Three days later the eggs hatched out, by which time the leaf had lost its colour and had dried out considerably. The lighting was intensified, this time well above the subject, which is now black instead of white, and moving. A change in the emulsion had to be made to assist in giving an instantaneous exposure and at the same time produce finer details in the blacks.

Magnification: × 25 (total × 100). *Microscope: Leitz. Camera: Watson. Objective: 1 in. Eyepiece:* × 2. *Substage: nil. Tube length: 170 mm. Bellows length: 8 in. Emulsion: H.P.3. Illumination: reflected, two intensity lamps. Exposure: 1/25 second.*

EGGS OF LARGE CABBAGE WHITE BUTTERFLY, *Pieris brassicae*

These eggs were found on a cabbage leaf and were allowed to remain undisturbed until they were due to hatch (indicated by a dark band around the top of each egg). As depth of field is limited one egg was pushed over at an angle to give a better idea of its shape. A heavy general shadow was also introduced. One lamp was used to illuminate the subject. The light was placed fairly low to illuminate the tops of the eggs from the side.

Magnification: × 35 (total × 70). *Microscope: Leitz. Camera: Una ¼-plate. Objective: 2 in. Eyepiece: 45 mm.* × 6. *Tube length: 170 mm. Bellows length: 12½ in. Emulsion: P. 1500. Illumination: reflected. Exposure: ⅕ second.*

EGGS OF CABBAGE MOTH, *Barathra brassicae*

These eggs were photographed two days after they were laid. The leaf on which they were found was cut around the eggs, leaving approximately ½ in. each side, and then strapped to a microscope slide by means of transparent tape. The butterfly and ladybird eggs were mounted in a similar manner.

Magnification: × 35 (total × 70). *Microscope: Leitz. Camera: Una ¼-plate. Objective: 2 in. Eyepiece: 45 mm.* × 6. *Substage: nil. Tube length: 170 mm. Bellows length: 12½ in. Emulsion: P.1500. Illumination: reflected. Exposure: ⅕ second.*

EGGS AND LARVAE OF SEVEN-SPOT LADYBIRD

GS OF LARGE CABBAGE WHITE
BUTTERFLY

EGGS OF CABBAGE MOTH

PLATE 26

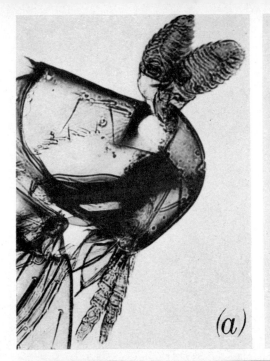

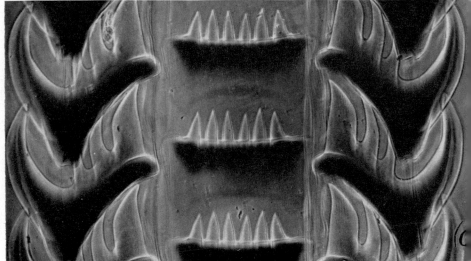

(a) HEAD OF FLEA OF MOLE, × 40 (total × 170)

This photomicrograph gives all the detail available. The sharp sucker has a tube passing through it which runs up to the dark area in the head. Small trumpet-like drums can be seen in the antennae. These cannot be seen when the antennae are lying down.

(b) PARASITE OF SHAG, × 25 (total × 75)

Specimen taken from nest of Shag on Gannet Rock, Lundy. It will be noticed that this parasite of a diving bird is completely covered with fine hairs, which it is assumed assist in forming an air-bell around itself.

(c) PALATE OF WHELK × 55 (total × 140)

Mounted specimen. This is an interesting subject for phase contrast, without which the chitinous teeth are not visible. Often when photographing such a specimen as this the inclusion of foreign matter cannot be avoided.

See facing page for data.

PLATE 27

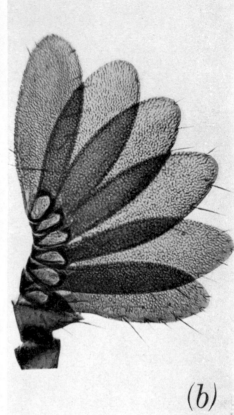

(a) EGGS OF PARASITE OF PHEASANT, *Phasianus colchicus*, × 80 (total × 250)

A beautiful subject for reflected oblique lighting. With the aid of a reflector hard shadows have been eliminated and detail shown in the delicate shells.

Microscope: Leitz. Camera: Watson. Objective: 25 mm. Eyepiece: 45 mm. × 6. Substage: nil. Tube length: 160 mm. Bellows length: 16 in. Emulsion: P.1200. Filter: diffuser only. Illumination: reflected. Exposure: 10 seconds.

(b) ANTENNA OF COCKCHAFER, × 20 (total × 25)

Mounted antenna of cockchafer.

Microscope: Leitz. Camera: Una ¼-plate. Objective: 1 in. Eyepiece: 45 mm × 6. Substage: lower condenser only. Tube length: 170 mm. Bellows length: 4 in. Emulsion: O.250. Filter: blue. Illumination: transmitted. Exposure: 5 seconds.

PLATE 28

Data for Plate 27, on facing page

Microscope: (a) Watson, (b and c) Leitz. Camera: Watson. Objective: (a) 16 mm. N.A. 0·30, (b) 25 mm. N.A. 0·30, (c) ⅔ × 10 N.A. 0·25. Eyepiece: (a and c) 45 mm. × 6, (b) nil. Substage: (a and b) less bull's eye condenser, (c) phase contrast. Tube length: (a) 160 mm. (c) 170 mm. Bellows length: (a) 6 in., (b) 15 in., (c) 9 in. Emulsion: (a) P.1200, (b) O.250. (c) chromatic. Filter: (a and c) green, (b) blue and two diffusers. Illumination: (a) daylight transmitted, (b) transmitted, (c) phase. Exposure: (a) 4 seconds, (b) 6 seconds, (c) 13 seconds.

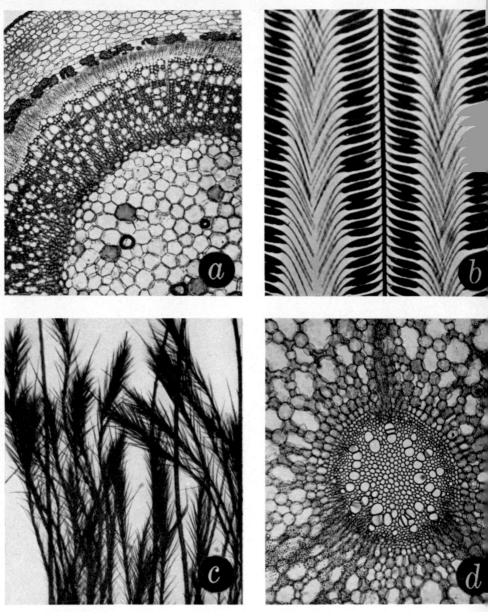

(a) TRANSVERSE SECTION OF OLD LILAC STEM,
Syringa vulgaris, × 150 (total × 400)
(b) SECTION OF FEATHER OF HUMMING BIRD, × 20 (total × 100)
(c) HAIRS ON BACK OF LARVA OF VAPOURER MOTH,
Orgyia antiqua, × 50 (total × 150)
(d) TRANSVERSE SECTION OF NUPHAR-ADVENA, × 20 (total × 120)

Microscope: (a and b) Leitz, (c and d) Watson.   *Camera:* (a) Sanderson $2\frac{1}{4}$ × $3\frac{1}{4}$ in., (b and d)
Zeiss Ikon, (c) Una $\frac{1}{4}$-plate.   *Objective:* (a) 16 mm. N.A. 0·30, (b) 25 mm. N.A. 0·30, (c and d) 25 mm.
Eyepiece: (a) 22 mm. × 11, (b) 45 mm. × 6, (c and d) 45 mm. × 6.   *Substage:* (a) complete with
bull's eye condenser, (b) lower condenser, (c) lower condenser only, (d) less bull's eye condenser.
Tube length: (a, b and c) 170 mm., (d) 160 mm.   *Bellows length:* (a and c) 14 in., (b and d) nil.
Emulsion: (a) P.300, (b) Ortho film, (c) O.250, (d) H.P.3.   *Filter:* (a and d) green, (b) blue, (c) pale
yellow.   *Illumination:* transmitted.   *Exposure:* (a) 5 seconds, (b) 10 seconds, (c) 2 seconds, (d) 12 seconds.

PLATE 29

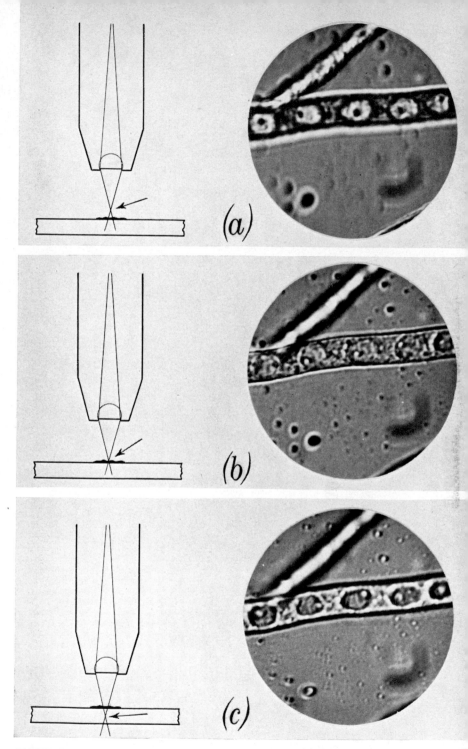

PLATE 30.   EFFECT OF FOCUSING AT THREE DIFFERENT LEVELS

(a) Focusing above the specimen.
(b) Critical focusing.
(c) Focusing below the specimen.

  Magnification: × *800.*

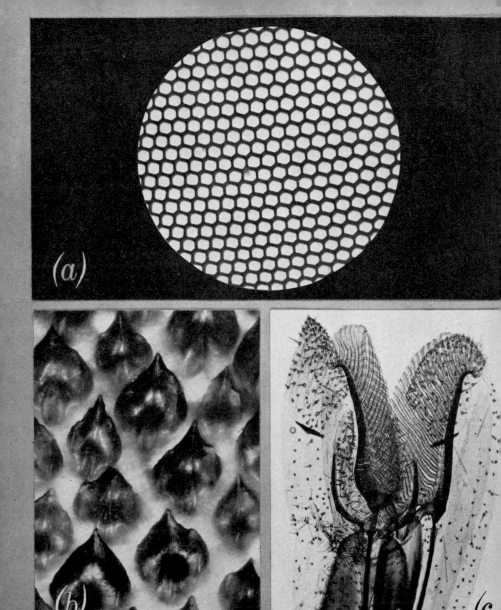

(a) SECTION OF EYE OF GAD FLY, *Tabanus sudeticus*, × 180 (total × 250)
   Specimen mounted with pressure between slide and cover glass.

(b) SKIN OF DOG FISH, *Scyllium canicula*, × 35 (total × 45)
   Note depth of field.   In place of the filter a thin diffused glass was used, for softer illumination.

(c) TONGUE OF DRONE FLY, *Eristalis tenase*, × 40 (total × 64)
   Taken from a mounted specimen.   Two filters were used to assist in recording the finer details.

*Microscope: Leitz.   Camera: Una ¼-plate.   Objective: (a) 8 mm. N.A. 0·65, (b and c) 25 mm. N.A. 0·
Eyepiece: 45 mm. × 6.   Substage: (a) complete with bull's eye condenser, (b) lower condenser only, (c)
bull's eye condenser.   Tube length: (a) 160 mm., (b and c) 170 mm.   Bellows length: (a) 14 in., (b) 9
(c) 11 in.   Emulsion: (a) O.250, (b) P.1200, (c) Special Rapid.   Filter: (a) blue, (b) nil, (c) deep green
orange.   Illumination: (a and c) transmitted, (b) reflected.   Exposure: (a) 25 seconds, (b) 6 seconds,
10 seconds.*

PLATE 31

The electrodes are 2 mm. apart, and this minimizes instability in the arc. Owing to this special design, this lamp is very suitable for general compact-source work as well as for fluorescence microscopy. The surface brightness of this lamp is given as 25,000 stilb, a stilb being one candle per square centimetre. The associated control equipment is for 220 volts a.c. (approximately) and is housed in a compact single case, the lamp being started by the depression of a button (Fig. 41). This button switch converts the running choke ballast to a leak-transformer. In view of this the insertion of an electrode in the discharge tube is not required. Where an arc length of 30 mm. is in operation it is sometimes necessary to use the quartz discharge tube without an outer

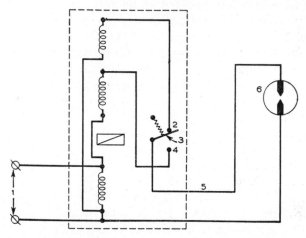

Fig. 41. Circuit and operating data, ME/D 150-watt lamp

(1) mains a.c.; (2) normal contact position for lamp operating switch retained by spring; (3) starting switch; (4) starting contact—lamp ignited by depressing button 3 for 10–20 seconds; (5) no-load voltages: 2—5, 145 V; 4—5, 540 V; (6) lamp

envelope. With the MB/U 125-watt high-pressure mercury lamp there was some oxidation of the lead-in wires, thus shortening the total burning hours. To overcome this the makers have found it essential to introduce a special discharge tube, the MBL/U 125-watt, fitted with leads shrouded in quartz. Another special feature of this lamp is the annular discs which have been added to minimize movement of the arc. The lamp is, of course, burnt in the vertical position and its life is estimated to be 200 hours.

Hanovia High-intensity Mercury-vapour.—Specially designed for photomicrography, this lamp is also suitable for high-power photomicrographic work employing the ultra-violet region of the spectrum. It is housed in a Beck lamphouse, which has an iris diaphragm and provision for necessary filters. The No. 14 filter transmits a band of light around 3,650 Å and this wave-length can be shortened by the maker's filter No. 15. The lamp can be used for fluorescence photomicrography, in which case a longer wave-length is necessary, and the usual condenser and silvered-glass mirror may be brought into operation; a quartz lamp-condenser is used when light of a shorter wave-length is required. The lamphouse is fitted with a control unit and the a.c. model operates with a transformer. Heat-absorbing filters are an essential addition to the apparatus, to eliminate the possibility of any undue heat being passed on from the lamp. An aluminium reflecting-surface mirror fitted to the microscope is a feature for ultra-violet illumination when direct illumination is not available.

Zirconium Concentrated-arc.—Zirconium is a metallic element which is very suitable for electrodes. It has been discovered that when an electric arc is struck between such electrodes in hydrogen or ammonia, the metal fuses and melts into grey drops on to the negative electrode.

The Sylvania enclosed concentrated-arc lamp has a permanent metallic anode and a specially prepared refractory zirconium-oxide cathode. These two elements are sealed within a glass bulb filled with argon, an inert gas.

When an arc is established between the two electrodes, the oxide surface of the cathode is raised to its melting temperature and molten zirconium is liberated. As a result of the high temperature to which the cathode surface is raised, a brilliant white light is emitted by the molten zirconium and a cloud of vaporized zirconium and zirconium oxide extends for a few thousandths of an inch from the cathode. Slightly larger than the cathode is a metal ring which forms the positive electrode. The light is emitted through the aperture in the anode, forming a narrow intense beam of light with a continuous spectrum and a colour temperature in the region of 3,200° K. There is no particular position in which this lamp must be burnt, as with others; the molten metal is held in position by surface tension. Its radiations extend from one end of the spectrum to the other; from 2,500 Å, through the visible region of the spectrum, reaching a maximum at 10,000 Å, and then on to the infra-red.

The diameter of the spot which gives the intense light is 0·0025 in. (2-watt lamp) and approximately 0·008 in. (100-watt lamp). Although this latter spot is considerably larger than the first mentioned, it is still minute. The surface intensity of this lamp is estimated as being approximately ten times that of an ordinary tungsten lamp of normal voltage. The lamp becomes a useful tool in photomicrography and for many applications replaces the carbon-arc lamp. The size of the 1,500-watt light-source is approximately ⅜ in., which is still amazingly small. As the current is increased it automatically increases the candle-power of the lamp, and as the current increases the luminous spot becomes larger, producing a far higher degree of illumination.

The concentrated-arc lamp is ideally suited for photomicrography, as the light-source sends out a very narrow beam of light. Perhaps, at times, it might be thought too critical because it shows up any imperfections which may exist, such as fine dust, finger marks, slight air bubbles and stresses in the glass—scratches and striae in glass show up as luminous bodies.

The concentrated-arc lamps ranging from 25-watt to 300-watt are particularly suited for colour photomicrography, owing to their colour balance. Moving subject-matter can easily be photographed on account of the short exposure time and no correction filter is normally necessary. The colour reproductions taken with this means of illumination are slightly more crisp perhaps than those produced with coiled-filament and ribbon-filament. The author's colour work illustrated in this book was illuminated by the two last-mentioned lamps and the Pointolite lamp. The results of the former are quite pleasing in spite of the source's being considerably less bright. A colour film suited to artificial light was, of course, used.

The high-wattage concentrated-arc lamps are also used with great success for phase-contrast, interference and dark-ground illumination.

The Mikrark illuminator (Plate 12) houses a 100-watt concentrated-arc lamp and can be used with any photomicrographic set-up and is, in itself, unique in all respects. The illuminator outfit is divided into two units: the lamphouse which houses the high-intensity lamp, and an efficient optical system mounted on an adjustable stem and held firmly in position by a heavy base-plate. The second unit is the power supply, suitably housed and consisting of the apparatus for rectification, starting and running current. The lamp can operate from a.c. or d.c.

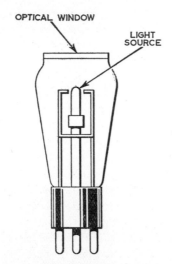

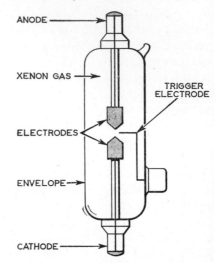

Fig. 42. Sylvania C. 100 concentrated-arc lamp, as fitted in Mikrark
illuminator

Fig. 43.   F.A.5   xenon-arc   lamp
(flash tube)

The successful use of the intense, small source of light is greatly
enhanced by the fine optical system which allows the light to be
focused from 10 in. to infinity.

Fig. 42 illustrates the C.100 concentrated-arc lamp as fitted
in the Mikrark illuminator. Details of the lamp are as follows:

Wattage	100
Operating current	6·25 amperes
Lamp volts	16
Starting volts	2,000
Rated life	375 hours
Light-source diameter	0·072 in.
Normal colour temperature	3,200° K
Average brightness	24,500
(candles per sq. in.)	
Average axial candle-power	100

F.A.5 Xenon-arc Lamp (Flash Tube).—The British Thomson-
Houston F.A.5 is a dual-purpose lamp capable of giving a continuous light and also an instantaneous flash of very short duration.
The photomicrographer would be well served by its use, but
unfortunately, at the time of writing, there is no standard
lamphouse for photomicrography in which the F.A.5 tube is

fitted (Fig. 43). Experimental work has been carried out by Langham Photographic Instruments Ltd., and is continuing with a view to producing a compact lamphouse, together with a suitable capacitor. The author has handled an experimental lamphouse which houses the tube, apart from the lamp. The lamp itself is housed directly above the intensity lamp, if in use. A metal tube or case between source and microscope base is an essential additional fitting, to prevent stray light from interfering with the image. Both the intensity lamp and flash lamphouses are in true alignment with the optical system of the microscope. The intensity lamp, better known as the secondary lamp, is used to frame the picture and to focus the image on the ground-glass screen.

· On the other hand, the F.A.5 can be used alone to illuminate the specimen for visual means. Once the necessary preparations in readiness for the flash and the usual focusing have been carried out, no other operation such as swinging the secondary lamp away, or swinging the flash lamp into position, is necessary. When a secondary lamp is used, it illuminates through the envelope of the F.A.5 without any ill effect being detected on the screen. The light emitted from the F.A.5, when burning as a continuous arc, is slightly lower in brightness than the carbon-arc; but a filter is required to decrease the brightness for visual

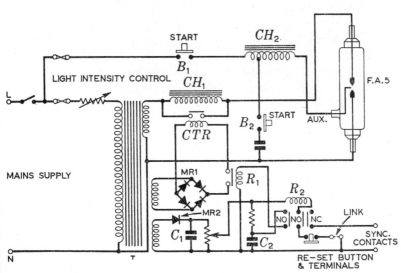

Fig. 44. Xenon lamp pulse circuit

inspection of the specimen without any undue eye-strain. It is felt that there is a necessity for a far shorter tube, which would in turn allow a much smaller lamphouse.

The circuit design (Fig. 44) is for normal 200/250-volt 50-cycle a.c. operation, and provides current for the F.A.5 lamp at 40 volts. On closing the main switch the two main lamp electrodes are made alive. As the gas pressure in the lamp is high at room temperature, it is necessary to provide a surge of voltage from transformer CH_2 to the auxiliary electrode on the lamp by closing push-button B_1 and intermittently opening and closing the start-button B_2. The intermittent operation of button B_2 causes a peaking 50-cycle a.c. voltage to initiate the auxiliary arc. Once this arc discharge has been established by further intermittent closing and opening of B_2, B_1 still being held closed, the main arc-gap breaks down, and once the two main electrodes have reached a sufficiently high temperature the auxiliary arc is extinguished by releasing the button B_1. The lamp is now running at a steady power of approximately 150 watts.

To pulse the lamp, synchronizing contacts are provided which, when shorted together, close the relay R_2. The contacts on this relay in turn close and complete a further circuit to cause the charged condenser C_2 to be discharged through relay R_1. The closing of relay R_1 in turn closes a high-speed contact CTR which momentarily allows a heavy current to flow through the lamp. Normally the current in the lamp is limited by the series choke CH_1. The value of the current in the lamp is controlled by the variable resistance in the primary circuit of the main transformer, and the duration of the flash by the energy stored in the condenser C_2 and discharging this through relay R_1. The timing of this circuit is pre-set to give a flash of light with a duration of 1/20th to 1/25th of a second. After each flash the circuit must be reset, and as well as the toggle switch provided for this purpose, a link is also supplied so that automatic resetting and tripping of the circuit can be arranged independently of any manual operation.

The voltage and current necessary to trip the circuit are of such a value that a micro-relay or normal contacts are adequate to trip the flashing of the lamp.

Linear Flash Tube.—Langham Photographic Instruments Ltd. have designed a lamphouse for electronic flash, using a linear tube of approximately $2\frac{1}{2}$ in. in length (Fig. 45); unfortunately, at the time of writing, this has not been produced on a commercial

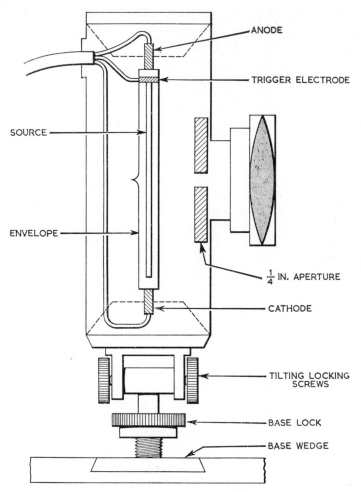

Fig. 45. Linear flash tube and lamp

scale. This lamphouse is small, compact and efficient in its manipulation and output, and can be used in either the vertical or horizontal position. The linear-source tube fitted to this lamphouse has a flash duration of 1/600th of a second, and its output is 150 joules. The light is directed through a $\frac{1}{4}$-in. aperture close to the tube, and this directs a beam of light into a lens system some 2 in. from the source. A directional tube can also be fitted between the lamphouse and the substage or mirror, thus controlling the whole output.

A secondary light-source must be used in connection with this lamp. In such cases the flash lamphouse is swung away at an angle of 45°, returning to the exact position in front of the secondary lamp when required. This particular tube can be used for colour work, the brightness being in the region of 5,800° K. In addition, the lamphouse can be used with any microscope; it has already been used with the Holophot and other models. The device used for fixing the lamphouse to the Holophot will not, of course, suit all cameras (Fig. 45). When this is the case, a fixing swivel and brackets can be fitted by Langham Photographic Instruments Ltd.

There is a demand for a small flash-tube operating in the vertical (similar to that shown in Fig. 42) and incorporating a secondary light-source, this being suitably housed in a lamphouse such as the Beck (Fig. 31). A window could be provided in the end of the short tube, enabling the specimen to be illuminated and a search to be made, the flash being used at will. The bulb could operate in the vertical or in the horizontal. If synchronized with the camera shutter, moving objects could be held in focus with the aid of a viewing eyepiece right up to the time of (flash) exposure.

The Xenon Combination Lamp.—Designed for use with the Ortho-lux microscope (Plate 11), this is equipped with the xenon lamp, XBO 162, which has a light-source of very high intensity. This unique lamp gives a practically continuous spectrum in the visible region and also covers the medium- and long-wave ranges in the ultra-violet. The colour temperature is 6,000° K and the light intensity per unit area near to the cathode exceeds 100,000 stilb, but in the centre of the arc approximately 25,000 stilb is registered. The light output of this particular lamp is suitable for all work likely to be encountered in photomicrography, especially in recording moving objects in colour. This can be done with daylight colour material without the introduction of a colour-correction filter. It should, however, be noted that the heat-absorbing filter necessary with this lamp slightly reduces the red portion of the light and slightly increases the blue tones. Should a compensation-filter be necessary, the Kodak 30 R filter can be used with great success without affecting the film speed.

If the lamp is used for long periods at a time, its life is approximately 1,200 hours, but if used with frequent intervals the lifetime of the bulb is considerably increased.

The XBO 162, 150-*watt lamp.*—This is an alternative to the standard 6-volt 5-amp filament lamp, and must be used with a rectifier connected to 220 volts a.c. The ignition requires 20 kV and this is arranged automatically, by means of a sliding contact, on switching on the lamp. After it has been switched off, and while still hot, this lamp may be switched on again immediately. A special feature of the lamphouse is the lock on the door which prevents the latter from being opened while the mains connection is in position. On no account should the lamp door be opened while the lamp is hot, in fact, it should not normally be necessary to open the lamphousing for adjustments after the lamp has been inserted.

The optical arrangement of the lamphouse gives an arc of the xenon high-pressure discharge lamp which is reflected into its own plane, compensating for the slight decrease in brightness which occurs. The special three-lens collector system permits a beam of light to be directed into the substage condenser and, when the lamp is used for long periods, the Schott K.G.1 heat-resisting filter should be inserted.

Another special feature of this lamp is the inclusion of four filters which can be brought into operation independently, by an easily operated switch. The fitted filters are as follows:

Panchromatic green for monochrome photomicrography.

Grey filter, 1 per cent transmission (2·3 mm. NG3).

Grey filter, 0·5 per cent transmission (2·4 mm. NG9).

In addition to these dimming filters, a dispersion disc is fitted; its function is to blur the structure of the source, thus ensuring a far greater degree of evenness of illumination. The BG 12 filter can also be inserted; this is required for fluorescence work when the SC 150 ultra-violet high-pressure mercury-vapour lamp is in use.

A swing-out mirror is arranged in front of the filter box for alternative use with the standard microscope lamp (5-amp 30-watt) as supplied for the Ortholux.

SPECIAL METHODS

Bubble Illumination.—Often one is confronted with a subject which just will not fit on to the microscope stage; in such cases ways and means must be devised as illustrated in Fig. 46. This arrangement was devised to photograph gas bubbles (Plate 57) on the inner surface of a bottle of aerated soft drink. The figure illustrates the microscope, less stage and condenser, with the foot in a reversed position, thus enabling the objective to operate close to the bottle.

The Watson microcamera was used for this particular task and was modified to operate in the horizontal position. Three brackets, two of which are seen in Fig. 46, at *B* and *D*, held the camera firmly in position. Focusing on the inner side of the bottle was carried out on the ground-glass screen. A special stage housed the bottle resting on a piece of Perspex, *I*, held within the metal tube *H*. Glass would, of course, be better, but this is more difficult to cut. The stage could be racked up and down by *J* and thumb-screw *K* (Fig. 47) to enable a survey to be made over a large area. The bottle was turned manually.

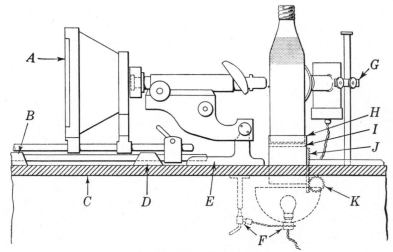

Fig. 46. Bubble illumination

The main source of illumination came from *F* (Fig. 46), a 500-watt Photoflood bulb, situated beneath the bench top. This lamp was fully adjustable and could be locked in position on a ball joint. A second source was provided at *G*. This top light played an important part in illuminating the area to be photographed, but care and patience were required in establishing its position, since a great deal of reflection occurred at the curved surface of the glass. When the light was correctly positioned, the bubbles were seen in relief, making observation of the hydrophilic and hydrophobic surfaces quite simple.

Shutter speeds in work of this sort must be short, because the bubbles are in constant motion.

'*Strap*' *Method.*—It is not always possible to cut pieces off a specimen and some manufacturers object to their samples being defaced. To overcome this, the author devised the 'strap' method of photomicrography. Illuminating a subject such as is seen in Plate 22 is not always easy, and more than one lamp is often necessary. In such cases the microscope stage and foot often restrict one's movements.

The Watson microcamera was used (Fig. 48), the bellows extension added to the magnification produced by the microscope. A heavy base is absolutely a necessity in such work to ensure

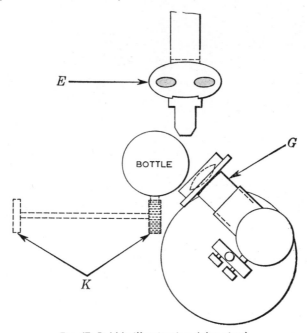

Fig. 47. Bubble illumination (plan view)

rigidity. The microscope body was taken out of the limb; this made the stage, condenser and foot unnecessary. The microscope tube was held rigid and vertical by a strong light alloy 'strap' *B* to provide coarse adjustment *D*, while *C* held the two sections together. This 'strap' can be seen in Fig. 49. A hole was drilled through the halves to house the microscope tube, coarse-adjustment and camera-supporting pillars. Major adjustments were made by *C* and final focusing by adjustment *F*. Low-power objectives can be used, there being no restriction in the height

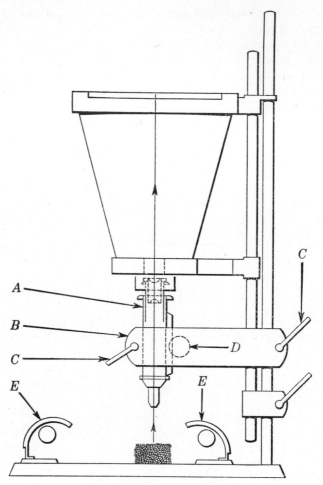

Fig. 48. Oblique illumination

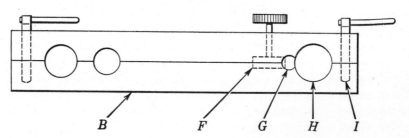

Fig. 49. Plan view of strap

movements. It is possible to move any required distance from the specimen and to photograph very large areas. The specimen must be moved manually.

Two tubular lamps, 63 mm. in length, 25 mm. diameter and 50-volt, were suitably housed in adjustable reflectors E, illuminating the subject from a low angle. Care must always be taken to ensure even illumination which becomes more difficult as the magnification is decreased.

PHOTOMETERS

Many types of Photometers have been adequately described by J. F. Dunn in his book *Exposure Meters and Practical Exposure Control* (Fountain Press). George L. Royer and Marie E. Wissemann, of the Microscopic Laboratory, Calco Chemical Company, Inc., Bound Brook, N.J., however, place on record the successful use of an exposure meter with the Leica camera, using Kodachrome Type A film.

The C.G. Grand Microphotometer is small and compact and has been specially designed for photomicrography. Its removal from the microscope is not necessary after a reading has been taken and before the exposure is made. This meter fits any microscope, the eyepiece resting in a bayonet fitting which clips into the exposure meter. Provision has also been made for any type of camera to fit on the top of the meter. The light-sensitive selenium photo-electric cells are quickly and effectively removed from the path of light rays by a quick release lever. There is also a range switch which enables reduction of sensitivity of the meter by a ratio of 10:1. To calibrate the instrument for exposure time, for instance, an adequate light-source, adjustable to such an extent that a convenient scale reading may be obtained, should be employed. When the best exposure time for a certain reading has been determined, it is an easy matter to correlate values for the entire scale. If, say, an exposure time of 10 seconds for a scale reading 5 is found to be satisfactory, and with a different specimen the reading is 2·5, only half the original amount of light is available in the second instance.

Photovolt Corporation, New York, produce a wide range of exposure meters for photomicrography and over the years have specialized in these instruments.

Models 501-M, 514-M and 200-M are of particular interest to the photomicrographer. The two first-mentioned operate with

phototubes of the photo-emissive type and are capable of registering lower light values. Thus, they lend themselves to direct light
measurements in the focal plane. In the 501-M the phototube is
housed in a search unit having a circular window of 1 in. diameter.
The spectral response is shown by curve *C* in Fig. 50. The response
covers the visible spectrum from the red region of about 650 mμ
through the yellow, green and blue and near ultra-violet. With
the aid of suitable filters the response of the instruments can be
modified for approximate agreement with the spectral sensitivity
of the panchromatic, orthochromatic and non-colour-sensitized
material.

The panel of the photometer has an indicating meter, zero
adjustment and a four-position range switch enabling the instrument to operate at high sensitivity for light of low intensity.

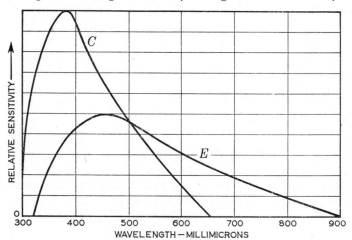

Fig. 50. Relative sensitivity curves of Photovolt exposure meter

For applications in which high response in the far red is needed,
this model can be fitted with a phototube having a response as
shown by curve *E* in Fig. 50. The overall sensitivity of phototube
E is somewhat lower than that of phototube C. The 200-M is also
capable of recording the slightest change in light values, and uses
barrier-layer photocells. It is suitable for use with panchromatic
and colour materials. The effect of colour filters is also properly
indicated by barrier-layer cells. It is worth while pointing out that
the makers of this instrument claim that it is twenty times more
sensitive than usual exposure meters and also permits at least ten

times more accurate readings by having a longer scale length. Perhaps it can now be realized that with the usual exposure meter some judgement of exposure must be exercised in addition to the given reading, before an exposure is made.

The search unit of model 200-M is fitted with a metal extension tube $\frac{1}{2}$ in. long and has an outside diameter to fit into the standard 0·917 in. inside diameter of the eyepiece sleeve. The inside diameter of the body tube is usually 37 mm. The instrument measures the intensity of the total light beam entering the ocular. It may be necessary to measure at a slightly increased distance from the eyelens; this can be done with the ocular adapter.

Ocular Adapter.—When the search unit is placed in position directly on the ocular, the photocell surface will be a distance of $\frac{1}{2}$ in. above the eyelens. The size of the light spot on the photocell then depends on the height of the eye point of the eyepiece in use. When operating with a high-magnification eyelens, the beam is spread out sufficiently to give a reliable light reading. A little care is necessary when applying the search unit to oculars of low power; the photocell may be just at the eye point or slightly above it so that a small spot of high intensity is formed on the photocell. Barrier-layer cells may give erroneously low readings if strong light is concentrated in a small area. To ensure accurate readings and avoid errors, always make certain that the light spot on the cell has a diameter of at least $\frac{1}{4}$ in. A means of testing the correct distance from the ocular is to lift the search unit $\frac{1}{4}$–$\frac{1}{2}$ in. from the top lens; if the needle deflection is thereby increased, this shows that the light spot was too concentrated for correct results. It is then necessary to hold the search unit at the level at which no further increase in the needle reading is obtained and to use this needle reading for the actual exposure determination. Or, for greater convenience, one may employ the ocular adapter as seen in Fig. 51. The choice of the method depends mainly upon how frequently objectives, eyepieces, bellows extension, various apertures, types of films and distance of illumination are being changed. The instrument is provided with a scale divided into arbitrary units and must initially be calibrated to conform with the particular microscopic and photographic technique adopted. In general, it will be found more convenient to adjust the intensity of the image to give a standard reading on the instrument, rather than attempt to interpret various scale readings in terms of exposure.

Much useful advice on using the exposure meter is given in a booklet published by the manufacturers.

Colour Balance.—Regarding the use of the Photometer 514-M for obtaining the correct colour balance in photomicrography with Kodachrome and Ektachrome film, see a comprehensive article by R. P. Loveland, *Analytical Chemistry* (1949) **21**, No. 4, 467.

EXPOSURE CONTROL

A change in the overall magnification will produce a corresponding change in the intensity of the image. By the direct

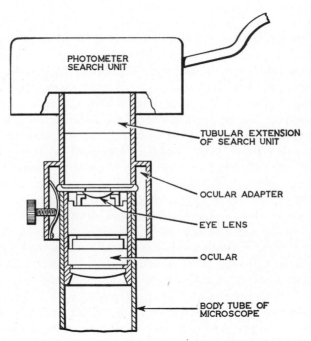

Fig. 51. Photometer search unit of Photovolt exposure meter

application of the inverse square law, if the magnification is increased by a factor of n, then the corresponding exposure will be n^2 times the original exposure. If, for instance, the original magnification was $\times 100$, with an exposure of 2 seconds, at a magnification of $\times 200$ the correct exposure will be 8 seconds. This simple relationship is not valid if changes are made in anything other than the camera bellows-extension and the fine-focusing control.

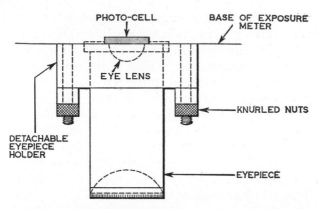

Fig. 52. Detachable eyepiece and photo-cell of exposure meter

The exposure time for opaque specimens is normally fairly constant; there will, however, always be the exceptional case. There are occasions when it is difficult to determine the correct exposure time; particularly with such specimens as those consisting of a network of cells with transparent material between. A reading cannot be made of the colour cells due to the bright light being transmitted around the colour area. If the specimen transmits a complete colour-band, the correct exposure time becomes easier to record on the meter.

The use of an exposure meter is almost essential in this type of photography; when one is not made specially for the microscope, it can only be regarded as an approximate guide to the correct exposure or negative density. The term correct

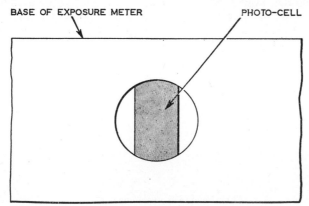

Fig. 53. Plan view of photo-cell and base of exposure meter

exposure bears little relationship to negative density, because negatives of various densities can be printed on different grades of paper to give similar prints. A photographer who regularly makes photomicrographs can usually judge the correct exposure from the intensity of the image on the screen.

In photomicrography there are so many variable factors which govern the final exposure. Any exposure meter must be capable of recording or translating any alteration in the light value, however slight. The exposure meter illustrated in Plate 9 was made for the author and was calibrated by a series of tests, giving an indication of the correct exposure time with the emulsion for which it was calibrated. When first calibrating a light meter such as this there are several points to remember: the emulsion speed, developing time and temperature must be constant, and also the optical system and bellows length. This type of meter is simple and easy to make. It consists of a photo-electric cell which points downward to the eyepiece, the eye-lens of the eyepiece fitting flush to it (Figs. 52 and 53). When light falls upon the photocell it causes an electric current to flow, and this causes the needle to move along the scale, indicating the amount of light reaching the photocell.

With some mounted specimens, the light reaching the photocell may be direct from an area of clear glass on the slide. This reading, therefore, has no relationship to the stained areas. In such cases it is advisable to move the stained part of the slide directly under the objective while a reading is taken. The detachable eyepiece-holder allows for any eyepiece to be used with this meter and can be quickly changed by means of two knurled thumb-nuts, the meter being used only when the microscope is in the vertical position. The meter box simply houses the photocell, the meter being attached to the top and having a switch on one side. The aluminium box is finished in a slate-grey hammer-finish paint.

7

DARK-FIELD
ILLUMINATION

Most photomicrographs are taken under conditions of bright-field illumination. But subjects which have a refractive index very similar to that of the medium in which they are retained are extremely difficult to observe by the transmitted-light technique. Since diffraction and refraction effects are most marked at the boundaries of such subjects, they may usually be rendered visible if the direct rays of light from the condenser are prevented from reaching the objective, and the subject is illuminated only by marginal rays as shown in Fig. 54. This is called dark-field or dark-ground illumination, and depends for its efficiency upon accurate location and adjustment of a suitable condenser, a high-intensity light-source and a very clean specimen.

The importance of the latter factor is not always appreciated, but a slide which appears tolerably clean and well prepared under bright-field illumination often looks very dirty under dark-field. In fact, air bubbles and minute particles of foreign material may become so obvious that they confuse the details of the actual subject-matter.

Consideration of the conditions necessary to illuminate a transparent specimen for dark-field examination will show that the condenser must have a N.A. greater than that of the objective, and

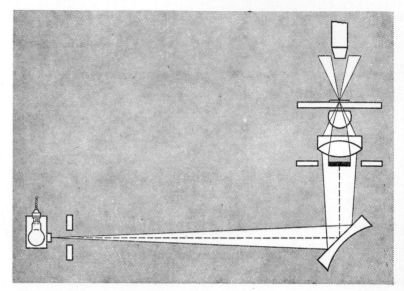

Fig. 54. Dark-ground illumination

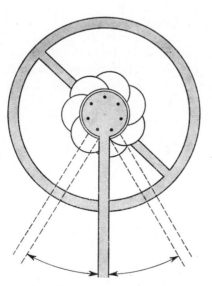

Fig. 55. Traviss expanding stop

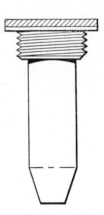

Fig. 56. Funnel stop

the central stop placed in the condenser must block all the central rays which contribute to a N.A. equal to or less than that of the objective. If this is not so and the condenser transmits any rays of smaller N.A. than that of the objective, these will be able to enter the lower lens of the objective as direct transmitted light.

A central expanding stop, such as the Traviss expanding stop (Fig. 55), or one of a set of fixed stops (Baker) may be placed

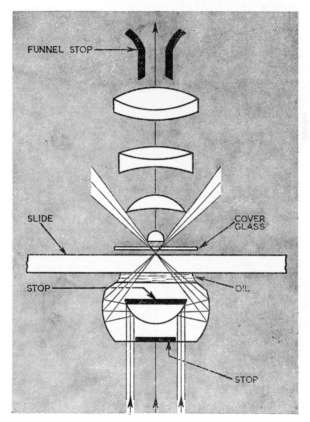

FUNNEL STOP

SLIDE

COVER GLASS

STOP

OIL

STOP

Fig. 57. Light rays and optical system in dark-ground illumination

below the condenser to block the central rays. Whichever type of stop is used, care must be taken to see that the stop is accurately centred and arranged to be just large enough to obliterate all direct illumination of the specimen.

An ordinary Abbe condenser may be used with objectives having a N.A. up to 0·40, but an achromatic condenser must be used with objectives of N.A. in the range 0·40–0·75 or so. With objectives of higher N.A., specially computed oil-immersion dark-field condensers are required. In an extreme case, the N.A. of the objective may be reduced by the introduction of a funnel stop (Fig. 56) as shown in Fig. 57, but this clearly decreases the resolving power of the lens.

The Abbe chromatic condenser N.A. 1·20 is ideal for this application and gives brilliant results with most objectives, especially with a dry objective of N.A. 0·65. The insertion of an immersion medium between the condenser and the slide will often improve the brilliance of the image.

The Abbe chromatic condenser of N.A. 1·40 has three lenses and its large aperture allows a large stop of 22-mm. diameter to

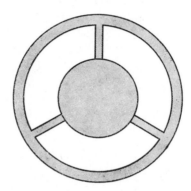

Fig. 58. Dark-field stop

be used between the two lower lenses. A condenser of this type can be used successfully for the photography of soap crystals (Plate 55(e)) which can, as a rule, be quite difficult. Bacteria in a live state, fungi or minute colloidal particles can be recorded quite well if an objective of N.A. at least 0·85 is used with this condenser. There is an efficient stop (Fig. 58) now in production in the U.S.A. which has been designed to be attached beneath the condenser.

The achromatic condensers, back-lens types, are by far the best for dark-field illumination and should always be used when objectives of N.A. 1·30–1·40 are used.

The first bispheric reflecting condenser (Fig. 59(a)) was made by Leitz in 1908 and a short time later H. Sredentopf designed an efficient cardioid condenser for Zeiss. The light rays

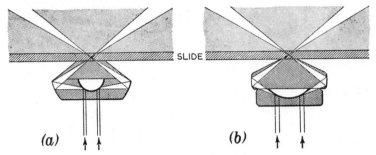

Fig. 59. Bispheric double reflecting dark-ground condenser (*a*); cardioid reflecting dark-ground condenser (*b*)

(Fig. 59(*a*)) strike the convex surface and are reflected to the concentric concave reflector, bringing the rays to an aplanatic focus at the specimen. Owing to the perfection of focusing achieved, fine details can also be recorded in bacteria and in subject-matter such as crystals having a similar refractive index to that of the medium in which they are mounted. The aperture of this condenser varies from N.A. 1·20 to 1·33, allowing objectives up to N.A. 1·05 to be used.

The Bausch and Lomb cardioid condenser (Fig. 59(*b*)) provides efficient illumination for work at lower magnifications, but it does not fill the field when used with oil-immersion objectives. These condensers are manufactured in various focal lengths, 3·6 mm. for oil-immersion and 5·5–6 mm. for work of a general nature.

The alignment of the microscope must be very carefully conducted for work by the dark-field technique. First, remove the eyepiece, objective and substage condenser. Next, set up a very intense light-source and use the substage mirror to project the beam of light exactly up the microscope body tube. If a lamp with a very small source is being used (such as a Pointolite) it may be necessary to use an auxiliary condenser in the light-train in order to fill the whole of the substage condenser lens. If this is so, the preliminary adjustment of the mirror should be carried out with the auxiliary condenser in position. The condenser may then be inserted together with the rest of the optical equipment.

Since the adjustments are most exacting for high-power work, we will discuss the technique from this aspect. An ordinary condenser will have to be centred by inspection of the position of the cone of light which it provides, but most dark-field condensers bear some sort of centring mark on their upper lens. This should be focused by the objective and centred by the substage-condenser centring screws. If the condenser is corrected for one thickness of slide, this should be checked against the slide to be used. Some condensers are equipped with a correction device for slide thickness; if so, this must be checked.

The top lens of the condenser may now be oiled and the slide placed in position. The subject should be focused with an objective of moderate power, and the condenser may be racked up and down to give the optimum illumination. This will occur when the illuminated area on the slide is a spot of minimum diameter. Any deviation from this position will result in a larger and more diffuse spot and finally in a ring of light. Having established this optimum condition and made any necessary minor adjustments to the condenser centring, etc., the high-power objective may be brought into position. Some final, very delicate adjustments will almost certainly be required to produce the best results.

It is, of course, most important that all immersion oil be care-fully removed after the work is finished.

8

MONOCHROMATIC ILLUMINATION

FILTERS play an important part in photomicrography. Often a prepared microscope slide suggests richness of colour to the naked eye, but when it is photographed and a negative produced, there is sometimes a disappointing result, such as a flat negative image and lack of colour contrast, which could have been improved had a correction filter been used.

No two filters of the same nominal colour, manufactured by independent firms, can possibly transmit exactly the same wavelengths. Filters of similar type can vary as much as 70 mμ in peak transmission. The following is an approximation of the wavelengths corresponding to the peak transmission of the most popular colour-filters:

Violet	400 mμ
Indigo	440 mμ
Blue	490 mμ
Green	530 mμ
Yellow	580 mμ
Orange	610 mμ
Red	730 mμ

The use of the correct filter in photomicrography may increase not only the contrast of the photographic image but also definition, owing to reduction in chromatic aberrations. This is particularly true of an achromatic lens system combined with a yellow-green filter.

An objective having a N.A. of 1·37 resolves 132,082 lines per inch with white light, but when a green filter is used with this objective, it resolves 143,170 lines per inch. An objective having a N.A. of 1·30 increases from 125,333 to 135,854 lines per inch when a green filter is introduced into the light-train. These figures show that the correct filter can improve the resolving power of an objective.

Colour screens may be made of coloured glass or dyed gelatine, and the latter can be used between glass or unprotected. In either case, however, the gelatine filters must not be overheated. Another means of producing a colour filter is by using a suitable coloured solution contained in a trough.

TYPES AND USES

Liquid Filters.—These are in some respects better than glass, since it is possible to control their characteristics over a wide range, but they are not so convenient to use or handle. The cells used for this purpose are made of optically flat glass, and the cell itself is not less than 2 in. deep. Liquid filters also serve as heat filters. When preparing liquid filters, some attention must be given to the strength of the light-source. The Pointolite bulb requires a much stronger solution than, say, a 12-volt 24-watt coiled-filament lamp. It is difficult to state the concentration required for liquid filters, and experience is the only guide.

A popular liquid green known as Zettnow's filter comprises saturated aqueous solutions of copper nitrate and chromic acid. The strength of these two solutions can be varied to control the density of the green. There are, however, many chemicals which will give a green solution and many which will produce a blue-green. Iodine-green, acid-green and methyl-green are the most popular and can provide very dense filters.

Acetate of copper and bichromate of potash, together with a strong solution of glacial acetic acid, will produce a yellow-green. By controlling the proportion of each chemical, the colour saturation, either the green or the yellow, can be emphasized, acetate of copper giving the green and bichromate of potash the yellow.

A very useful liquid blue, suitable for blue-light fluorescence, is prepared by the addition of concentrated ammonia solution to a saturated solution of cupric sulphate until the precipitate of cupric hydroxide is re-dissolved. This method produces a deep blue solution known as cupric tetraminosulphate or cuprammonium sulphate. Other filters suitable for pure ultra-violet fluorescence are mentioned in Chapter 9 under the heading 'Fluorescence Illumination'.

Gelatine Filters.—There are times when a specimen is far too contrasty, in which case it is essential to reduce the contrast in one colour in order to emphasize another. For instance, when a specimen is stained both red and blue, the two colours may reproduce at similar densities in a monochrome negative. To separate these colours, and thus produce a difference in tone in black and white, a filter must be chosen which is complementary to one colour and identical with the other. Another example can be given here. A specimen which is stained red and stained green (Plate 46(a)) is to be photographed and the maximum colour contrast is required. The following points should, therefore, be borne in mind. A green filter holds back the red parts, which now appear dark, and the greens are now light because this colour was allowed to pass. The golden rule to be remembered is to choose a filter which is complementary to that colour of the specimen which is required to be dark in the finished print.

The use of a blue filter increases the resolution considerably, and a deep filter, such as violet, increases the resolution still more, to approximately twice that attained without a filter.

The subject which shows multiple colours should be photographed with the insertion of the Ilford Gamma (No. 402) filter to give correction to all colours on a par with their visual luminosities. The colour-correction filter (Addacolor C.C. filter) manufactured by Harrison and Harrison can be used with similar effect. If the choice of negative and processing is not used to advantage, the results might not be entirely satisfactory in black and white.

When photographing a colourless subject, such as diatoms, it is advisable to use a blue filter, coupled with a process plate, the details therefore appearing dark. The use of a green filter with a chromatic plate gives approximately the same results (Plates 38(c) and (d) and 49(d)). It is as well to remember that the shorter the wave-length of light the greater the resolving power. Should chromatic aberration appear in the optical system, the use of a deep yellow filter with an orthochromatic emulsion, or a green with panchromatic film, will be necessary to counteract this fault. The exposures will, of course, be long.

Gelatine filters, such as the Wratten 'M' series (Table 6), sandwiched between glass, are indispensable for this type of work.

TABLE 6. USES OF WRATTEN 'M' SERIES FILTERS

Name	Code	Colour	Trans- mission per cent	Uses
A	25	Red	15·0	For infra-red photography and for objects stained red and brown.
B	58	Green	26·0	For maximum contrast in transparent specimens and red-stained specimens —particularly useful in medical work.
C	47	Blue- violet	3·2	Enables high resolution to be achieved with orthochromatic plates, also enhances contrast of colourless specimens (Plate 54).
D	35	Purple	—	Rarely used alone (requires long exposures).
E	22	Orange	34·0	General purposes, isolates the yellow band from various light-sources.
F	29	Red	7·0	Enhances contrast in brown subjects.
G	15	Deep yellow	67·0	Enhances detail and contrast of blue-stained specimens and is often used with a green filter.
H	45	Blue- green	5·07	Increases resolution and contrast of colourless and orange-yellow specimens.
XI	11	Light blue	40·4	Gives high resolution with panchromatic material; used with high-intensity tungsten light.

For further reference, the *Wratten Filter Manual*, a 96-page book dealing with Wratten light filters and supplied by Kodak, will be of value to all photomicrographers.

Further information dealing with ultra-violet radiations is given in Chapter 9 under the heading of 'Reflecting Microscopy'.

TABLE 7. MAXIMUM CONTRAST FILTERS FOR STAINED SPECIMENS

Stain	Colour	Filters Recommended
Acid Fuchsin	Magenta	Deep Green + Yellow-orange
Aniline Blue	Blue	Deep Green + Orange
Azure I	Violet-blue	Deep Green + Orange
Basic Fuchsin	Magenta	Deep Green + Yellow-orange
Carmine	Light Magenta	Deep Green + Yellow-orange
Crystal Violet	Lavender	Deep Green + Yellow-orange
Eosin	Orange-red	Yellow-orange + Blue-green
Gentian Violet	Deep Violet	Deep Green + Orange
Haematoxylin	Deep Blue	Deep Green + Yellow-orange
Light Green S.F.	Light Green	Deep Red
Methylene Blue	Light Blue	Purple + Yellow-orange
Methyl Green	Blue-green	Deep Red
Methyl Violet	Deep Violet	Deep Green + Orange
Orange II	Light Orange	Medium Blue
Saffranin O	Orange	Yellow-orange + Blue-green
Sudan III	Reddish-orange	Yellow-orange + Blue-green

Corresponding Ilford filters are listed below:

No. 305 Micro 1 (blue-violet)
No. 303 Micro 2 (blue)
No. 405 Micro 3 (green)
No. 110 Micro 4 (deep yellow)
No. 202 Micro 5 (deep orange)
No. 501 Micro 6 (purple)
No. 502 Micro 7 (magenta)
No. 104 Micro 8 (yellow)
No. 108 Micro 9 (pale yellow)

Figs. 60, 61 and 62 illustrate the curves relating to these filters.

All filters should, of course, be placed between the subject-matter and the light-source, not between subject and objective.

The filter controls the density of the background which can be either light or dark, the colour of the specimen controlling this point. Before filters can be used to advantage, however, the worker should have full knowledge of the negative material available, ensuring that the combination of filter and emulsion will produce the best possible negative. Table 7 can be used as a guide for colour contrast.

Rarely does the same filter give colour contrast and detail. If, however, this does happen, it is always advisable to concentrate on the latter (Plate 25). When focusing on an object which is stained yellow, it is as well to do so with the complementary colour filter in position, as this gives a different point of focus

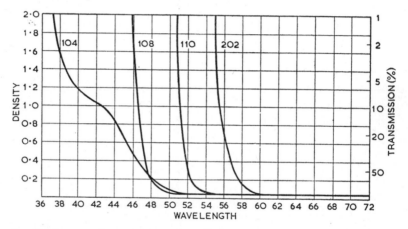

Fig. 60. Curves relating to Ilford Filters 104, 108, 110, 202 (Micro 8, 9, 4 and 5)

to the normal unfiltered light. Apochromatic objectives are to be preferred when one photographs stained specimens using filters. The objective, being fully corrected, brings the blue-violet, yellow and blue-green all into focus on the same plane. It must be remembered, however, that a compensating eyepiece should be used to ensure the colour correction of the particular objective. This is not possible when using infra-red material, as there is a vast difference between the visual focus and the infra-red focus. The sensitivity of the eye falls off at approximately 7,000 Å, but photographic material goes beyond this point, having a peak at approximately 9,000 Å. In view of this it is recommended that an Ilford Tricolour Red or a Kodak Wratten No. 25 be used when

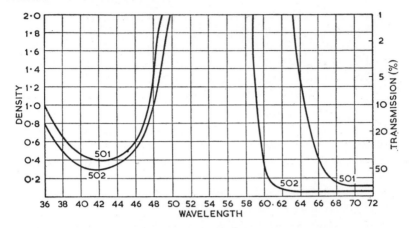

Fig. 61. Curves relating to Ilford Filters 501 and 502
(Micro 6 and 7)

focusing and be replaced with an infra-red filter before the exposure. It must be borne in mind that focusing has taken place in light of a wave-length less than the infra-red and that some further focusing must be done by careful adjustment. It is recommended that the fine adjustment be used, the degree of movement being determined by trial and error. The objective, of course, should be racked away from the specimen. There are a number of filters which transmit beyond 7,000 Å, as follows:

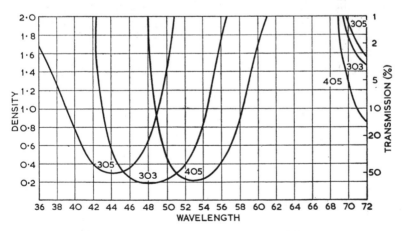

Fig. 62. Curves relating to Ilford Filters 303, 305 and 405
(Micro 2, 1 and 3)

Wratten 88A transmits from 7,200 Å;
Wratten 87 transmits from 7,400 Å;
Ilford 207 + 813 also transmits from 7,400 Å.

(See page 147 for infra-red.)

As can be seen, a filter absorbs part of the light which is
thrown on to the specimen; therefore, the exposure will be greater
than if no filter were used. The filter factor is governed by the
colour-sensitivity of the particular emulsion in use, and the type
of light used to illuminate the subject about to be photographed.
Ilford and Kodak supply a printed guide to the approximate
exposure factors for their own filters, but this can only act as a
rough guide to the photomicrographer, there being so many
variable factors to be taken into account. Because of this it will
be found that trial and error is one of the best methods. It is
suggested that the worker keep a strict note of all exposures made.
To do this properly takes a considerable time, as the following
information should be recorded: type of lighting; filter; aperture
of substage, lamphouse and objective; focal length of objective;
dry or oil objective; magnification of eyepiece; camera bellows-
length; whether condenser used or not; distance of light-source
from condenser; and type of emulsion. All these points, and many
others, affect the exposure time.

Ultra-violet Filters.—Work in the ultra-violet is difficult. The
eye is not sensitive to light of wave-length less than 4,000 Å, but
the special ultra-violet lamphouse already referred to can also
be used in the visible region of the spectrum. For this type of work
the optical parts should be made from quartz, fluorite or lithium
fluoride, which transmits radiations in the ultra-violet, i.e. from
3,500 Å to 2,000 Å.

When using ultra-violet as a means of illumination and filters
for mercury lamps, it is essential to separate any fluorescent
radiation which may be produced. All visible radiations must be
excluded from the emulsion and, as fluorescence is a visible
illumination, means must be employed whereby these radiations
are filtered out from the ultra-violet. The lamphouse or substage
is fitted with a filter which transmits ultra-violet and at the same
time absorbs all visible rays. The filters capable of doing this are
the Corning 586 and the Wratten 18A. These two are very effective when panchromatic material is used. The Wratten 17A filter
is slightly inaccurate when used with panchromatic film, as it

allows a small proportion of visible rays to enter, but it is effective when non-colour-sensitive emulsions are in use, as the transmission is in the region of 2,000 Å.

The Wratten 32 filter, which is minus-green, absorbs heavily the two most prominent bands from a mercury lamp, 5,460 Å and 5,770 Å. The mercury-vapour lamp is becoming increasingly popular and its value in producing monochromatic illumination is recognized; therefore, the Wratten 77 and 77A filters are incorporated with this source to produce monochromatic light. A yellow band is produced by the Wratten 22 filter, blue-violet by Wratten 50 and green by the Wratten 62.

Interference Filters.—The Fabry-Perot interference filter consists of two highly reflecting silvered surfaces separated by a very thin and uniform spacing layer of air or cryolite. With this type of filter it is possible to select a very narrow band of radiation in any part of the spectrum. Dye filters cannot approach the selectivity of a Fabry-Perot filter, and the effect obtained with an ordinary filter (Plate 43) is therefore not so pronounced as with an interference optical system.

The Multiple Reflection filter consists of two semi-transparent films of silver separated by what is known as a dielectric spacer, which is transparent and of a low refractive index. The three layers are fixed on glass by evaporation in vacuum. The thickness of the dielectric layer controls the spectral position of the transmitted light. The spacing of the reflecting layers is comparable with the wave-lengths of light and interference phenomena enable the filter to be highly selective.

Heat-resisting Filters.—The special Pyrex glass heat-resisting filter, blue-green in colour, absorbs the infra-red heat rays and also part of the visible red. Care should be taken when obtaining one of these filters to ensure that it is free from air bubbles and defects in the glass. These Aklo filters can be purchased in light, medium and dark shades of 2–3 mm. in thickness. Some loss of light is experienced, the light filter transmits 25 per cent, the medium 60 per cent and the dark filter 42 per cent of the incident light. These filters do not absorb all the heat as can be seen from the following: 75 per cent is absorbed by the light filter, 93 per cent by the medium and 96 per cent by the dark filter.

9

SPECIAL METHODS OF ILLUMINATION

IN the previous chapter we were concerned with the colour of light and the way in which this could be modified by the introduction of various filters. The colour of light depends upon the wave-length or group of wave-lengths of which it is composed. In this chapter we shall review some of the ways in which the wave *nature* of light can be exploited to assist in the observation of microscope specimens.

NATURE OF LIGHT

In order to be able to discuss polarization and interference phenomena it is necessary to form a simple picture of the nature of light. If we imagine a rope supported loosely in a horizontal position, we can transmit a 'wave' along the rope by jerking one end quickly up and down. The wave travels along the rope to the far end, but none of the rope itself is transmitted along its length. This travelling wave is therefore made up of a series of transverse displacements of short lengths of the rope and is known as a transverse wave. Before we apply this elementary analogy to the nature of light, we may press the similarity a little further. If we imagine that the rope passes through a small hole in a fence, the 'wave' cannot be transmitted through the hole. If, however, we enlarge the hole into a slit, the wave will pass through the slit, but only when the plane of the wave is parallel to that of the slit.

Light consists of a series of transverse vibrations in space, which may be imagined to be very similar to a series of transverse waves passing along a loose length of rope. There is one very important difference, however: the wave motion of light is not confined to one plane but occurs simultaneously all around the rope. The only way to picture this is to imagine that, just for an instant, the rope is 'frozen' with a wave somewhere along its length. If the rope is now spun about its length as an axis, the wave will sweep out a circular shape. Reverting to light we may therefore try to form a picture of a series of transverse waves, which expand and contract through 360°, at right angles to the direction in which they are travelling.

If we now project a beam of such light through a substance which behaves optically in the same way as the slit in the fence, all the vibrations which do not lie in the plane of the slit will be blocked, and the only light transmitted will be that in which the vibrations are parallel to the slit. Such an emergent beam is said to be plane-polarized because its vibrations are confined to one plane. If a second piece of similar material is placed in the path of the emergent plane-polarized beam, the beam will be transmitted only if the plane of polarization of the second sheet of material is parallel with that of the first. If it is perpendicular to it, no light will pass. At intermediate angles a proportion of the light will pass. If two such sheets were arranged close together, the rotation of one relative to the other would provide the effect of an infinitely variable neutral density filter—although, of course, the polarization introduced would make such a filter of very limited value.

This simple analogy with wave motion in a rope cannot be pressed too far. In ordinary non-polarized light, the amplitude of the transverse waves, measured normal to the direction of propagation of the light, is entirely random. When the light is plane-polarized, the vibration occurs in one plane, and the waves are of constant amplitude. But it is also possible to have light which is polarized in two directions, at right angles. If the amplitude of vibration differs in the two directions, the light is said to be elliptically polarized. In the special case when the amplitudes are equal, the light is said to be circularly polarized. These concepts are not easily understood, and can only be properly explained in the mathematical terms of simple harmonic motion. The phraseology is introduced here, since most photomicrographers are faced with the necessity of having some sort of mental picture by which they can understand the mechanism of polarization effects. For a full explanation of the phenomena the reader may consult any of the standard text-books on light.

POLARIZATION

There are several materials which may be used to produce polarized light. The Nicol prism is composed of two pieces of Iceland Spar, suitably cut and polished and mounted together with Canada balsam. Iceland Spar is known as a doubly refracting material, which means that a beam of light incident to its surface is split into two beams within the crystal. These two beams travel at slightly different angles to each other, depending upon the relative disposition of the incident light-beam, the face upon which it impinges and the direction of the optical axis of the crystal. But the really important thing about these beams is that they are both plane-polarized.

The angle of the balsam-cemented interface between the two components of the completed prism is arranged so that one of these two beams is reflected to the side of the prism where it is absorbed, while the other is allowed to proceed and emerge from the opposite face of the assembly to that at which the beam entered. A complete description of the theory of the Nicol prism is outside the scope of this book, but is readily available in works dealing with physics and light.

The efficiency of a Nicol prism is very high, but its application is limited due to difficulty in obtaining large pieces of optically perfect Iceland Spar. The effective diameter of Nicol prisms is, therefore, rather small, commonly of the order of 1 cm. The most convenient modern method of producing polarization is by the use of a synthetic material known as Polaroid. This has the great advantage that it is available in large sheets and is quite thin.

Polarized light has many applications. Light reflected from a surface suffers a degree of polarization, and this effect is often used in conventional photography. If a display behind a glass window is to be photographed, trouble is often experienced due to strong reflections from the surface of the glass. By using a piece of Polaroid over the lens, a position may be found in which the intensity of these reflections is decreased. This is a comparatively unimportant application, but in the examination of transparent materials polarized light is invaluable.

A crystalline material is one in which the atomic lattice is a regularly repeated, more or less precise, geometrical arrangement.

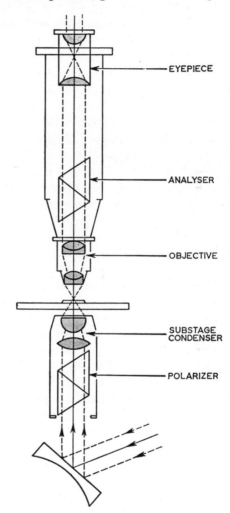

Fig. 63. Optical lay-out of illumination by polarized light

EYEPIECE

ANALYSER

OBJECTIVE

SUBSTAGE CONDENSER

POLARIZER

Such structures are referred to three mutually perpendicular lines known as axes, in order that the various properties of any given crystal may be discussed in relation to the direction in the crystal for which the property is investigated. Isotropic materials are ones in which the properties are similar in any direction within the crystal. Many materials are, however, anisotropic; which simply means that the physical properties of the crystal vary with the direction in which they are measured. In the case of transparent materials, the optical properties vary in various directions within the crystal.

Bausch and Lomb Polarizing Microscope LC and the Leitz Polarizing Microscope are recommended if a considerable amount of photomicrography in polarized light is to be carried out. There are also several body tubes equipped for work in polarized light which may be interchanged with conventional body tubes.

The application of polarized light in microscopy is a specialized subject, and the technique is invaluable in the examination of a very wide range of materials. No book on photomicrography can be expected to deal exhaustively with this aspect of the subject, but the photomicrographer must be able to appreciate the basic technique and able to conduct the simple manipulations which are necessary during the adjustments that precede exposure. The following brief notes are written with this aim in mind.

In order to be able to use polarized light in microscopy, a polarizing element must be fitted in the light-train. This is usually done beneath the condenser when the microscope is to be used for work by transmitted light. A Nicol prism is shown in this position in Fig. 63, but a sheet of Polaroid may also be used—not so effectively, however, as a prism. When the plane-polarized light passes through a specimen, a number of changes may be produced in the nature of the emerging beam which is received by the objective. In order that the nature of these changes may be examined, a second polarizing element is mounted above the objective and within the microscope body tube. The only difference between this component, called the analyser, and the lower polarizing element, is that the analyser is capable of rotation through 90° about the optical axis of the microscope, whereas the polarizing element is fixed in position. A graduated quadrant is provided with the analyser in order that its degree of rotation may be observed, and it is also usually provided with a click stop, or some similar means of establishing when it is 'crossed'. This condition occurs when the planes of polarization of the two polarizing elements are mutually at right angles (Polaroid sheet does not create this condition), and corresponds to the position in which the minimum amount of light appears at the eyepiece (in the absence of a specimen on the stage). The whole of the analysing equipment is sometimes carried on a slide by means of which it can be inserted into the optical path, or quickly removed. For the most part, the analysing equipment is fitted above the objective (Plate 9(a) and (b)).

A disadvantage of the Nicol prism for this work is that the prism mounting is rather long. Unless the body tube of the microscope has been specially constructed to carry the analysing Nicol the lengthening of the body tube resulting from fitting an analysing adapter may introduce complications. For all serious microscopic work with polarized light, a graduated rotating stage is essential, and a further facility often provided is a slot at 45° to the fixed plane of polarization of the polarizer. Various accessories, such as quarter-wave plates and quartz wedges, may be inserted in this slot to facilitate interpretation of the nature of the subject material.

The analyser illustrated in Plate 9 can be rotated through 360° by thumb and forefinger. This delicate adjustment does not upset the focus of the objective, which is immediately beneath it. If the stage and analyser be fixed, polarized light can be obtained by revolving the polarizer around its axis.

When a crystal of an optically isotropic material is examined under the microscope, with the analyser inserted and in the 'crossed' position, the crystal will appear dark. This is due to the fact that the plane of polarization of the light transmitted by the polarizer is at right angles to the plane of polarization of the analyser, and, since the specimen examined is isotropic, the beam of light undergoes no change in character (other than a slight loss in intensity) between the polarizer and analyser. This condition will still be obtained if the specimen stage is rotated. Thus, if a transparent crystal appears uniformly dark under crossed Nicols, irrespective of the degree of rotation of the specimen the crystal is probably isotropic.

Anisotropic crystals may be of either two or three refractive indices; the latter are called biaxial crystals and the former are known as uniaxial crystals. These differing refractive indices mean that a beam of light incident to one face of the crystal is divided into two or three beams within the crystal, each travelling in different directions and at different velocities. When these rays leave the upper face of the specimen under observation, the various beams combine and the result depends upon the precise nature of each of the emergent beams. Since the refracted beams within the crystal travel at different speeds, and since also the optical path length must depend upon the angle of each beam, it is clear that the emergent beams will not bear the same phase relationship to each other. The result is the introduction of a varying measure of ellipticity in the emergent beam and this is then 'analysed' in the analysing element to give a series of patterns which bear a marked similarity to interference figures. In fact, they are not similar, but this distinction is not very important from the purely practical point of view.

If monochromatic light is used, and an optically anisotropic crystal is examined under crossed Nicols, the specimen will go black, or 'extinguish', four times for each complete rotation of the

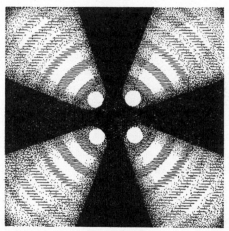

Fig. 64. Uniaxial interference figure, showing isochromatic curves

stage. To establish whether the crystal is uniaxial or biaxial, it is necessary to examine the interference figure, and this is shown when the stage is rotated to be midway between two extinction positions. At this position, uniaxial crystals present the pattern shown in Fig. 64 and biaxial crystals present the appearance of Fig. 65. Both these illustrations represent a particular case. In Fig. 65 the section is normal to the optical axis and in Fig. 66 the two optic axes lie at the centre of the series of concentric circles.

Under crossed Nicols, most sections of optically anisotropic crystals exhibit colour when in any position other than their extinction position. In general, the highest polarization colours are produced by crystals in which there is the maximum relative retardation between the refracted beams. These colours are

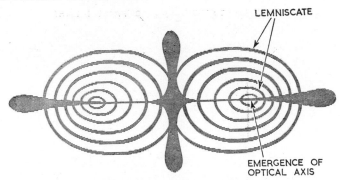

LEMNISCATE

EMERGENCE OF
OPTICAL AXIS

Fig. 65. Biaxial interference figure

usually referred to in terms of Newton's colour scale. The lowest colours in the scale vary from grey to red, the second order consists of violet, blue, green, yellow and red, which sequence is repeated in the higher orders. Seven orders can usually be distinguished, of which the second and third are the most brilliant. From the fourth order the colours become more pale, until after the seventh order they merge into white. The precise order of the colours observed may be determined by the introduction of a quartz wedge in the slot at 45° to the plane of polarization of the analyser. For a complete description of these techniques the reader is referred to *Crystals and the Polarising Microscope* by Hartshorne and Stuart (Arnold, London), and similar works.

Although much of the literature on identification of substances under the microscope is based on morphological or structural appearance, better identification of chemical substances can be obtained when crystals are illuminated by means of polarized light. Films entitled 'The Polarizing Microscope', available from

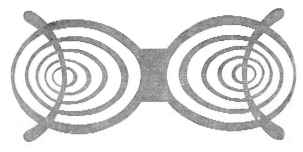

Fig. 66. Biaxial crystal illuminated between crossed Nicols

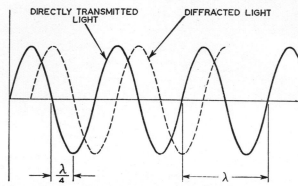

Fig. 67. The directly transmitted light and the diffracted light differ in relative

phase by one-quarter of a wavelength $\left(\dfrac{\lambda}{4}\right)$

Cooke, Troughton & Simms, illustrate beautifully the method for determining some of the basic optical properties.

PHASE CONTRAST

The principles of phase-contrast illumination are not new, although they have been applied to microscopy only since the work of Zernike in the early 1930s (see 'How I discovered phase contrast', ZERNIKE, F., *Science* (1955) **121**, 345–9). In ordinary transmitted-light work we rely upon differences in optical density or colour to form an image. When light passes through such a specimen, the emergent light consists of the directly transmitted light, and light which has been diffracted through various angles depending upon the nature of the fine detail in the subject. By virtue of the small changes in refractive index and thickness which accompany these structural features within the subject, the direct and diffracted emergent light differ slightly in phase. When the

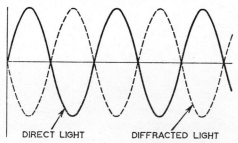

Fig. 68. The action of the phase plate used to increase the phase separation to $\dfrac{\lambda}{2}$

variations in refractive index and path length are small, this
phase difference is of the order of one-quarter of the wave-length
of the light used. Fig. 67 illustrates this effect. If the directly
transmitted light can be separated from the diffracted light, and
the direct light can be given a further acceleration or retardation
of one-quarter of a wave-length, the two types of light emerging
from the specimen will become 180° out of phase, or will be phased
together. The former case is illustrated in Fig. 68, and it is obvious
that the two beams will now interfere with each other. If the
relative intensities of the two beams are equal, the interference will
result in complete suppression of the light. In this way the slight
differences in refractive index and thickness of a *transparent*
specimen may be clearly seen in a black-and-white photograph.
The human eye is insensitive to these phase differences, so that
special methods must be employed if they are to be utilized for
image formation. There are many ways in which the actual
devices required to produce phase contrast may be introduced,
but the basis of the method remains unchanged. The result may
be termed positive or negative phase contrast, depending upon
whether the direct ray is accelerated or retarded by the necessary
quarter wave-length. From the practical point of view these
methods differ rather as do positive and negative images.

Fig. 69 illustrates a simple phase-contrast arrangement for
work in transmitted light. A diaphragm having a narrow circular
iris is placed beneath the condenser, *A*, and permits light to pass
only through the annular opening. An image of this annulus is
formed in the plane of the phase plate, *B*, and the phase plate
carries an exactly matching annulus of material which will either
accelerate or retard the light falling upon it by the necessary
quarter wave-length. In use, the image of the substage diaphragm
must be exactly focused and centred upon the ring in the phase
plate. Then, all the light transmitted directly through the specimen will pass through the ring in the phase plate and receive the
necessary acceleration or retardation. All the diffracted light
received by the objective will be projected upwards and only a
very small proportion of this light will pass through the ring in the
phase plate; the bulk of the diffracted light will pass through the
remainder of the phase plate and suffer no phase change. The
two beams are then received in the eyepiece, where they interfere.
For maximum interference the intensity of the direct beam must
be reduced to match that of the diffracted beam, and this is

accomplished by the deposition of a thin film of metal over the ring on the phase plate, to act as a neutral density filter.

The particular arrangement shown in Fig. 69 varies in detail

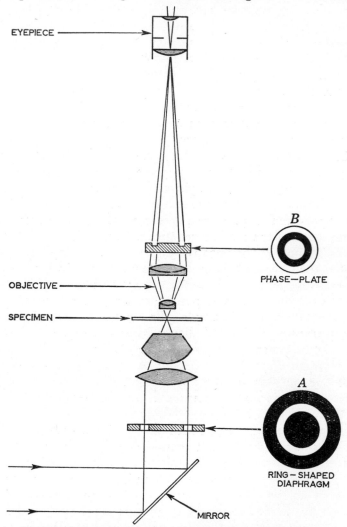

EYEPIECE

B

PHASE—PLATE

OBJECTIVE

SPECIMEN

A

RING — SHAPED
DIAPHRAGM

MIRROR

Fig. 69. Diagrammatic arrangement of phase-contrast equipment

in the equipment provided by various manufacturers, but the principle remains unaltered. With any particular equipment the manufacturer invariably provides the necessary information for alignment.

A typical instance of the value of phase-contrast technique is provided in Plate 27(c). This shows the palate of a whelk. Under ordinary transmitted light, it is very difficult to discern any structure at all. The technique can also be applied to the examination of opaque materials by reflected light, when it is capable of differentiating between very small differences in the level of the surface. This method, first described by F. S. Cuckow in 1949 (*J. Iron St. Inst.* (1949), **161**, 49), is a very valuable tool in metallography, also applied to the study of fibres, crystals and other materials. M. Françon (*Optica Acta* (1954) **1**, 50) described a method by which two movable quartz plates, cut at 45° to the optical axis and interposed between polarizing units, could be used to form a colour-contrast technique. This method has not been very widely adopted yet.

A. Wilska (*Mikroskopie* (1954) **9**, 1–10) introduced a modification of these methods by the use of annular zones coated with lamp black in place of the conventional phase rings; he also made the ring apertures much larger than the normal types and claims that this method gives a much better contrast and resolving power than conventional phase-contrast equipment. The new Leitz phase-contrast apparatus with the Heine condenser permits narrow or wide annular illumination, phase contrast and dark-field or intermediate stages of illumination to be achieved by suitable adjustment of the condenser.

INTERFERENCE MICROSCOPY

Since the development of phase-contrast techniques, further changes have been brought about in the methods of image formation within a microscope. Phase contrast is a form of interference where a beam of light is separated, or retarded, causing image details to be surrounded with a very slight bright fringe or halo to give a second image line, one less sharp than the other. Interference technique provides an image free from such haloes.

Although phase-contrast and interference microscopy are comparatively new, a simple lens system was devised in 1862 in which a beam of light was split into two beams and then recombined to form an image in which interference effects could be observed. This technique proved to be a great success in the study of smooth surfaces and now enables irregularities to be measured. The fringe pattern can be likened to a map which shows contours.

The depth or height can be determined by observing the corresponding fringe deformation. These patterns (Plate 35) are easily interpreted: plane surfaces generate straight lines or fringes, while spheres are shown by circular patterns and cylinders show either elliptical or straight fringes. In a photographic record it is, however, difficult to discriminate between a ridge and a groove, although the difference may easily be determined during visual

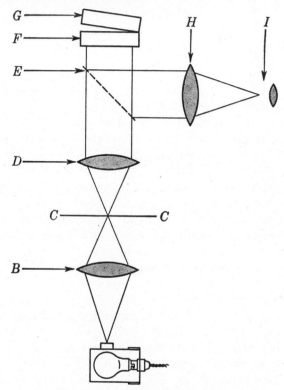

Fig. 70. Early method of interference

observation by observing the movement of the fringes as the fine focusing control is racked gently up and down. Thus, although the height (or depth) may easily be calculated from a photograph, it is necessary to specify whether the observed area lies above or below the remainder of the surface. Refractive index determinations have been applied to liquids, Canada balsam and cadmium sulphide. The interference microscope has also been applied to research in many fields, especially on wood, cotton, rayon and synthetic fibres, as well as on the sharpness and nature of the extreme edge of a razor blade (Plate 56). Little was it realized at that time that this simple system would be the fore-runner of the complex interference methods used today. One or two illustrations of the most up-to-date multiple-beam interference techniques are shown here; there are far too many to illustrate

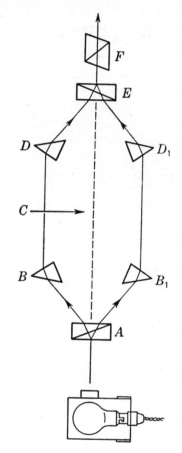

Fig. 71. Cyclic interference,
after F. H. Smith

them all—additional reference is made in the bibliography. Multi-beam interference makes possible the study of the surfaces of materials which appear to be completely smooth, such as glass, film, metals, plastics and crystals. In addition, transparent specimens can be studied. This special technique is also capable of providing a means whereby measurements can be made of very small features of molecular dimensions.

A typical two-beam method used by Fizeau (*Comp. Rend.* (1862) **54**, 1237), by which he studied smooth surfaces, is seen in Fig. 70. The images produced by this method of illumination are known as Fizeau fringes and the term is now universally used. The Fizeau system is a series of lenses, together with a very thin transparent wedge, as can be seen in the illustration. The light-source, after passing through lens B, is projected on to C, which is an iris diaphragm with a small aperture, set at the point of focus of B and D. The parallel beam of light from D now passes on and through the half-silvered glass plate E, striking the lower of the two inclined plates at normal incidence. The angle of the wedge, produced by G, is very shallow.

Some of the light is reflected by the upper surface of plate F, back on to the inclined plate E and thence to the lens H to produce an image at I. Some of the remaining light passes across the wedge-shaped gap and is reflected by the lower face of the plate G and then traverses a similar path back to I. Thus, two images are formed at I, the difference between them being due to the difference in optical path length between the light reflected from the upper surface of F and that reflected from the lower surface of G. This difference in path length means that the two beams of light interfere, i.e. 'crests' neutralize 'troughs' in the wave-form, and an interference image appears at I. If one of the two reflecting surfaces at F or G is perfectly flat (an optical flat), the image may be interpreted to show the variation from true flatness of the other surface comprising the wedge.

Multiple-beam micro-interferometry has been developed by Professor S. Tolansky, as the outcome of which *Multiple Beam Interferometry* (Clarendon Press, Oxford, 1948) was written. A little before this, F. H. Smith developed a number of methods whereby a beam of light could be split (Patent Specification 639,014, referred to in Figs. 71, 72 and 75, the experimental work being carried out over a number of years). At about the same time, J. St. Ledger Philpot carried out extensive research on a technique which differed from those above and the final Patent Specification 645,464 was also made public in 1950; the technique is illustrated in Figs. 73 and 74. There are other fine examples of the genius of these and other workers who contributed to science; the result is that a more up-to-date and effective method of interference microscopy has been introduced, which now plays an important part in science and also serves humanity.

Translucent specimens can be studied with comparative ease when viewed through the usual microscope optical system. Although translucent, they may at times appear to be transparent, due to the intense light passing through. The difference between a translucent and transparent material is that the former is a turbid medium, causing light rays to be absorbed and many rays

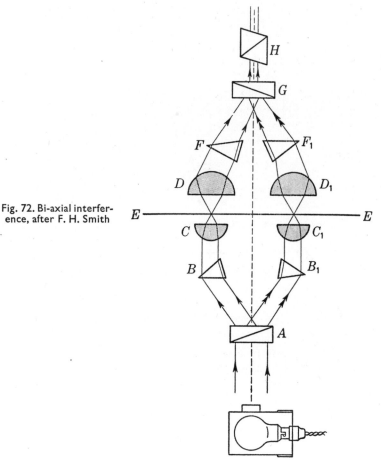

Fig. 72. Bi-axial interference, after F. H. Smith

to be scattered within the medium, while a truly transparent medium does not allow light to be scattered within that medium. It will be remembered that when using oil immersion, the glass slide, mounting medium, specimen, cover glass and oil allow a light ray to travel through without being scattered, because they

T.P.—10

are transparent. Interference microscopy enables two transparent
specimens (lying upon each other in a transparent medium) to be
separately examined. Staining can be introduced to render visible
that which hitherto was invisible, but on occasions the introduction

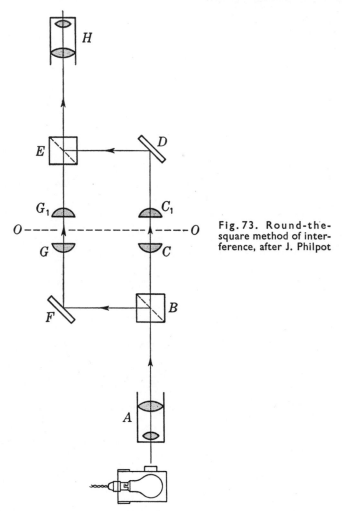

Fig. 73. Round-the-
square method of inter-
ference, after J. Philpot

of stains destroys delicate cells. In addition, there are many subjects which do not lend themselves to staining. Interference
microscopy provides a means of studying transparent objects
without having first to stain them or treat them in any similar
way. Lacy, D., and Blundell, M., *J. Roy. Micr. Soc.* (1955) **75**, 48,

describe a method whereby they have examined freeze-dried and stained tissues with the interference microscope.

If, after a beam is split, the two halves are allowed to traverse

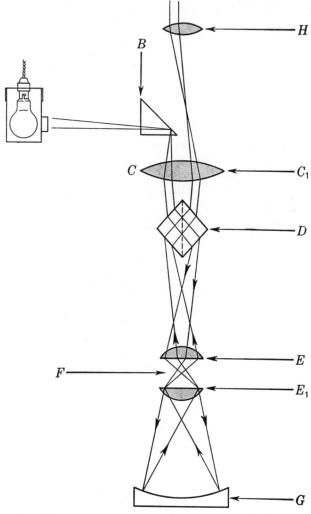

Fig. 74. Simple lens system interference, after J. Philpot

equal optical paths of the same length, they will not produce a phase difference, i.e. they will not interfere with each other. But if one of two beams of light traverses an optical path length which is slightly different from the other, interference is created between the beams and the tiny differences in optical path length are at once apparent.

A method of cyclic-interference microscopy has been developed by F. H. Smith (Fig. 71). As can be seen, monochromatic light from the source is a parallel beam passing on to, and being divided by, the double prism, and emerging as two divergent beams, one to the left and one to the right. By virtue of the prisms B and B_1, they are plane polarized in planes at right angles one to the other. The beams are now deflected to be parallel to each other by prisms B and B_1, one beam passing through the object C. There is thus a difference in the optical paths of the two beams owing to the object at C. The beams are then combined by the prisms D and D_1, and the double prism E. A single beam, consisting of two superimposed beams, plane polarized in two mutually perpendicular planes emerges from this double-image prism on to F. Rotation of the analysing prism F may then be used to vary the intensity of either of the polarized beams, and in this way the condition for maximum contrast in the image may be achieved. This condition is simply that the two beams should be of equal intensity.

Another beam-splitting method, similar to the previous one, and also developed by F. H. Smith, is seen in Fig. 72. The light from the source is directed into, and split into two beams by the prism at A. Prisms B and B_1 cause the two beams to alter their direction and pass through the corrected lenses C and C_1 and then through the object plane E. After passing through D and D_1 the beams are brought together by a similar series of prisms F and F_1, and entering G as two beams, finally pass through an analyser H. It is claimed that if the double-image prisms A and G be Wollaston's prisms, the two emergent beams will be plane-polarized light, polarized in planes at right angles to one another. Viewing of the image formed by these beams must be carried out through the analyser seen above G.

The round-the-square system (Fig. 73) may be regarded as a form of the Jamin interferometer with a microscope and is included here in contrast to those already mentioned. The light-source in this particular case is projected by a collimator, indicated by A, on to an obliquely inclined partial reflector B. The latter consists of two prisms separated by a thin partial reflecting layer of aluminium, silver or rhodium. From this composite prism the light is transmitted through the lens C, and having passed through the object plane O and lens C_1, is reflected at the mirror D on to another partial reflector E, this being identical with B. Thence the reflected light forms what is described as the odd beam and continues on to the eyepiece H, the image forming in the normal

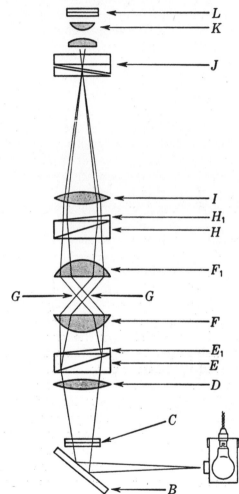

Fig. 75. Uniaxial interference, after F. H. Smith

manner. Returning to B, where part of the beam is bent after being reflected, it now shines on to the mirror surface of F, is bent at right angles and passes through lens G, object plane O and second lens G_1, to the partial reflector E. Thence the transmitted light blends with the odd beam to form an image at H. The inventor states that if no object is in position, and the media at the two object planes are similar, the system may be adjusted for any desired degree of interference. Then, the introduction of an object modifies the phase relationship, and an interference image results.

A rather different method is illustrated in Fig. 74. The equipment required is simple and is mainly contained within the microscope tube. The light is directed down the microscope tube by the prism B and enters the double prism D. This has a partial reflecting surface as shown by the dotted line, and some light passes through to be directed down to the objective.

The light then passes through the objective E, object plane F and lens E_1 to be reflected back by the mirror G through the lens system. By suitable design of the prism D the light from the object interferes with that reflected from the source to produce the interference image. This method is particularly suitable for the photography of minute transparent specimens.

By way of contrast, and as an example of the genius of the inventor and the flexibility of an optical system, Fig. 75 illustrates the uniaxial optical system. The diagrammatic drawing shows a compound microscope, with a means of dividing a single beam into two which then traverse the specimen. After passing through the specimen the beams cross and re-combine. In this manner the optical path lengths differ slightly one from the other, so as to produce an interference effect which can be viewed or projected on to a sensitive emulsion in the normal manner. The beam is reflected at the surface of the mirror B and is directed through a polarizing screen C to a collimating lens D situated between the latter and a Wollaston prism E–E_1.

The incident beam of light is now divided into two mutually divergent beams which pass through lens F and object plane G, where they are brought to a point of focus, entering the objective on either side, as shown. These beams are polarized in planes at right angles one to the other. The beams pass through lens F_1 and the double prism H and collimating lens I, which brings the two beams together. After passing through the Soleil Babinet compensator J, the joint beams now pass through the eyepiece K, which is fitted with a polarizing screen L.

As already mentioned, the inclusion of a particular lens condenser or prism may introduce difficulties, and may cause the light beam to go 'off course'. In this particular case the additional prisms E_1 and H_1 have been added to maintain the correct relationships. The use of the prisms E and H on their own introduces dispersion.

Another method, whereby the formation of variable deviation between two beams takes place, is through a pair of double-refracting double-image prisms, positioned one in front of the other, and in true alignment so that deviations are in opposition. The introduction of adjustable movement into one of the double prisms would, therefore, automatically vary the deviation.

The use of monochromatic light in interferometry results in images in which differences in optical thickness of an object are indicated by variations in intensity in the image. If white light is used, the image becomes coloured. There are many other interference techniques which cannot be mentioned here, but reference is made to them in the bibliography.

The Baker Interference Microscope.—The wave-changing mechanism in this microscope is caused by an interferometer system which, like others, is built into the microscope, thus affecting the condenser and objective light waves as already described. By virtue of the optical system a double-image effect is obtained, the results being far more distinct and sensitive to structural changes than those obtainable with phase-contrast equipment.

The condenser and objective are arranged to form two images of immediately adjacent parts of the field under examination. The two images are then formed together in such a position that they interfere. A valuable feature of this particular equipment is that the degree of interference may be varied at will by the special double-refracting phase-shifting system incorporated in the instrument.

Green mentions an application of interferometry to biological surfaces (*Austral. J. Sci.* **9**, 26); when a certain surface has sufficient reflectivity, it can be studied with this type of microscope. The basis of interference photomicrography with an ordinary microscope is the use of a metallized slide and a cover glass with which to sandwich the specimen. The illumination is solely monochromatic light, conveniently obtained by an interference filter.

Quartz Wedge Eyepiece Method.—For some purposes it is more convenient to view the effect of the specimen upon a field crossed by a uniform series of interference fringes. The Baker fringe field eyepiece consists of an ocular tube which fits into the top of the microscope. In this tube is a slip which houses one of a series of interchangeable quartz wedges. Various wedges are required to produce a range of fringe separations. The Ramsden eyepiece is fitted with a focusing eyelens and the quartz wedge is positioned at the focal planes of the eyelens. The wedge can be rotated through 90°, and a slide carrying an analyser is placed above this. To use the fringe eyepiece, the quartz-wave plate and rotating analyser in the microscope body tube must be withdrawn. By rotating the wedge in the eyepiece the spacing of the bands can be varied, enabling measurement to be made of optical retardation introduced by the specimen.

REFLECTING MICROSCOPY

The eye is sensitive to radiations of wave-lengths from approximately 4,000 Å to 7,000 Å, the shorter end of the spectrum being ultra-violet and the longer infra-red. Between 4,000 Å and 136 Å is the ultra-violet region which may produce effects not encountered with visible radiations. These radiations may induce fluorescence (i.e. cause the substance upon which they impinge to emit visible radiations); they also ionize gases and may be recorded on a photographic emulsion.

Quartz is transparent down to 1,850 Å, whereas fluorite remains transparent down to 1,200 Å. The behaviour of a silvered surface is indeed very interesting at this end of the spectrum. A considerable amount of ultra-violet radiation may be absorbed by it; in fact, only some 4 per cent of the radiation is reflected at 3,160 Å. As a point of interest the same silvered surface will reflect some 95 per cent of visible radiation. The thickness of a coating of metallic silver controls the amount of reflected radiations, which in turn affects the reflecting ability of reflecting objectives.

Wave-lengths of 7,500 Å to 400,000 Å are known as infra-red waves and constitute the band of thermal radiation. The amount of infra-red radiations penetrating optical systems varies considerably and should be of interest to the photographer who is constantly using systems of various types incorporating all forms of illumination.

Although reflecting microscopy might be thought to be a recent invention, it was in fact first introduced in the middle of the seventeenth century by Sir Isaac Newton. This first reflecting microscope consisted of a concave ellipsoidal mirror and a diagonal flat. In 1738 R. Smith described a number of compound reflecting microscopes, these having single and double mirrors. This method was outdated by the introduction of the achromatic objective in 1824. From then until the early 1930s little progress was made in the production of the reflecting microscope. In 1931, however, various types were manufactured. Three years later, B. K. Johnson (*J. Sci. Instrum.* (1934) **11**, 384) produced the single-mirror objective (Fig. 76). This was the first to be used in an ultra-violet microscope.

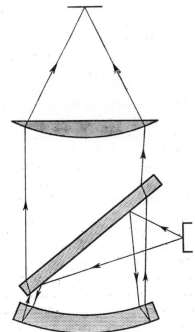

Fig. 76. Single-mirror reflecting objective

In 1950 a reflecting objective was introduced by E. J. Ambrose, A. Elliott and R. B. Temple (*J. Sci. Instrum.* (1950) **27**, 21) for use in the near infra-red of the spectrum. Used with ordinary microscopes, these covered from approximately 2,400 Å to 10,000 Å. Today, the reflecting microscope is used to further the advance of research in many fields. One of the functions of this particular method is the examination of photographic emulsions by ultra-violet and infra-red radiations, thus overcoming some of the limitations of the conventional microscope. The applications of the reflecting microscope now cover phase contrast and interference using polarized and unpolarized radiations from one end of the spectrum to the other.

The use of quartz objectives now makes possible illumination with ultra-violet radiation and gives a great increase in the detail of the image, as the resolving power of the optical system increases with decreasing wave-length. If these quartz objectives are used at a wave-length other than the one for which they are designed, there will be a general deterioration in the resolving power. The normal transmission band of quartz ranges from 1,850 Å to 30,000 Å. These objectives are, therefore, unsuitable for very short wave-length ultra-violet work.

The manufacturers of quartz monochromatic lenses have encountered numerous set-backs due to the presence of aberrations. To overcome these aberrations a lens was produced with seven individual lenses, mounted in air. Thus, twelve air surfaces caused a deterioration of the image by back reflection. Therefore, the refracting objective with a back-coated lens mirror and one auxiliary lens was introduced by B. K. Johnson.

The present-day reflecting microscopes are free from aberrations. The use of aspheric reflecting mirrors minimizes the possibility of glare and other optical faults and, in addition, the reflecting system permits a far greater working distance. The Burch microscope has a working distance of approximately 12 mm. as compared with 0·5 mm. for a refracting objective of similar N.A. Details may be found in *The Microscope* (1951) **8**, No. 9, 242–3. It is very suitable for photomicrography. The N.A. of one objective is 0·65 dry and of the other, 0·95 dry; the latter increases to 1·4 when oil immersion is introduced. The photographic image is practically free from curvature of field, owing to the aspheric surface of the mirrors.

The use of a cover glass over the specimen will, however, cause defects in the photographic image when working with reflecting objectives, owing to the introduction of spherical aberration. To overcome this difficulty it is suggested that a specimen cover glass, having the same thickness as the test slide, be used when setting up the apparatus and focusing the field of view. The cover glass used for immersion purposes creates a certain amount of chromatic aberration which can be cancelled out by introducing a suitable lens element into the system.

The illumination used with the Burch microscope can be either a tungsten filament lamp or a Littrow monochromator, together with a medium-pressure mercury-arc lamp, giving either white light or ultra-violet radiations respectively. Photomicrographs are usually made without the eyepiece, avoiding the possibility of aberrations caused by its introduction. The tube-length of the Burch microscope differs from others and is operated at 34·5 cm. Normal optical filters should not be used with this apparatus. There are two points of focus in almost the same plane, one due to fluorescent light which radiates from the unstained areas of the specimen and the other to transmitted ultra-violet radiation. For work in the ultra-violet the visible radiations must be filtered out.

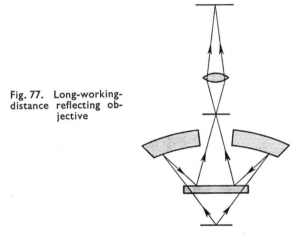

Fig. 77. Long-working-distance reflecting objective

The production of an optical system without the presence of quartz has enabled photographic records to be made in ultra-violet of even shorter wave-length. Further details involved in this special technique can be found in B. K. Johnson, *J. Roy. Micr. Soc.* (1953) **73**, 24.

There are, however, various types of reflecting objectives which, of course, cannot all be illustrated here, but a few are shown, to give an idea of their general features.

The long-working-distance objective was designed by J. Dyson and constructed to enable the surfaces of metal specimens in a furnace to be examined by metallurgists. For the purpose of inspection, the specimen was placed at the centre of curvature of a concave mirror with a hole in its centre (Fig. 77). A small lens was placed between the specimen and the mirror, the latter reflecting an image into a plane behind the mirror. This reflecting objective had a long working distance, enabling the specimen to be viewed through the transparent side of a furnace.

The Newtonian objective (Fig. 78) is of different construction. In this particular case the light from the specimen was reflected through an axial aperture in a concave mirror to a very slightly convex mirror situated behind a meniscus lens. The light was then reflected on to the concave surface which in turn directed the beam through the meniscus lens, to form the primary image.

A few years ago, K. P. Norris and M. H. F. Wilkins (*Nature, Lond.* (1952) **170**, 883) described an objective which could be used

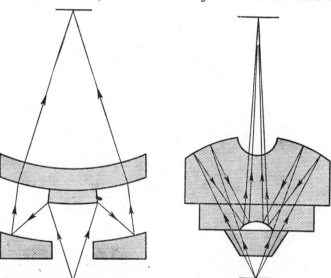

Fig. 78. Newtonian reflecting
objective

Fig. 79. Ultra-violet reflecting
objective

for ultra-violet microscopy (Fig. 79). This objective comprised three quartz lenses, which were centred and placed in optical contact one with the other, some surfaces being coated with an aluminium deposit. The course of the reflected light can be followed from the diagrammatic drawing.

In addition to the Burch reflecting microscope, there is the model made by the M. H. F. Wilkins group of the Medical Research Council, King's College (*J. Roy. Micr. Soc.* (1953) **73**, 77–81).

The Beck reflecting objective ×74, 0·65 N.A. was designed by the above group primarily for microspectrography, but gives a fair performance when used for photomicrography. The advantage of this microscope is that it is possible to focus and take pictures with visible light and then photograph the same section with ultra-violet radiations (Plate 41).

Living cells can now be photographed in their natural state with the visible spectrum and also with ultra-violet, and in addition to this, records can also be made in the infra-red part of the spectrum.

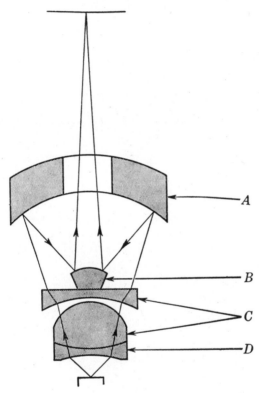

Fig. 80. Polaroid-Grey reflecting objective

The Polaroid-Grey reflecting objective (Fig. 80) was designed by L. V. Foster of New York. Its focal length is 2·8 mm. and N.A. 0·72 with a magnification of × 53. It has two reflecting surfaces of aluminium film evaporated on glass; there is a quartz fluorite doublet and also a fluorite refracting component which reduces the residual spherical aberration set up by the spherical surfaces. (A and B indicate the glass components, C the fluorite and D the

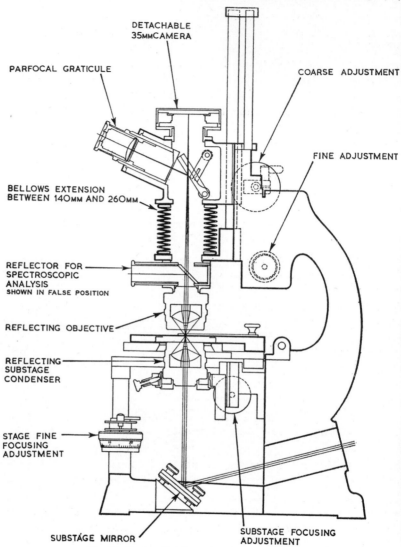

Fig. 81. Beck reflecting microscope and camera

fused quartz lens.) Chromatic aberration introduced by the quartz cover glass is also corrected. This unique objective has an occluded aperture of 0·21 and is operated with a × 4 negative-type eyepiece, to give an overall magnification of × 212 at 160-mm. tube-length. For higher magnifications, the use of a × 10 quartz eyepiece of the Huyghens' type is recommended. The Grey

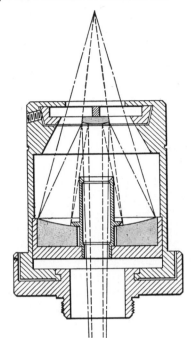

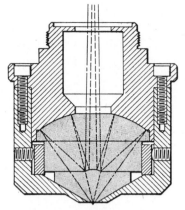

Fig. 83. Beck oil-immersion reflecting
objective

Fig. 82. (*left*) Beck long-working-distance reflecting objective

objective can be used in the visible ultra-violet or infra-red
regions with a very slight change in the focus. The Burch, Brom-
berg and Grey 10-mm. reflecting objectives are absolutely free
from chromatic aberration provided the specimen is mounted in
air, but if the specimen is mounted with a cover glass, an alteration
in the optical path length is unavoidable. This introduces chromatic aberration.

Beck Reflecting Microscope.—General interest in microscopical
problems concerned with the ultra-violet and infra-red regions
of the spectrum has created a demand for a laboratory microscope
capable of fulfilling such demands. Thus, after much research and
development, the Beck reflecting microscope is now available
(Fig. 81).

Although the apparatus was originally designed for the in-
vestigation of problems in biophysics, it is in no way limited to
this particular field, for, since its production, it has fulfilled
demands put upon it in very many fields. The infra-red trans-
missions of the lower-power objectives have been invaluable for
investigations connected with germanium and allied metals used
in transistors.

All objectives can be used for the purpose of photographing transparent objects. In addition to this, they can also be employed with vertical illuminators. The objectives are available in various magnifications, ×15 to ×172, as seen in Figs. 82 and 83.

The objective is carried on a fitting fixed to a slide, and gives the usual movements when attached to a microscope. Coarse and fine adjustments are calibrated by a micrometer to 0·005 mm. There is a detachable 45° reflector, fitted above the objective, which projects the image in a horizontal direction, allowing it to fall upon the slit of an analytical spectrograph.

The observing eyepiece is of the inclined parfocal graticule type. After the specimen has been viewed, and a field selected and focused, the detachable reflector is removed, thus permitting axial light rays to pass on to the film in the camera. The tube eyepiece is a ×10 Ramsden type with a graticule, and having its focal plane parfocal with that of the 35-mm. camera. The eyepiece tube will accommodate any standard-size eyepiece, and by employing a bellows extension in place of the usual draw-tube, a much wider range of adjustment can be obtained. The position of the focal plane of the viewing eyepiece and camera can be adjusted to suit the 'tube-length', and this ranges from 150 mm. to 285 mm. A fixed scale makes this easy to adjust.

The mirrors are surface aluminized, which enables radiations from the ultra-violet to the infra-red to be reflected. The substage mirror is illuminated by an external source through an aperture in the vertical limb of the base, as illustrated in Fig. 81. The mirror does not have the free movement associated with the conventional type of microscope, but optimum results are obtained when illuminating by short and long wave-lengths.

There is ample movement in the substage. It travels 3 in. in a horizontal direction and 1 in. in the vertical. This allows quite large specimens to be housed and examined by vertical illumination. It is possible to make an accurate re-location of the same area in a specimen, as the slide-holder has a 1-mm. stage scale.

In addition to the normal focusing, an extra fitting can be used to allow movement in the direction of the optical axis, and by this means accurate focusing can be carried out as required for ultra-violet photomicrography, where the permissible depth of field is extremely small.

The 35-mm. camera houses the normal perforated film and can take up to 40 frames, each of 1 in. diameter. The negatives

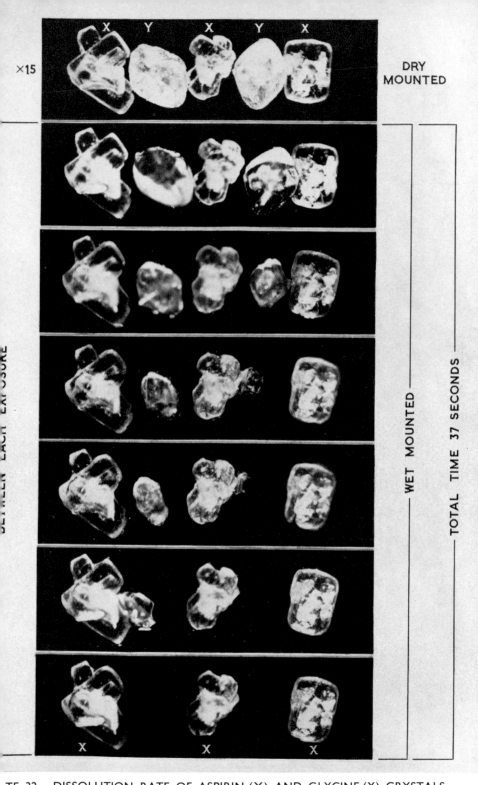

×15

X   Y   X   Y   X

DRY MOUNTED

WET MOUNTED

TOTAL TIME 37 SECONDS

X   X   X

TE 32. DISSOLUTION RATE OF ASPIRIN (X) AND GLYCINE (Y) CRYSTALS

he crystals were placed on a piece of blackened blotting paper fastened to a microscope slide, photo-
hed dry mounted, and the exposure determined.   The blotting paper was then moistened.

icroscope: Leitz.   Camera: Watson.   Objective: × 1.   Eyepiece: × 6.   Tube length: 160 mm.   Bellows
h: 10 in.   Emulsion: 0.250.   Illumination: oblique.   Exposure: 2 seconds.

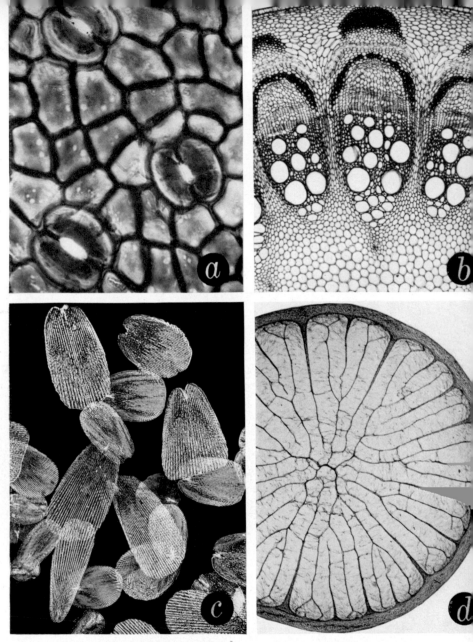

(*a*) STOMATA ON LOWER SURFACE OF LEAF, × 150 (total × 250)
   Section stained red, to enable the stomata to be clearly seen against the leaf itself.

(*b*) TRANSVERSE SECTION OF STEM OF CLEMATIS, × 30 (total × 100)
   Stained with carmine and iodine green.

(*c*) SCALES OF SILVER-FISH INSECT, × 110 (total × 200)
   The scales were sprinkled on a slide; no cover glass was used.   Normal transmitted light proved inadequate to give a clear impression of the 'silvery' nature of the scales.

(*d*) TRANSVERSE SECTION OF QUILL OF PORCUPINE, × 7 (total × 30)
   Camera iris wide open.   Transmitted light was used to illuminate the centre section, and reflected light for the outer shell, so that the latter gives detail instead of being opaque.
   See facing page for data.

PLATE 33

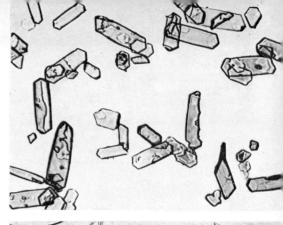

PLATE 34.
6-AMINOPENICILLANIC ACID
CRYSTALS, × 160

(upper) This is an historic photomicrograph, as it shows the first pure crystals obtained. So valuable was it as a record that it was taken without first mounting the crystals in a fluid.

(centre) These are the crude crystals obtained during the later stages of production. Mounted in Detel.

(lower) The normal appearance after the final stages of purification. Mounted in Detel.

Microscope: Leitz. Camera: Watson. Objective: 4 mm. Eyepiece: × 4. Substage: complete. Tube length: 170 mm. Bellows length: 8 in. Emulsion: B.40. Filter: blue. Illumination: transmitted.

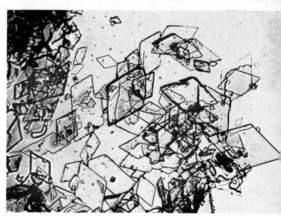

Data for Plate 33, on facing page

Microscope: Leitz. Camera: (a, b, c) Una $\frac{1}{4}$-plate, (d) small folding $2\frac{1}{4} \times 3\frac{1}{4}$ in. Objective: (a) 16 mm. N.A. 0.30, (b) 25 mm. N.A. 0.30, (c) 8 mm. N.A. 0.65, (d) $\frac{1}{2}$ in. Eyepiece: (a) 22 mm. × 11, (b and c) 45 mm. × 6, (d) × 2. Substage: (a) complete with bull's eye condenser, (b) lower condenser only, (c) less bull's eye condenser, (d) nil. Tube length: (a, b, d) 170 mm., (c) 160 mm. Bellows length: (a) 16 in., (b) 8 in., (c) 8 in., (d) nil. Emulsion: (a and c) chromatic, (b) Special Rapid, (d) Pan roll film. Filter: (a and c) green, (b) green and yellow (d) blue. Illumination: (a and b) transmitted, (c) dark-ground, (d) transmitted and reflected. Exposure: (a) 6 seconds (c) 10 seconds, (b and d) 2 seconds.

PLATE 35. INTERFEROMETRIC CONTOUR PATTERN OF TRIGONS

A good example of the interferometry technique. Trigons are small triangular pits, seen here in
interferogram given by a minute region of the octahedron face of a small diamond.

(*Courtesy of Professor S. Tolansky, D.Sc., F*

Details of Plate 36, on facing page

(a) One-second exposure was given with transmitted light and 5 seconds' with the oblique light.

(b) Focusing was carried out on the claw because of the thickness of the leg.

(c) The hundreds of fine hairs must be clearly recorded if the photomicrograph is to be of value.
eyepiece was dispensed with, the bellows and objective giving the magnification.

(d) Contact print. A similar subject to the last-mentioned, but this time a × 2 eyepiece was used
the bellows length reduced by half.

Microscope: (a and d) *Leitz,* (b and c) *Watson. Camera:* (a and b) *Una ¼-plate,* (c and d) *Watson. C
tive:* (a and b) *25 mm.,* (c) *2 in.,* (d) *16 mm. N.A. 0.30. Eyepiece:* (a) *45 mm. × 6,* (b) *× 2,* (d) *22 mm. ×
Substage:* (a, b, d) *lower condenser only. Tube length:* (a and b) *170 mm.,* (d) *172 mm. Bellows length
15 in.,* (b) *10½ in.,* (c) *11½ in.,* (d) *6½ in. Emulsion: 0.250. Illumination:* (a) *transmitted and reflected,* (b,
d) *transmitted. Exposure:* (a) *6 seconds,* (b and d) *3 seconds,* (c) *9 seconds.*

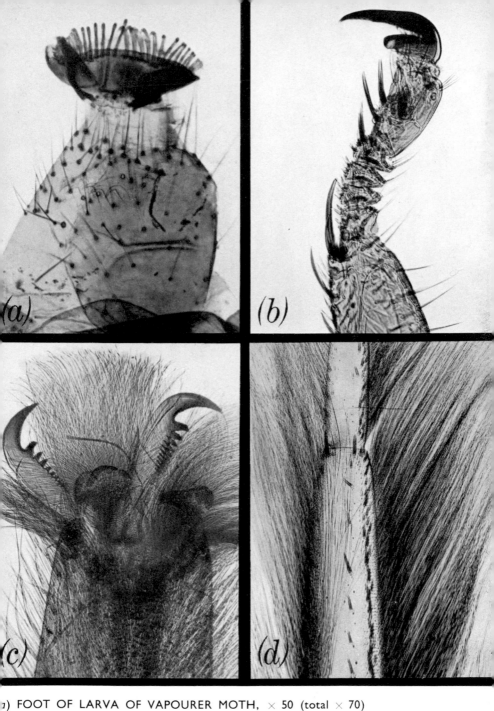

(a) FOOT OF LARVA OF VAPOURER MOTH, × 50 (total × 70)

(b) FOOT OF SHEEP TICK, × 35 (total × 70)

(c) FOOT OF SPIDER, × 12 (total × 50)

(d) PART OF LEG OF WATER BOATMAN, × 70

PLATE 36

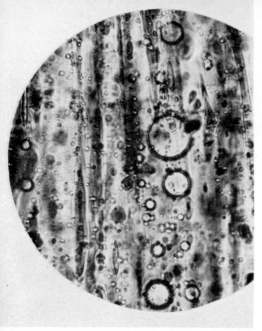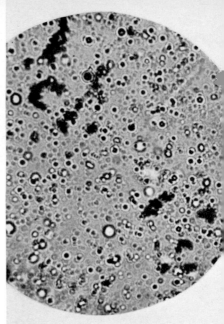

PLATE 37. FLAVOURING ESSENCE WITHIN A BOILED SWEET, × 130

It was impossible to photograph this subject with the orthodox method of transmitted illuminati◦
the source was not bright enough or large enough. Although a 500-watt Photoflood was used t◦
minate the subject the exposure was still long. The photomicrograph on the left shows the particl◦
and dispersion of flavouring essence within a boiled sweet produced to the old formula. The dark◦
are shadows from particles well below the plane of focus. The dark bands around the essence◦
caused by the scattering of light within the sweet. The second photomicrograph (of a sweet produc◦
a new formula) shows a great reduction in particle size of the flavouring essence, a greater dispersio◦
a more even distribution.

*Microscope: Leitz. Camera: Watson. Objective: 25 mm. N.A. 0.30. Eyepiece: 22 mm. × 11. Sub◦
one lens. Tube length: 170 mm. Bellows length: 12 in. Emulsion: 0.250. Filter: blue. Illumination:◦
mitted. Exposure: 1 minute.*

Details of Plate 38, on facing page

(a) Substage iris half closed. These bell-shaped creatures are seen attached to their retractile s◦

(b) The colony of vorticella has moved in search of food. The subject was photographed float◦
water in the hollow of a slide. Not narcotized.

*Microscope: Leitz. Camera: Una ¼-plate. Objective: 16 mm. N.A. 0.30. Eyepiece: 22 mm.
Substage: less bull's eye condenser. Tube length: 170 mm. Bellows length: 4 in. Emulsion: H.P.3.
pale yellow. Illumination: transmitted using an intensity lamp. Exposure: 1/25 second.*

(c) Intensity lamp with iris half-closed was used. Not narcotized.

*Microscope: Leitz. Camera: Macca ½ ×. Objective: 25 mm. Eyepiece: 45 mm. × 6. Substage:
condenser only. Tube length: 170 mm. Emulsion: P.300. Filter: green. Illumination: transm◦
Exposure: 3 seconds.*

(d) Lamp-house as for (c). The cyclops moves and swims freely with eggs in this position. Not n◦
ized.

*Microscope: Leitz. Camera: Watson. Objective: 25 mm. Eyepiece: 45 mm. × 6. Substage: lowe◦
denser only. Tube length: 170 mm. Bellows length: 8 in. Emulsion: chromatic. Filter: green. Illu◦
tion: transmitted. Exposure: 4 seconds.*

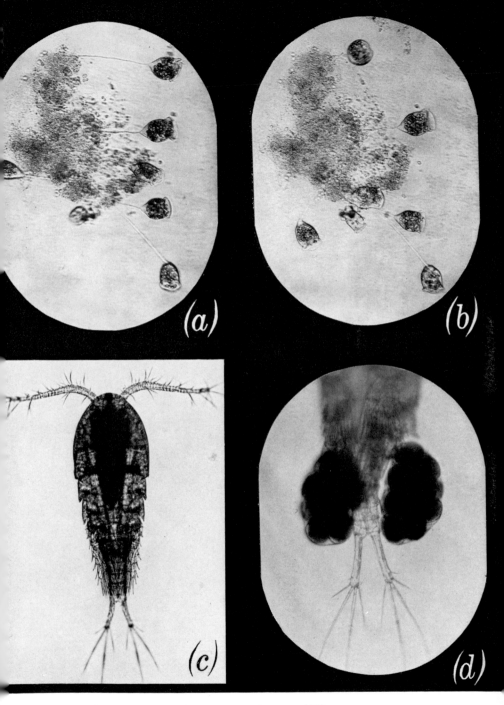

(a, and *b*) COLONY OF VORTICELLA, × 70 (total × 150)

(*c*) MALE ADULT CYCLOPS, × 20 (total × 75)

(*d*) TAIL OF CYCLOPS WITH BROOD SAC ATTACHED, × 30 (total × 200)

PLATE 38

PLATE 39.   PARASITE OF MOORHEN

The subject was photographed with various objectives, illustrating the field and depth covered with each.   Note the change in exposure times.

	(a)	(b)	(c)	(d)	(e)	(f)
Magnification	× 15	× 40	× 65	× 140	× 300	× 500
Microscope	Leitz	Leitz	Leitz	Leitz	Leitz	Leitz
Camera	Una ¼-plate	Una ¼-plate	Una ¼-plate	Una ¼-plate	Una ¼-plate	Una ¼-plate
Bellows length	10 in.	10 in.	10 in.	10 in.	10 in.	10 in.
Objective	× 1	25 mm. N.A. 0·30	16 mm. N.A. 0·30	8 mm. N.A. 0·65	4 mm. N.A. 0·75	2 mm. apochromatic N.A. 1·0 oil immersion
Eyepiece	× 6	× 6	× 6	× 6	× 6	× 6
Substage	nil	nil	lower lens only	less bull's eye condenser	complete with bull's eye condenser	
Tube length	160 mm.	160 mm.	160 mm.	160 mm.	160 mm.	160 mm.
Emulsion	0.250	0.250	0.250	0.250	0.250	0.250
Filter	blue Wratten H	blue Wratten H	blue Wratten H	blue Wratten H	blue Wratten H	blue Wratten H
Illumination	transmitted	transmitted	transmitted	transmitted	transmitted	transmitted
Exposure	10 sec.	16 sec.	24 sec.	30 sec.	1 min.	2½ min.

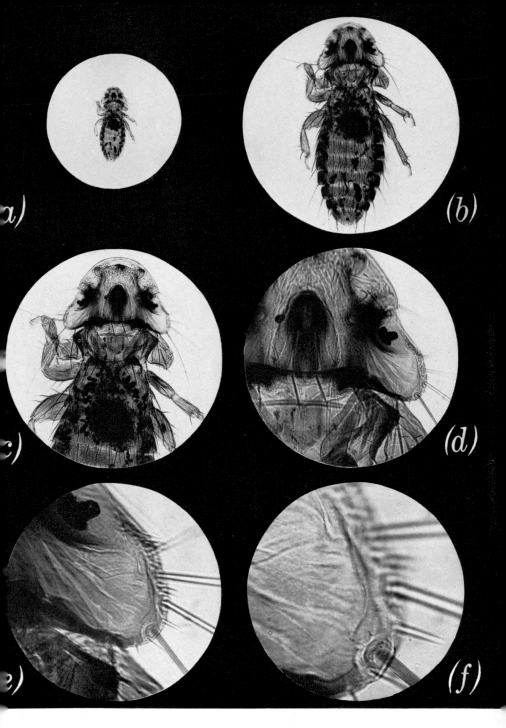

(a)

(b)

(c)

(d)

(e)

(f)

PLATE 39

PLATE 40

(a) TEETH OF SAW OF SAWFLY, × 140 (total × 260)

Subject natural colour—brown. Only the female sawfly, *Trichiosoma tibialis*, possesses the saw-like implement illustrated here and situated at the tip of the abdomen. The saw is used to make an incision in twigs in which the insect places its eggs.

Microscope: Leitz. Camera: Watson. Objective: 8 mm. N.A. 0·65. Eyepiece: 45 mm. × 6. Substage: complete. Tube length: 170 mm. Bellows length: 10½ in. Emulsion: P.1500. Filter: green. Illumination: transmitted and reflected. Exposure: 4 seconds.

(b) JAWS AND TEETH OF PARASITE OF BEE, × 250 (total × 500)

Lamp iris wide open. Both reflected and transmitted light used. It seems incredible that such a small insect as a bee should carry a parasite. They have a double set of jaws and live mainly on the fine hairs of the bee's back.

Microscope: Watson. Camera: Watson. Objective: 4 mm. N.A. 0·75. Eyepiece: 45 mm. × 6. Substage: less bull's eye condenser. Tube length: 160 mm. Bellows length: 8 in. Emulsion: P.1200. Filter: green. Illumination: reflected and transmitted. Exposure: 12 seconds.

(c) HEAD AND MOUTH PARTS OF NYMPH OF DRAGONFLY, × 8 (total × 12)

This specimen was photographed with only objective and the camera bellows length, which gave the magnification. The lighting was transmitted to the specimen after being reflected from a white card, which was also beneath the subject. Two micro lamps were used to illuminate the spot. Subject unstained.

Microscope: Leitz. Camera: Una ¼-plate. Objective: 3 in. Tube length: 170 mm. Bellows length: 8 in. Emulsion: H.P.3. Filter: green and diffuser. Illumination: reflected and transmitted. Exposure: 3 seconds.

(d) SECTION OF TOOTH OF SAWFISH, × 15

Normally this would be an opaque subject, but a thin section was cut on a microtome, thus allowing the subject, *Pristis perotteti*, to be illuminated by transmitted light and permitting the inner details of the tooth to be recorded.

Microscope: Leitz. Camera: Una ¼-plate. Objective: 2 in. Eyepiece: 45 mm. × 6. Tube length: 170 mm. Bellows length: 8 in. Emulsion: O.250. Filter: orange. Illumination: transmitted. Exposure: 4 seconds.

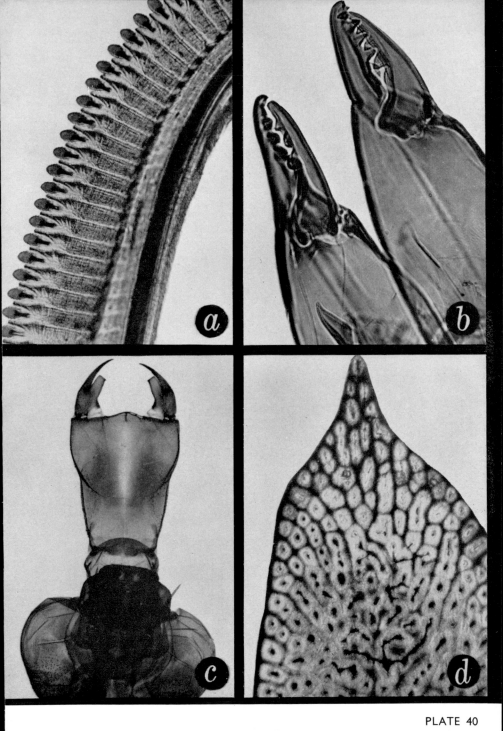

PLATE 40

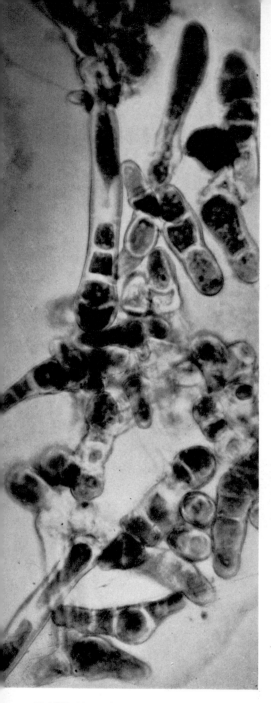

PLATE 41. LIVING CELLS OF YEAST, × 1,200

The specimen was photographed without an eyepiece direct on to Micro-File 35 mm. film. The photomicrograph on the left (ultra-violet light, 2650 Å) clearly shows increased resolution compared with that on the right (visible light, 5460Å).

Beck reflecting objective N.A. 0.60; reflecting condenser N.A. 0.50; compact-source, high-pressure mercury arc, 250-W; and a quartz prism monochromator, to separate wavelengths, were used.

(Courtesy of Dr. M. H. F. Wilkins, Biophysics Research Unit, King's College, London,

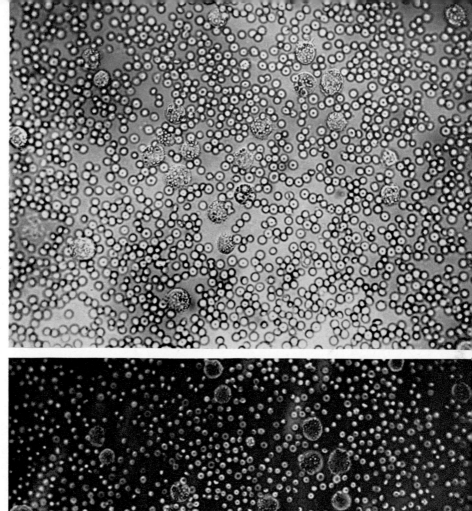
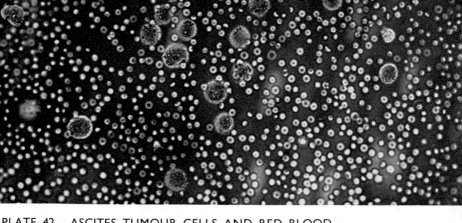

PLATE 42. ASCITES TUMOUR CELLS AND RED BLOOD
CELLS, × 80 (total × 400)

Photographed with normal transmitted light. Transmitted light substage was used
for the upper illustration and interference for the lower; other data similar.

*Microscope: Baker I/84. Camera: Leica. Objective: × 40. Eyepiece: 6. Tube length:
standard. Bellows length: Micro-Ibso I/3. Emulsion: Mico-neg Pan (Ilford). Filter: nil.
Illumination: zirconium arc. Exposure: 4 seconds.*

(Courtesy of Dr. G. Easty and K. Moreman, Chester Beatty Research Institute, London)

Microscope: Watson.
Camera: Watson. Objec-
tive: 25 mm. Eyepiece: 45
mm. × 6. Substage: complete.
Tube length: 160 mm.
Bellows length: 12 in. Emul-
sion: Ilford N.40. Filter:
blue. Illumination: intensity
lamp. Exposure: 3 seconds.

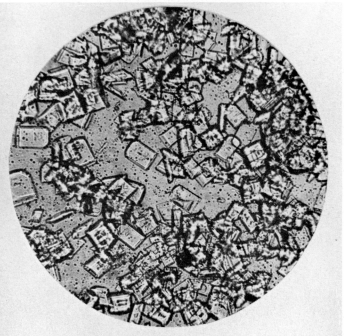

Microscope: Watson.
Camera: Watson. Objec-
tive: 25 mm. Eyepiece: 45
mm. × 6. Substage: complete.
Tube length: 160 mm. Bellows
length: 12 in. Emulsion:
Ilford N.40. Filter: interfer-
ence. Illumination: intensity
lamp. Exposure: 5 seconds.

PLATE 43. SUCROSE CRYSTALS, × 55

(*upper*) Sucrose crystals formed in a boiled sweet exposed to moist conditions and subsequently dried out. The sugar has lost its glassy state and become devitrified. A number of
the crystals have become transparent and their form is difficult to define.

(*lower*) This is the same field as above. Owing to an interference filter being used between
substage and source, the crystals now take shape. The filter slightly alters the focus, the
three-dimensional structure of the crystals is more clearly demonstrated.

PLATE 44.   GROUP OF SPONGE SPICULES,   × 30 (total × 200)

Siliceous deposits, such as these, are a favourite subject for the photomicrographer, their glass-like skeletons being very attractive.   The upper section of the plate was illuminated by transmitted lighting and processed in the normal manner, in Pyro-soda. The lower half was photographed in exactly the same way, but the reversal process was used.

Microscope: Leitz.   Camera: Watson.   Objective: 25 mm.   N.A. 0.30.   Eyepiece: Leitz 2.   Substage: single condenser.   Tube length: 169 mm.   Bellows length: 10 in. Emulsion: B.20.   Filter: diffuser only.   Illumination: oblique.   Exposure: 3 seconds.

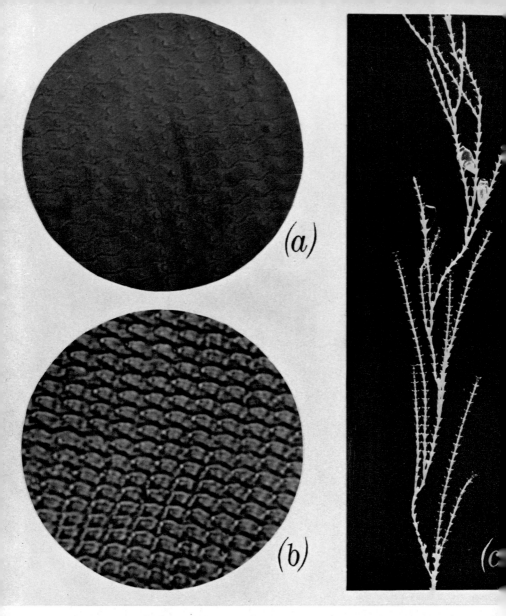

(*a* and *b*) PALATE OF SNAIL, × 85 (total × 180)

(*a*) Although a contrasty emulsion was used to increase the contrast, the subject is flat. A blue f
also helps to produce an image with more contrast, but, as can be seen, this subject does not lend itself to
use of transmitted illumination. The print was printed on grade 4 contrasty paper, but the result is
very much flatter than (*b*).

(*b*) Mounted specimen of *Helix arbustorum*. Without phase-contrast it is very difficult to produ
record of this subject. A process plate was used to give an even greater contrast in the subject.

(*c*) HYDROID ZOOPHYTE, × 6 (total × 24)

Wet mounted specimen of *Sertularia opercutulata*. A very delicate subject photographed with
substage or eyepiece, which gave an image size of × 6 on the plate. Reversal process used to give
image its original whiteness.

Microscope: Leitz. Camera: (a and b) *Watson,* (c) *Una ¼-plate. Objective:* (a and b) *2/3rd × 10 N.A.*
(c) *2 in. Eyepiece:* (a and b) *22 mm. × 11. Substage:* (a) *complete,* (b) *phase-contrast. Tube length*
and b) *172 mm. Bellows Length:* (a and b) *9 in.,* (c) *4 in. Emulsion:* (a and b) *B.20 contrasty,* (c) *soft grade*
pan. Filter: (a) *blue,* (b) *green. Illumination:* (a) *transmitted,* (b) *phase,* (c) *transmitted light with a 60*
bulb. Exposure: (a) *6 seconds,* (b) *5 seconds,* (c) *2 seconds.*

PLATE 45

are subsequently enlarged as necessary. There is an eight-speed shutter ranging from 1 second to 1/250th of a second, as well as a time and bulb position, operated by a cable release.

The ×15, 0·28 N.A., 24-mm.-working-distance objective (Fig. 82) has the largest exit pupil of the range of six and is particularly useful for work in the infra-red where energy values are often low. The exceptionally long working distance of this objective makes possible investigations into effects associated with both high and low temperatures, since the specimen may be viewed from outside a suitable chamber. The objective is adjusted for use at 160-mm. tube-length when using an 0·18-mm. thick cover glass, but the appropriate correction must also be carried out when incorporating thick cover glasses or a window. The reflecting mirrors are adjustable and careful centring must be carried out to ensure optimum results; these mirrors are altered by means of a mirror key.

The ×36, 0·50 N.A. objective has a higher resolving power and possesses a far greater working distance than that associated with conventional 8- or 16-mm. objectives. A spacing collar is inserted when working with a window of 4 mm. thickness. This thickness of window should be adhered to, because if it differs in any way, chromatic aberration will appear and impair the final results.

The third and fourth reflecting objectives × 52 and × 74, 0·65 N.A., are mainly for use with ultra-violet and give results of the highest quality. These are fitted with an engraved scale on a movable ring which indicates the matching cover-glass thickness, registering 1/1,000th of an inch. This scale moves against a second scale on the objective body, which indicates the tube-length at which the objective should be worked. The value of these scales can well be appreciated by those connected with photomicrography. An additional objective is used as a condenser, fine adjustments being necessary to allow for the thickness of the slide in use. If a refracting condenser is used with a reflecting objective, the objective is apt to be flooded with light, thus producing an image of very low contrast. It has therefore proved to be most satisfactory to use a second objective as a condenser; the aperture of the condenser then corresponds with that of the objective.

The immersion objective gives a magnification of ×172 and has been constructed differently from the others. The system can be considered as a complete single block of fused quartz. All reflecting surfaces are internal (Fig. 83); therefore atmospheric conditions cannot interfere with its effective operation. Allowances have been made so that the chromatic aberration introduced by the immersion water is cancelled out. In this particular objective the refraction at the recommended 'tube-length' brings the 5,461 Å and 2,650 Å mercury lines to a common focus. The residual secondary spectrum is so small that the system can be considered colour-free.

When used for photomicrography, the highest resolving power is necessary; thus the 'tube-length' must be used at 250 mm.; any other length will introduce aberrations. The separation of the mirrors and the centralization need no special adjustments. This

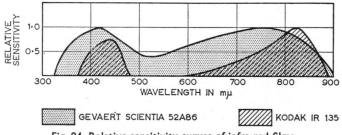

Fig. 84. Relative sensitivity curves of infra-red films

has been taken care of, but it is recommended that a quartz cover glass be used 0·18 mm. in thickness. The ×52 objective can be used as a condenser for this particular objective, but a special condenser can be fitted if so desired.

INFRA-RED PHOTOMICROGRAPHY

There is a wide choice of illuminants for infra-red photomicrography, some of which have already been mentioned. Opaque objects do not reflect infra-red radiations in the same manner as when recorded with ordinary light. Further, since infra-red radiation is invisible, it is possible to take photomicrographs in apparent darkness. Many objects regarded as opaque to visible light are in fact transparent to infra-red radiation; among these are wood and ebony. This explains why infra-red film should be treated with caution when loaded or in storage.

An incandescent source produces a large amount of infra-red; this includes several discharge lamps. Low- and high-intensity arcs and filament lamps are efficient radiators in the infra-red. The lower the colour temperature of a filament lamp, the greater its efficiency in the infra-red. The peak emission is usually in the region of 9,000 Å. When employing the illuminants already mentioned as infra-red sources, it is absolutely necessary to incorporate an infra-red filter. There is a wide choice of filter material transmitting wave-lengths from 7,000 Å and upwards. A selection is listed below:

Wratten	88	transmits from 6,800 Å
Wratten	88A	transmits from 7,200 Å
Wratten	87	transmits from 7,400 Å
Ilford	207	transmits from 7,200 Å
Ilford	207 + 813	transmits from 7,400 Å
Muster Schmidt K.G.	100	transmits from 7,200 Å
Muster Schmidt K.G.	500	transmits from 7,600 Å

When using direct infra-red sources, it is not necessary to employ an infra-red filter.

When using a filament bulb of the 500-watt type, the lamp must be enclosed in a lightproof housing, with the aperture facing the microscope covered by an infra-red filter, to eliminate all visible radiation. The spectral transmission of the filter should reach its maximum around 8,000 Å; thus, maximum sensitivity of the emulsion will permit maximum image contrast. Fig. 84 illustrates the sensitivity of infra-red film manufactured by Gevaert and Kodak respectively. In both cases the film reaches its maximum sensitivity in the region of 8,000 Å; thereafter it quickly falls off into the visible region.

The infra-red transmission limits of substances of optical interest are as follows:

Glass	30,000 Å
Quartz	40,000 Å
Calcite	50,000 Å
Fluorite	90,000 Å
Rock salt	150,000 Å
Sylvine	230,000 Å

FLUORESCENCE ILLUMINATION

Although fluorescence has been present in animals, insects, rocks and many other substances since the beginning of time, this particular technique was not applied to microscopy until Lehmann, Heimsted and Reichert did so just before World War I.

Dr. Karl Reichert demonstrated his first model before a meeting of scientists in 1911. Nevertheless, for many years fluorescence microscopy was ignored.

After the end of World War II interest was revived in this special technique, the application of which is limited, but which is nevertheless an important scientific tool in such sciences as histology, quantitative analysis, cytology and microbiology.

Fluorescence is the ability of a material to absorb light of one wave-length and emit light of a different (usually longer) wave-length. Some substances continue to emit radiations for long periods after the external stimulus has ceased; this is known as phosphorescence. Instruments which measure the light intensity of fluorescence are known as fluorimeters. In microscopy ultra-violet radiations are used to study natural fluorescence, since these are the radiations principally absorbed in the production of fluorescence. It is wise to remember that care must always be taken when working with ultra-violet radiations, since, if the radiations are intense, the eyes may be damaged. In addition to the natural fluorescence of an object, a fluorescent material may be used to 'stain' it.

There is a wide range of fluorescent stains, which have been given code names and numbers by Reichert's, the manufacturers. A comprehensive list of colours is given in their booklet which contains recipes and tables.

The specimen is immersed in the fluorescent impregnant for periods ranging from seconds to as long as 20 minutes or more, according to the subject, before passing through the other processes, after which it is placed on an ultra-violet glass slide in readiness for photographing. Ultra-violet rays will induce fluorescence in many unpigmented plant and animal cells and tissues, which can then be photographed in colour, giving a good colour differentiation.

Canada balsam, Venetian turpentine, styrax, euparal and sirax have certain fluorescence properties and, therefore, cannot be used as a mounting medium. The Leitz fluorescence microscope BX has been specially designed for this particular application and is capable of working with ultra-violet fluorescence and blue-light fluorescence. With this model it is possible to use pure ultra-violet fluorescence and thus to observe the images in their natural colours and to record them with any one of the makers' interchangeable cameras.

The unique fluorescence photomicrographic apparatus illustrated in Plate 10 is manufactured by Reichert, and is the first with this special means of illumination. The beautiful Reichert colour photomicrographs reproduced in this book are ample evidence of the performance of this superb apparatus (Fig. 85).

No special microscope is really necessary for fluorescence photomicrography, but unfortunately there is a possibility that some of the optical parts themselves may become fluorescent.

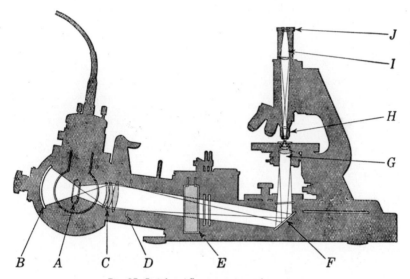

Fig. 85. Reichert fluorescence microscope

A, High-pressure mercury-vapour burner; B, reflecting mirror; C, lamp collector prisms; D, lamp (field) iris diaphragm; E, heat-absorbing and red-excluding filter; F, deviating mirror; G, condenser (quartz glass); H, objective; I, eyepiece; J, u.v.-excluding eyepiece filter.

Modern microscopes, however, are fluorescence-free. During the construction of the optical parts Canada balsam, which is also a fluorescent material, is used as an adhesive; if the cement is very thin, however, no visible fluorescence occurs. On the other hand, very old optical parts might cause some alarm if fluorescent techniques were being used.

The type of optical glass used in the condenser slightly affects the image brightness, and if ordinary crown glass is used, some 10 per cent of ultra-violet radiation becomes absorbed; the more expensive quartz condensers, however, do not absorb the ultra-violet. As the percentage of light being absorbed by the crown glass is so low, it does not make a lot of difference to the final image. The image brightness is, however, increased when using immersion-oil and high-power objectives; this has already been discovered when using tungsten light. The usual cedarwood immersion oil cannot be used because of its fluorescent properties which would interfere with the fluorescence of the specimen.

Methoxybenzene is a good substitute immersion fluid which does not fluoresce and has a high refractive index. Some loss of light is experienced when using a mirror to reflect the ultra-violet radiations from the source, but a quartz prism used instead of a mirror will retain the original output of ultra-violet radiation. If the prism is not available, the illumination can be direct from beneath the substage condenser, as illustrated and referred to earlier.

The special equipment needed for this highly specialized branch of photomicrography is: firstly, two ultra-violet radiators, which are rapidly and conveniently interchangeable; secondly, a maximum-pressure mercury-vapour lamp for less fluorescent material at high magnifications; and thirdly, a high-pressure mercury-vapour burner for low-power work with highly fluorescent material. These lamps can be used with any microscope. The carbon-arc lamp can be used for this particular application and of course transmits a certain percentage of ultra-violet light, but unfortunately there are many drawbacks associated with this form of illumination.

There are many types of mercury-vapour lamp. Like the carbon-arc, one of the most important features of the mercury-vapour is the intense brilliance which provides maximum image brightness. The light intensity of these lamps is measured by the candle-power per square centimetre. Therefore, the d.c. carbon-arc, being 18,000 candles/cm.^{2}, has a lower intrinsic brilliance than the HBO 200, which is 25,000 candles/cm.^{2}. This mercury-vapour arc lamp is specially designed for photomicrography by Osram.

For visual observation a much less intense light is necessary, and for this purpose the H.P. 80-watt and the H.P. 135-watt (both manufactured by Philips) are most suited. If no other lamp is available, these could be used for photomicrography, but in that event some heating effect would be evident on account of the exposure time factor. The microscope should not be subjected to intense heat, which causes the metals to expand and contract; this is even more serious when exposing for any length of time.

As on other occasions, when one is about to take a photomicrograph critical illumination should be ensured.

When blue-light fluorescence is carried out it is essential to use a filter, either glass or liquid. The liquid filter (already mentioned) is most suited to this particular apparatus, as it also acts as a heat filter; cupric tetraminosulphate is recommended. The fluorescence microscope BX has built-in filters which are not affected by the heat from the lamp. There are several makes of ultra-violet and blue transmission combined filters which give complete absorption of the longer wave-lengths. When there is an excess of ultra-violet and blue radiation, it can be absorbed by a yellow screen. The new eyepieces made by Leitz provide for these filters to be housed beneath the eyelens of the eyepiece. For ultra-violet fluorescence microscopy the Ilford Chance O.X.I. ultra-violet glass filter is satisfactory. These are manufactured as glass squares and circles 3 mm. thick. The Ilford 805 is a filter used solely for absorbing ultra-violet, and is used to protect the viewer's eyes from transmitted ultra-violet radiation. This filter is visually opaque and absorbs blue, green and all other colours, except a very small amount of red.

Focusing can take place in white light by adding a fluorescent screen to the equipment. The photographic material required for this work must be suitable for wave-lengths down to 2,500 Å. Normal process plates such as B40 suffice. These can be processed with either a process developer or a M.Q. type.

X-RADIOGRAPHY

X-radiography has only recently been applied to microscopy and has already proved to possess certain advantages over some techniques. One worthy feature is that this means of illumination permits a very high resolution; just under 1,000 Å has been attained. Although this resolution is an improvement over that obtainable with light, it does not surpass that of the electron microscope. Another advantage is that of contrast and fine detail, coupled with resolution, and a far greater penetration of thick specimens is also possible. Therefore, surfaces of considerable depth can be covered, especially with the metallurgical and biological subjects. No special means of preparation of the specimen is necessary before photographing.

Contact Radiography.—The employment of almost any X-ray tube makes the process fairly simple, as no focusing is necessary.

The specimen is placed in contact with a very fine-grained photographic plate, the X-ray beam being adjusted on the specimen (Fig. 86). The plate is processed and the X-ray image is then rephotographed through an optical system to improve the degree of enlargement. This second image can now be further enlarged to a third and final magnification. It is obvious that emulsions of a very fine grain size must be used so that the resolving power can be kept as high as possible, but of course it cannot possibly reach that of the optical system of the microscope. Some fine work has been carried out by Barclay (1947) and Mitchell (1950).

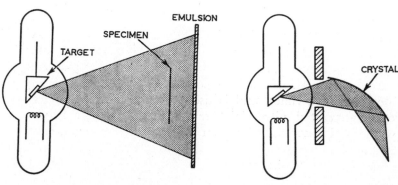

Fig. 86. Contact radiography   Fig. 87. Reflection radiography

Reflection Radiography.—Another method is to employ curved surfaces to focus the X-ray beam (Fig. 87). Here a highly polished metal mirror will serve the purpose well, although a curved crystal has also been used, but this projects an imperfect image.

Mirrors, having a shallow curve, serve to reflect rays at grazing incidence. The two mirrors are so arranged that one has its axis at right angles to the other. This arrangement of mirrors eliminates the possibility of astigmatism, whereas one mirror produces a somewhat inferior image due to astigmatism. This reflection X-ray microscope was developed and designed by P. Kirkpatrick and A. V. Baez (*J. Opt. Soc. Amer.* (1951) **38**, 392).

Shadow-projection Radiography.—Fig. 88 shows an apparatus developed by Cosslett and Nixon in 1953 from which some high-quality microradiographs have been published. This new method was made possible by using two magnetic lenses in series to form an image of the cathode on an area smaller than 1 sq.μ. The method adopted was to mount the specimen on a stage plate beyond the

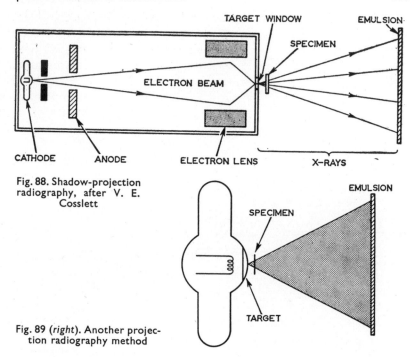

Fig. 88. Shadow-projection radiography, after V. E. Cosslett

Fig. 89 (*right*). Another projection radiography method

tube. Fitted to the stage were micrometer adjustments which provided the necessary accurately controlled movements across the X-ray beam and also along the axis of the apparatus. The positioning of the specimen along the axis controlled the degree of the magnifications of the projected image. An image of ×50 was attained and, by moving the specimen nearer the source, a higher magnification could be achieved. The final results have proved to be very successful and a high degree of resolution and depth has been achieved. The negative can undergo considerably further enlargement in an enlarger without loss of detail.

Fig. 89 illustrates another means of projection X-ray. Here the negative material can be enlarged to give further magnification.

General Electric X-ray Microscope and Camera.—This microscope is made by General Electric X-ray Corp., Milwaukee, and is based on the shadow-projection method and comprises an objective, aperture, condenser, accelerating anode, electron gun, target, and associated vacuum pumps, separate power supplies and contact systems (Plate 10).

A narrow cone of electrons emerges from the electron gun

(Fig. 90) and enters the condenser lens where it is collimated. This collimated beam enters the objective lens and is focused on to the target—a thin beryllium window ordinarily coated with tungsten. X-rays are then generated from this tiny target area, and the rest of the apparatus is simply a shadow-projection microscope. Therefore, a specimen placed near the X-ray source

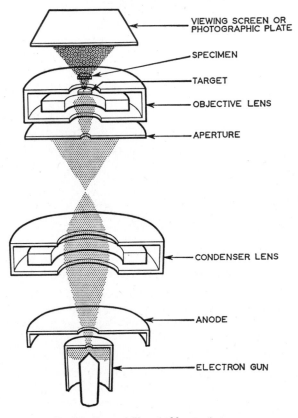

VIEWING SCREEN OR
PHOTOGRAPHIC PLATE

SPECIMEN

TARGET

OBJECTIVE LENS

APERTURE

CONDENSER LENS

ANODE

ELECTRON GUN

Fig. 90. General Electric X-ray microscope

casts an enlarged image on a fluorescent screen or photographic plate.

The complete electron-gun assembly is movable to enable alignment with the condenser and objective lenses; the output is controlled by varying the grid potential and the accelerating voltage on the anode is 20 kV.

The apertures referred to in Fig. 90 are designed to keep the spherical aberration to a minimum and the function of the four apertures of different sizes is to limit and vary the size of the electron beam.

The focusing of the objectives is electrostatic. There are two lower elements with apertures separated by an insulator and a top element in the target plane. This positions the target at the focal point of the lens, and governs the specimen size.

Situated in the centre of the target plate is the thin target disc which produces X-rays, and also acts as a vacuum seal.

One of the most useful accessories for this microscope is the Polaroid Land camera back. Operating with the microscope camera, this up-to-date device permits a developed image to be obtained in just 60 seconds after exposure (Plate 58). The Polaroid film has approximately the same speed as normal orthochromatic plates, but has a slightly better resolution than the fluorescent screen. This camera takes 5×4-in. cut film or plates. In addition to the speed of operation, one is furnished with direct viewing through the lead-glass fluorescent screen. The camera extension can be adjusted to change the magnification, and all settings are reproducible. Specimens can be mounted on $\frac{1}{2}$-in. diameter rings with films, and standard electron-microscope specimen grids can be accommodated.

This equipment has tremendous potentialities in many fields (Plate 58). Already the textile industry has made full use of this method of recording information and in medicine and dentistry it is proving to be a great boon.

10

CRITICAL ILLUMINATION

THE term *critical illumination* indicates that the microscope set-up is at its very best and that the adjustment of objective and substage condenser will produce the best possible image.

Critical illumination is that condition in which the maximum resolution is obtained. For photomicrography, it also means that the whole of the field of view is evenly illuminated. All the optical parts must be correctly adjusted if the illumination is to be critical. Critical illumination can, at times, be difficult to attain, but if the adjustments and principles are really studied and learnt the technique can become quite easy and any form of illumination can be mastered.

Critical illumination (Fig. 91) should always be the aim, and after a while this standard becomes second nature.

When working with a fixed optical bench, the apparatus is easily adjusted, compared with the portable microscope which has to be packed away in its case after the work is completed. When the instrument is used again it must be set up afresh, and it may be found that the fine adjustments required become trying and tedious and the worker will perhaps be tempted to get a little careless.

There are a number of details to be observed in lining up the equipment, the first of which is in connection with the baseboard of the camera, the lamp and microscope. If vertical lighting is used, the camera baseboard is placed into position about 10 in. over the

light-source. The next procedure is to centre the light on to the
ground glass, after which the microscope is placed into position
and correctly centred by means of light being projected on to the
ground glass. This is carried out without the optical system in the

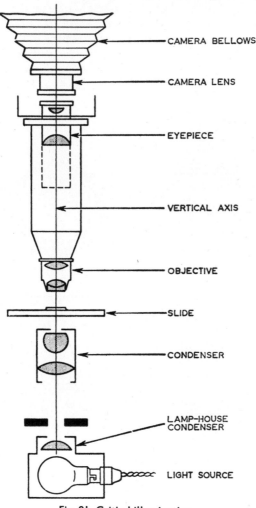

CAMERA BELLOWS

CAMERA LENS

EYEPIECE

VERTICAL AXIS

OBJECTIVE

SLIDE

CONDENSER

LAMP-HOUSE
CONDENSER

LIGHT SOURCE

Fig. 91. Critical illumination

microscope. Once the light is centred, the camera is swung away
and condenser and objective placed into position. The light now
shines directly into the condenser. Judging the correct aperture
of the substage diaphragm is easily carried out by removing the

eyepiece and looking down the microscope and examining the back lens of the objective while adjusting the diaphragm (Fig. 92); its image is clearly seen round the back lens of the objective.

At this point the light-source can be centred either by the mirror or by moving the condenser by its centring screws. On the other hand, the light-source may need a slight move. The lamp condenser, with iris wide open, is now focused on to the plane of the substage iris so that an image of the lamp filament is clearly seen. This can be done by using a small mirror to view the sub-stage iris. With the substage iris almost closed, an image of the lamp filament (Plate 14) should be clearly seen on the ground glass if the source is correctly centred. When the specimen slide is placed into position, the condenser is focused on to the under side of the

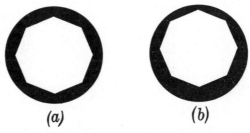

Fig. 92. Image of iris diaphragm formed in back of objective lens
(a) in critical alignment; (b) out of alignment

subject until the lamp iris is sharply seen in focus. This iris image should be in the centre of the subject. The eyepiece is added and the camera swung into position. The substage iris is then opened and the specimen focused on to the ground glass, when even illumination should follow. At this stage it may be necessary to rack the substage condenser up or down. The condenser iris should be carefully reduced, and any sign of diffraction should be avoided.

Any necessary filter is next placed in position and the subject once again focused on the ground glass. If high-power objectives are employed, it is advisable to use a focusing lens when focusing the image on the ground glass to provide a greater degree of accuracy. Once the illumination has been adjusted to secure the best quality, it is advisable to check for dust specks on the different lenses. This can be done by turning the eyepiece, etc., while looking at the image on the ground glass. If a dust speck is on any one of the lenses, it will be clearly seen to turn across the image as the lens is revolved between thumb and finger. Finally, before taking the photograph, check the light-source, lamp iris (and mirror if used), condenser and aperture, objective, eyepiece and camera, ensuring all are in their correct positions. Production of good photomicrographs can be assured by correct use of the apparatus and careful processing. Special attention should, therefore, be given to the illumination and use of correct light filters.

11

THE CAMERA

S TRANGE as it may seem, the camera is the least important
part of the photomicrographic set-up. The camera need in fact
be only a box in which to house the plate or film. Rarely does the
camera shutter come into operation unless, of course, moving
objects are to be photographed, and when a secondary source is
burning in conjunction with flash. On such occasions a fast
shutter is essential to arrest all movement.

The electric-light switch can be used to control the exposure
time when an exposure is longer than, say, 1 second. The plate
housing must be light-tight, with a free movement to the slide,
so that its removal will not shake the apparatus.

Any camera can be used in conjunction with the microscope.
It is advisable to remove the camera lens before taking a photomicrograph, since it serves no particular purpose in forming the
photographic image. If the camera lens cannot be removed, it
should be set to infinity (Fig. 93) and the camera iris opened to
its full aperture. It is possible, however, to make a photomicrograph with the lens in position, but a much clearer photographic
image is produced without the lens. There is no focusing to be
done with the everyday camera, such as a box (Plates 7 and 8),
miniature and others (Plate 2), and all these lend themselves to
photomicrography. With the addition of a metal tube, which
screws into the lens mount and fits around the draw tube, the
correct alignment is ensured, enabling shots to be taken of rapidly

moving objects, whereas with larger cameras it is more difficult
to do so.

MODELS AND USES

A similar microscope camera to that already mentioned is
the Macca (Plate 6), which takes a 4·5 × 6-cm. plate and also
the Makam, which takes 9 × 12-cm. plates. These are specially
designed for photomicrography. These cameras enable the subject to be seen during the whole process, both before and after the

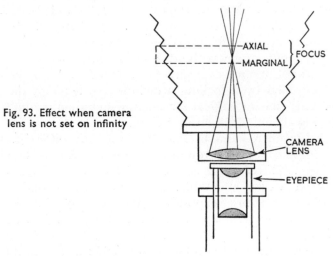

Fig. 93. Effect when camera
lens is not set on infinity

exposure is made. Unfortunately, the shutter speed, ranging from
1/125th to 1 second is not high enough to cater for some fast-
moving creatures. However, a quick series of shots can be taken
of growing or slowly-moving objects, the plates being easily
changed. The use of a long cable-release enables the worker to
sit in comfort until the field is suitable for photography. These
cameras also have an adjustable iris, which gives a good range of
stops. Magnifications range from low-power to ×200 and can
safely be carried out, but the camera is not as satisfactory when
working with high-power, because of vibration caused by the
operation of the shutter. The light switch can, of course, always
be used when making a time exposure, thus eliminating all movement; unfortunately, however, this method is not always successful, especially with free-swimming creatures.

The Golder Microflex camera (Plate 6) fits over the eyepiece and clamps tightly to the draw tube by three milled-headed

thumbscrews. This camera is light, has an efficient reflex shutter and is fitted with a fine ground-glass screen, which can be viewed comfortably while critical focusing is being carried out. When attaching this camera to the microscope no further adjustment is required, as all parts are automatically centred, thus ensuring the camera is in true and critical alignment with the optical system in use. The $2\frac{1}{4} \times 3\frac{1}{4}$-in. plate- or filmholder is easy to load and quickly placed into position when a photomicrograph is about to be taken. The slide can be inserted and removed without any fear of altering the adjustment of the microscope. The draw tube must not, of course, be slack. The eyepiece, which can vary in magnification, fits firmly into a clamping ring and is held tight by its top flange without fear of vibration. The shutter enables a brief or time exposure to be made, the time exposure being controlled by a locking attachment fitted into the cable release. This camera is ideal for making stereo-pairs, due to the safe-locking clamp which ensures rigidity.

The E.C.2 micro-camera (Plate 6) is slightly different. It has the viewing screen on the top of the camera and must be viewed from above. Therefore, it is necessary to have the microscope standing on a firm low table. The cable release operates the shutter for time or brief exposures. With this camera the subject cannot be viewed right up to the time of exposure, as with the previous camera.

When using the small folding pocket camera, such as the Zeiss Ikon, some device must be introduced to support the camera, as in Plate 4. A retort stand serves the purpose well, and allows for easy movement of the camera in all directions. While the operator is finding an appropriate field to photograph, the camera is swung away clear of the head, but when a photograph is about to be taken the camera is swung back into position without any further adjustments. When a long focal-length objective is used, it automatically raises the eyepiece and body tube, which in turn cause the camera to be raised. It is not advisable to have the camera lens or lens mount resting on the eyepiece, as this might easily push the draw tube down slightly and alter the focus of the microscope, besides causing possible vibration. The camera must be firmly secured to its stand or tripod, to enable the film to be wound over without altering the setting of the camera; the same applies to the plate camera when removing the plateholder. Great care should be taken in centralizing the camera over the eyepiece. The camera should be absolutely vertical or horizontal, ensuring that the optical axis is correspondingly vertical or horizontal, otherwise the negative will not be sharp all over. If the camera has no back plate on which to focus the image, focusing can take place on a piece of thin white paper placed in the plane of the film carrier. Failing this, a piece of ground glass can be laid over the back of the camera.

To prevent stray light from entering the camera when the lens is removed and the camera is in position for photomicrography, a light-tight ring should be placed around the eyepiece as seen in Plate 3. When using a plate camera such as Watson's vertical photomicro and Golder Microflex, focusing takes place on the ground glass. The use of double or treble bellows fitted to a camera allows for a variation in magnification without removing eyepiece or objective, this being a great advantage over the pocket camera where the magnification is controlled solely by the objective and eyepiece. Far better results can be obtained with the bellows type of camera, as the back can be raised and lowered, thus fitting the field into the plate area. In addition to this, far greater attention can be paid to the illumination of the subject which is viewed on the ground-glass screen, allowing complete control of both focus and illumination. Another great advantage the plate camera and optical bench have over the roll-film camera is that plates can be individually processed and any necessary alteration in exposure time, filter, field, focus and illumination can be made after visual inspection.

In all cases filters are placed below the substage condenser. A box camera was used to make the photomicrograph seen in Plate 46(c), the microscope being horizontal. Retort stands were used to support the Zeiss Ikon camera which was used to make the illustration seen in Plate 29(b). The camera lens system was left in both cameras when making the photomicrographs. The section of porcupine quill (Plate 33(d)) was taken with a Kodak folding camera with the lens system removed.

ADVANCED MODELS

The Holophot equipment seen in Plate 4 is especially suitable for the research scientist and is the result of the collaboration of many microscopists. It is compact, foolproof, rigid and easy to operate, and is used in all branches of science, including medicine. It can be seen that it is sturdily constructed, the main supports being vertical castings of a webbed pattern. These supports ensure permanent alignment of the complete optical system, the triple nosepiece bringing one of the objectives into alignment by one-third of a turn. An anti-vibration pad of sponge rubber is fitted under the base plate to ensure that if there is a slight vibration the camera and microscope move as one unit. Nevertheless, it is suggested that this unit, like others, be placed on a concrete base, preferably on a ground floor or basement, as it is essential that all microscopes should be free from vibration. The Pointolite is the permanent light-source and can be easily adjusted, thus guaranteeing that the lamp gives a centralized cone of light. This particular lamphouse enables specimens to be photographed by transmitted light and oblique illumination; macro-subjects can also be photographed by the same illumination.

An electronic flashlamp has also been devised, but is not a standard fitting (see Chapter 6). When using transmitted light the source is directed on to the two adjustable mirrors and re-directed into a $1\frac{1}{4}$-in. square-face prism situated beneath the substage condenser; vertical illumination then follows. The image can be examined by either a viewing eyepiece or a reflex mirror, which projects the image on to a finely etched screen conveniently placed in a vertical plane. When one views the illumination through the viewing eyepiece there is a minimum amount of glare. When the image is to be inspected in the reflex mirror, the viewing eyepiece is withdrawn, thus allowing an image to be projected on to the screen.

When required for low magnifications of $\times 2-\times 10$, the microscope unit is dispensed with simply by raising the camera. A spring-loaded clamp holding the microscope in position is withdrawn. The removal of the microscope enables the stage to be brought up to hold the specimen at the required distance from the camera lens. The low-power objective is fitted to the camera-lens panel immediately beneath the enclosed shutter, and focusing takes place by means of the rackwork motion of the stage. When one photogaphs large opaque specimens, the illumination is adjusted and directed by lowering one mirror to a position directly opposite the lamp iris. This mirror then directs the light to the other mirror, which is now placed at the top of the pillars and this in turn illuminates the specimen. For illuminating a transparent object the method is similar to that used in photomicrography. The top mirror is lowered to a position opposite the lamphouse iris; this mirror directs the light into the lower mirror—now lower than the lamp—and then redirects the light into the prism which is beneath the stage.

The Leitz Aristophot II incorporates a quarter-plate bellows camera with the usual fittings associated with such cameras. An outstanding feature of this combined microscope and illumination is the interchangeability of cameras. A Leica 35-mm. camera with micro-mirror reflex attachment can be fitted. There is a central shutter with a focusing telescope and an intermediate adapter $\times \frac{1}{3}$ or $\times \frac{1}{2}$ to be screwed between the two. With low magnifications, fine focusing of the image is carried out on the ground-glass screen and with high magnifications it is carried out with a focusing telescope on a finely-ground glass screen. It is possible to watch the specimen during the actual exposure; this is essential when photographing moving objects which have an irritating habit of swimming out of the picture or floating through (up or down) the point of focus. It is possible to use an extending bellows with the Leica camera to give additional magnifications.

The Beck whole-plate horizontal microscope and camera is carried on two triangular section benches, each 2 m. long. These are mounted on cross-bars with levelling screws. The Beck horizontal optical bench can be made to incorporate special requirements and can be made to employ quarter-plates or whole plates, the bellows having triple extension. The limb of the microscope is attached direct to a saddle piece, fitting on to the bench. The body has a rack-and-pinion draw tube. The stage has a rotating movement, like most of the latest models, which allows the image of the object to be correctly viewed and positioned on the plate.

The Panphot (Plate 5) is a large efficient research microscope with vertical camera and illuminating arrangement combined, and is suitably designed for work of a medical nature. This and similar models replace the horizontal optical benches, with all their disadvantages, especially as regards centring of the main components. The Panphot enables mobile specimens to be photographed in their free state. Furthermore, wet sections can be handled and photographed as they lie on the slide unmounted. This is a great advantage, as not every specimen lends itself to being permanently mounted in Canada balsam and similar mediums.

The interchangeable fittings of this instrument include monocular and binocular bodies with photographic tube combined and several types of object stages and substages. Nearly all standard microscope accessories can also be used to adapt the apparatus to practically all the requirements of photomicrography: transmitted light, incident illumination, bright-field, dark-field, phase-contrast, polarized light and fluorescence illumination can be used in the production of photomacrographs and photomicrographs. The illumination is directed on to the object by a highly reflecting plane glass, through a variable aperture. There are five interchangeable objectives on a revolving nosepiece. This gives a wide range of magnifications, which is sometimes necessary when forming a complete picture of a given specimen. A ring

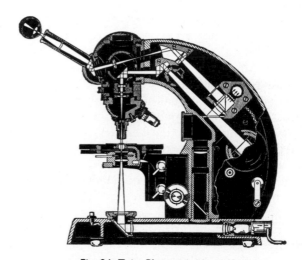

Fig. 94. Zeiss Photo-microscope

illuminator is fitted to enable photomacrographic specimens to be illuminated in such a way as to create an even spread of light.

The combined illuminating arrangement is a low-voltage filament lamp 6-volt 5-amp and arc lamp for 10-amp d.c. or 15-amp a.c. There is no fear of undue heat affecting the specimen, because a double heat-absorbing filter is fitted. This means of illumination can be changed over quickly and efficiently to the xenon lamp. The great advantage of this system of lighting is that it allows optional adjustment of the intensity even when changing from one light-source to another. The xenon lamp is optically and mechanically superior to the usual carbon arc light. Its colour, which is near to that of direct sunlight or daylight, is independent of mains voltage fluctuations. The current supply to the lamp is through a rectifier which is connected to 220-volt a.c. mains. The xenon lamp is always ready for immediate use, like the normal filament lamps. Short exposures can be made with this particular lamp. For convenience, the illuminating apparatus is at the side, which enables a quick change-over to be made. The lamp has a regulating transformer and also a spare lamp stowed inside. The xenon lamp is 150-watt, and altogether five filters are built into the Panphot, which makes handling quite easy. The low-voltage bulb is used for locating the field and during focusing, the xenon lamp being brought into position when the subject is ready for photography. The camera is an extensible mirror reflex type and is fitted to take plates 9×12 cm. or $3\frac{1}{4} \times 4\frac{1}{4}$ in. A very useful facility is the instantaneous exposure, which is available in addition to the usual time setting on the shutter.

Zeiss have completely revolutionized the appearance of the microscope-and-camera combination by introducing the Photo-microscope and the Ultraphot II, each of which has a sleek, streamlined and attractive air. In addition to the clean lines, these instruments are ultra-modern, as they are automatically controlled.

The Photo-microscope is the smaller of the two, with a built-in illumination arrangement, and the source is a low-voltage 6-volt 15-watt lamp, situated in the foot of the microscope (Fig. 94), thus making it easily accessible. After passing through a correction condenser the light is re-directed by a mirror, and vertical illumination follows. Above the objective there are mounted the Optovar magnification changer and deflecting prisms, as well as a protective device which is switchable into two stages. The Optovar system alters the eyepiece magnifications. (Similar systems are, of course, fitted to other makes of microscope.) A partial reflecting mirror then splits the course of the rays: one, the main beam, is directed to the film plane, and the other to a photocell and viewing eyepiece. For visual observation a deflecting mirror is inserted, thus directing the light into a ring-condenser, which is attached at the lower end of the tube head; the latter replaces the nosepiece. The nosepiece houses five Planachromat flat-field objectives ranging from $\times 2 \cdot 5$ to $\times 100$ oil-immersion, which gives a complete, smooth picture. These are therefore especially suitable for photomicrography.

The condenser has the usual rack-and-pinion movement and houses two filters. Thirty-five-mm. film is used in conjunction

with the Photo-microscope, the camera being housed in the un-
usually deep swept-back arm. After insertion, the film needs only
to be wound on to the receiving-side spool, after which it is
automatically wound from the feed spool. When the release
button has been pressed the camera shutter is opened and the
exposure time is automatically regulated. After the correct exposure has been made, the mechanism winds over the exposed frame,
leaving the film ready for a further exposure, and at the same time
operating a film counter. The shutter is then reset ready for a
further exposure. These operations are actuated by a spring-driven
motor, which is hand-wound at the time of loading the new film.

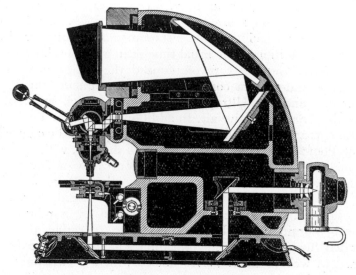

Fig. 95. Zeiss Ultraphot II

This initial charge is sufficient to repeat the cycle of operations
throughout the complete length of film, which can be exposed
completely to various subjects, each exposure being automatically
compensated.

The Ultraphot II is the larger of the two instruments (Figs. 95
and 96) and is designed to house 9 × 12-cm. plates, but 13 ×
18-cm. material can be used, as also can 35-mm. film. When
plates are used the automatic mechanism does not come into
use. The Ultraphot II fulfils the most exacting requirements. It is
easy to operate, the optical performance is of the highest order,
and bright- and dark-field methods of illumination can be

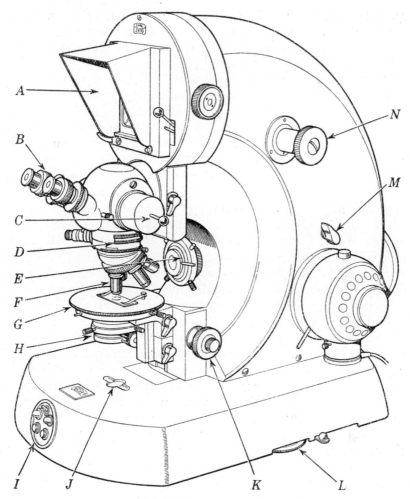

Fig. 96. Zeiss Ultraphot II

A. Photo-head 9 × 12 cm. with built-in setting lever for shutter
B. Normal oblique viewing, rapid changing mechanism for quick interchange of tubes
C. Adjustable ray director
D. Optovar with 3 magnification stages and focusable auxiliary microscope
E. Constant centring of lamp
F. Objective fitted with lower lens protection
G. Rotating stage for fine, rapid adjustment in all directions; interchangeable stage-carrier and carrier for illumination apparatus
H. Adjustment for illumination apparatus
I. Push-button for shutter and automatic camera
J. Constant centring of light-source for microscope, and filter carrier
K. Coarse and fine adjustment
L. Illumination field diaphragm for trans-illumination
M. Lamp switch for various forms of illumination
N. Adjustment varying length of camera to 30 cm.

used. In addition to this, phase-contrast and interference techniques can be introduced, besides ring illumination employing polarized or non-polarized light. A change in the path of light brings incident illumination into operation.

The instrument can be fitted with 1–3 lamps, according to requirements. The 12-volt 8-amp low-voltage bulb can be used for both transmitted and ring illumination. In addition to the low-voltage means of illumination a high-pressure mercury-vapour, or xenon lamp, can be used. The fully automatic carbon-arc lamp can also be used. When the latter is incorporated into the instrument it is housed at the rear of the microscope. With all types of illumination the light can be adjusted to give optimum illumination of all types of specimen.

Like the Photo-microscope, the Ultraphot II microscope has a nosepiece which contains five objectives. The range of magnifications covers a wide field—from 2:1 to 1,700:1—and by using the Luminars (63 mm. and 100 mm.), specimens as large as 60 mm. in diameter can be photographed. The new Zeiss plane objectives (apochromatic) are specially recommended for use when making photomicrographs.

The camera is fitted with a ground-glass screen and hood. A viewing eyepiece can also be used, and this is particularly welcome when photographing moving objects. The camera is also fitted with an automatic exposure mechanism which registers any change in intensity of illumination, whether by substage condenser, objective, density of specimen or otherwise. When using incident illumination the exposure time is solely in the control of the operator.

The Optovar system is also in use with this instrument. The ocular magnification can quickly and efficiently be changed by factors 1·25, 1·6 and 2.

The Polaroid colour-translating microscope has been designed to project a colour image within 30 seconds of the exposure being made. The microscope houses three colour-sensitive 35-mm. films, arranged to record different wave-lengths. These are exposed, processed and projected, the composite tri-colour picture appearing within the time stated. The apparatus used to establish this record is not at time of writing in mass-production, but several have been produced.

12

STEREOSCOPIC
PHOTOMICROGRAPHY

S TEREO-PHOTOMICROGRAPHY is a well-established branch of photomicrography which enables a better interpretation of the subject to be made. Strangely enough, this branch of photomicrography is practised very little today by either professional or amateur.

To appreciate stereo-photomicrography the principles must first be understood. When viewing an object on a flat print, any impression of depth (or height) can only be given by shadows. Such shadows can easily be interpreted the wrong way, and a feature which appears to be in relief may be a depression. Stereoscopic vision depends solely upon seeing two pictures with two eyes at the same time. It is largely a question of angles, as one eye sees slightly more of one side of an object than the other. Some animals and birds cannot see stereoscopically, particularly birds. It can be seen that birds hold their heads on one side, either to see an enemy or when about to pick up certain foods. Most insects have compound eyes composed of minute facets, which are believed to form images by a process known as mosaic vision. There are, of course, a few insects and pond creatures which have only one eye. In such cases the field of view covered is not seen stereoscopically.

To use a simple illustration indicating the practical value of stereoscopic vision, imagine knocking a nail into a piece of wood with one eye closed. How different and how difficult this job becomes and how often the fingers are hit. This is because the common faculty of seeing with two eyes has been removed. Using only one eye, one cannot see round the nail, and it becomes difficult to judge distances because the orthostereoscopic effect vanishes. In other words, a person with normal stereoscopic vision cannot judge depth accurately with only one eye.

When a stereoscope is not available for viewing stereo-pairs, the next best thing that can be done to create a stereoscopic effect is to make full use of shadows, which in themselves give the feeling of depth. For this reason many photomicrographs illustrated in this book have shadows, some darker and longer than others; in others the light has been used off-centre, the subject demanding its own particular treatment. Another method of giving a feeling of depth is to take a number of photomicrographs of a given subject at various planes or points of focus by slightly altering the fine adjustment. A permanent record of the various layers could be made by introducing ciné-photomicrography. By adjusting the picture to various planes the result achieved is exactly what the eye does when viewing an object, especially a near one. The eye automatically adjusts its focus as it goes from foreground to background and vice versa. This adjusting is known as accommodation. With the aid of a stereogram an object can be seen in far greater relief than a single image, so much so that one often feels that one could grasp the subject.

The production of stereoscopic photomicrographs consists in taking two photographs side by side, these two views being taken from two different view-points (Plates 59, 60 and 61). An important factor is depth of field. This means that to obtain maximum depth the magnification is limited to approximately ×250, although in some cases higher magnifications can be used. Transmitted and oblique illumination are equally effective in the production of stereoscopic effects.

APPARATUS AND TECHNIQUES

Although two eyes are used to view an object through the binocular microscope the image seen may not be stereoscopic unless twin objectives have been used. The binocular type of apparatus is not used for stereoscopic photomicrography.

Stereoscopic microscopes are manufactured with interchange-able units, and are made with both vertical and inclined (45°) eyepieces. The Research model, made by Watson's, now replaces the old Greenough model. It was as far back as the end of the nineteenth century that an American conceived the idea of combining two compound microscopes, thus giving one for each

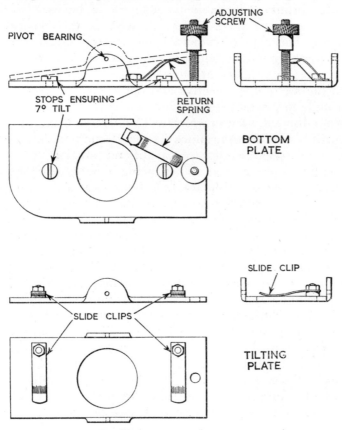

Fig. 97. Diagram of tilting stage

eye, controlled or operated by a master thumbscrew which moved the two tubes as one. Thus, stereoscopic vision started with paired objectives and eyepieces. This type of model is specially suited for stereoscopic vision, although the conventional binocular type is often confused with it. With the true stereoscopic model the optical axes of the two objectives converge towards the specimen, which is illuminated by the normal substage condenser.

For this type of microscope with paired objectives a special stereoscopic camera has been designed and can be purchased without any difficulty. Some twin-lens micro-cameras lack adequate stands, and when this is the case the use of a retort stand and clamp serves the purpose equally well, especially if an adjustable ball joint is used in conjunction with a small tripod. The extra fitting will enable the camera to be used with the inclined microscope (Wild M.5) as well as the vertical and horizontal. This type of camera is particularly useful when one is photographing moving subjects which do not, of course, permit the exposures to be taken at intervals.

With the use of one objective and one eyepiece, however, it is quite simple to produce stereo-pairs, and several methods are, in fact, at our disposal, a few of which will be covered here. With these methods it is possible to produce a stereoscopic photomicrograph by taking two photomicrographs at different angles.

The tilting-stage method of producing a stereo-pair of photo-micrographs is very satisfactory for both low- and high-power magnifications. It seems strange that this method should be so satisfactory, since in normal photomicrography endeavours are made to keep the slide truly at right angles to the optical axis of the system in use. The only extra piece of equipment required to produce stereo-photomicrographs by this method is a tilting stage which is quite easy to make (see Plate 8 and Fig. 97). The subject is photographed in two tilted positions, with the stage $7°$ or $7\frac{1}{2}°$ to the right, and with the same degree of tilt to the left without moving objective or eyepiece (Plate 60(*lower*)). This method can be used with oblique and transmitted lighting.

Once the illumination has been adjusted, there is nothing more to be done. The illumination should be centralized when the subject is aligned at right angles to the optical axis of the microscope. This operation may appear to be strange, especially as the subject will be in a tilted position when photographed, but at this stage even illumination is ensured and unevenness is prevented, as would be the case if adjusted when tilted to one particular side. Great care must be taken when centring the specimen to ensure that it coincides with the point of pivot, and the pivot must come in line with the axis of the objective, D, and A (Fig. 98). Tilting the subject gives two perspectives to the optical system, and two angles taken on planes B to B and B_1 to B_1. The axis of tilt must occupy the vertical bisector of the mounted image A.

The actual taking of the photomicrograph does not differ from straightforward oblique or vertical photomicrography. Care should be taken to get the best image the lens will record on the film. Here a word of warning about the introduction of foreign marking. Diffraction rings will spoil a picture. The picture obtained by the left tilt must correspond with that obtained by the right-hand tilt, the field being duplicated apart from its angle of tilt. The exposure of the negative material must be the same for each negative, as must be the development time.

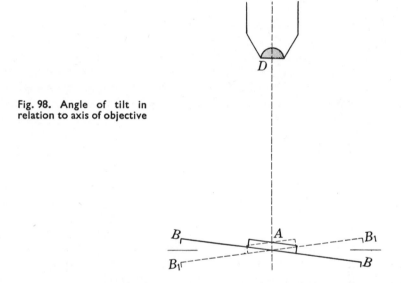

Fig. 98. Angle of tilt in relation to axis of objective

On certain exceptional occasions it may be necessary to refocus on the subject when about to take the second shot. In such cases great care should be taken to see that this is carried out on exactly the same spot as the first exposure. If focusing takes place on two different points, some considerable confusion will be caused when viewing these two views as one.

In this type of photomicrography extra attention should be paid when sticking the left- and right-hand prints down so that they are mounted on the correct side. If wrongly mounted, the subject is viewed under complete reversal conditions, known as pseudo-stereoscopic; shadows become 'embankments' and vice versa, as is the case when viewing aerial stereo-pairs which have been wrongly presented.

There is another method of tilting the specimen whereby two photomicrographs can be taken, and it is claimed that this tilting stage (the Moitessiers) gives up to 12° of tilt. This stage fits into the aperture of the microscope stage and is also pivoted so that the axis of the tilt occupies the vertical bisector of the objective-image. The author considers that 7° gives the best stereoscopic effect. In addition to the extra tilt available, this stage has a raising and lowering adjustment which allows for media of various thicknesses to be photographed.

In some exceptional cases oil-immersion objectives can be used with the tilting stage, the angle of tilt being reduced to approximately $4\frac{1}{2}°$. As the working distance of an oil-immersion objective is so limited, it is advisable to use one of the latest types, having the maximum working distance.

It has been seen that by tilting the subject stereo-pairs are obtained, provided the axis of the objective and eyepiece in use fall over the point of pivot of the slide. The specimen must also be positioned over the pivot of the slide (Fig. 98). Instead of tilting the subject to get the desired effect, we may incline the angle of the incident light. This is possible by the introduction of a single aperture mask below the substage condenser (as shown in Fig. 99).

At first it might be thought that this means of illumination is vertical, owing to the rays of light passing through the substage and on through the objective and eyepiece in the normal manner, but instead of the normal axial rays we use only oblique or marginal rays. The eccentric stop mask is housed in the filter-carrier and is as near to the lower lens as possible. This form of oblique lighting must not be confused with normal oblique lighting as used when photographing an opaque subject. By using an eccentric stop, the pencil of light is directed to the edge of the condenser, which is operated at full aperture, as can be seen in Fig. 99. The light rays strike and penetrate the specimen at an angle (also seen in the illustration). After the first exposure the stop is turned round to the opposite side and the same procedure carried out as for the first. Various sizes of hole can be used according to the subject about to be photographed.

On occasions, when the equipment allows, it is possible to use an eccentric stop with two holes, which gives off two narrow pencils of light running towards the axis of the condenser, but the instrument must be fitted with two oculars. The rays of light are,

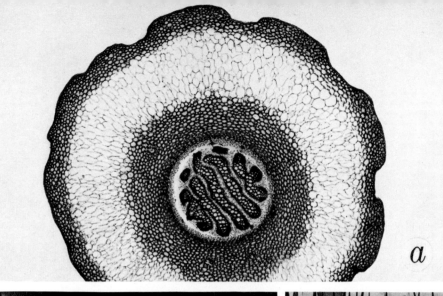

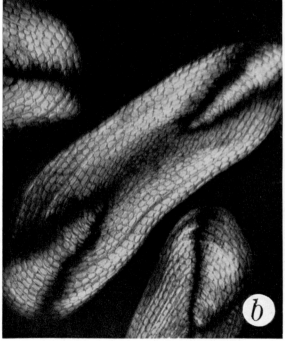

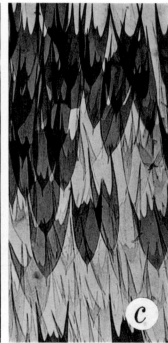

(a) TRANSVERSE SECTION OF CLUB MOSS, × 15 (total × 100)

Stained red and green. The green filter allows only one colour to pass; thus, the final image of the delicate cells of *Lycopodium selago* is in two tones.

(b) SCALES OF EEL, × 40 (total × 90)

Polarized light was used, enabling the fine structure of each *Anguilla vulgaris* scale to be seen. With normal transmitted light there is no visible image of this specimen.

(c) WING SCALES OF EMPEROR MOTH, × 45 (total × 70)

Microscope and camera in horizontal positions. Only part of the negative used.

Microscope: Leitz. Camera: (a) Watson, (b) Una ¼-plate, (c) box. Objective: (a and b) 25 mm. (c) 16 mm. Eyepiece: (a) nil, (b) × 2, (c) 22 mm. × 11. Substage: (a and b) less bull's eye condenser, (a) the two lower in use only, (c) nil. Tube length: (a and b) 170 mm., (c) 168 mm. Bellows length: (a) 6 in., (b) 12 in., (c) nil. Emulsion: (a) chromatic, (b) P.1200, (c) Verichrome. Filter: (a) green, (b and c) nil. Illumination: (a) transmitted, (b) polarized light, (c) reflected at 80°. Exposure; (a) 2 sec., (b) 5 sec., (c) 4 sec.

PLATE 46

PLATE 47

(a and b) GROUP OF DIATOMS

These minute algae, *Heliopeltametric*, are commonly found in both fresh and salt water. Because of their delicate and regular markings, certain species can be used to test the resolving power of a microscope. Careful treatment of the negative material prevents distortion of the very fine detail recorded. Transmitted illumination does not do justice to this beautiful subject.

Magnification: × 35 (*total* × 75). *Microscope: Watson. Camera: Una ¼ plate. Objective: 16 mm. Eyepiece: 45 mm. × 6. Substage: complete with bull's eye condenser iris ⅔ closed. Tube length: 170 mm. Bellows length: 6 in. Emulsion: Ilford Special Rapid. Filter: blue. Illumination: transmitted. Exposure: 5 seconds.*

Dark-ground illumination brings into view certain features that can scarcely be seen by transmitted light. It proved very difficult, however, to judge the correct size of dark stop to be used in order to achieve a sharply defined rendering of the outer circles. A blue filter was used in making the final image.

Magnification; × 35 (*total* × 75). *Microscope: Watson. Camera: Una ¼-plate. Objective: 16 mm. Eyepiece: 45 mm. × 6. Substage: less bull's eye condenser. Tube length: 173 mm. Bellows length: 6 in. Emulsion: Special Rapid. Filter: blue. Illumination: dark ground. Exposure: 13 seconds.*

(c and d) POLLEN GRAINS

Pollen grains of mallow, *Malva sylvestris*. Oil immersion was used together with phase contrast. A very difficult subject for photomicrography. The top of the grain is, of course, out of focus; this is termed an optical section.

Magnification: × 900 (*total* × 1,260). *Microscope: Leitz. Camera: Watson. Objective: 2 mm. N.A. 1·0. Eyepiece: 22 mm. × 11. Substage: complete with bull's eye condenser. Tube length; 160 mm. Bellows length: 9 in. Emulsion: P.1200. Filter: pale yellow. Illumination: transmitted phase contrast. Exposure: 25 seconds.*

The particular field shows a number of Caucasian fir pollen grains on a slide; some are flat and some are standing on edge, giving a clear picture of the "wings".

Magnification: × 200 (*total* × 550). *Microscope: Leitz. Camera: Watson. Objective: 8 mm. N.A. 0·65. Eyepiece: 22 mm. × 11. Substage: complete. Tube length: 160 mm. Bellows length: 7 in. Emulsion: P.1200. Filter: diffuser only. Illumination: transmitted. Exposure: 5 seconds.*

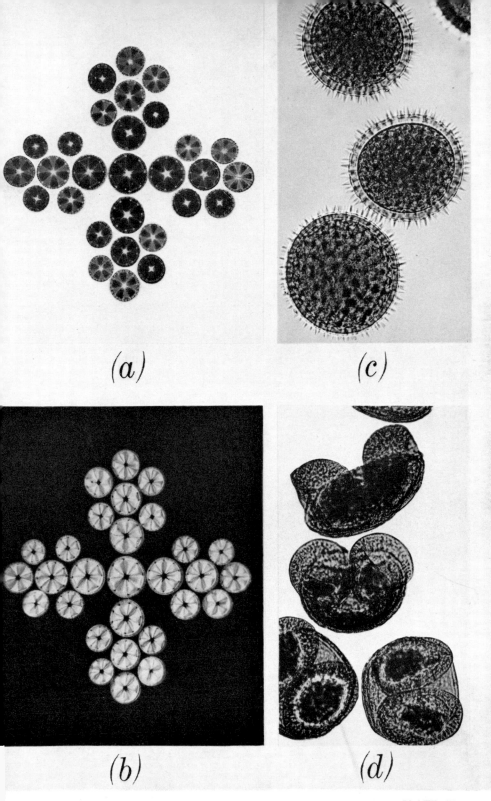

(a)

(c)

(b)

(d)

PLATE 47

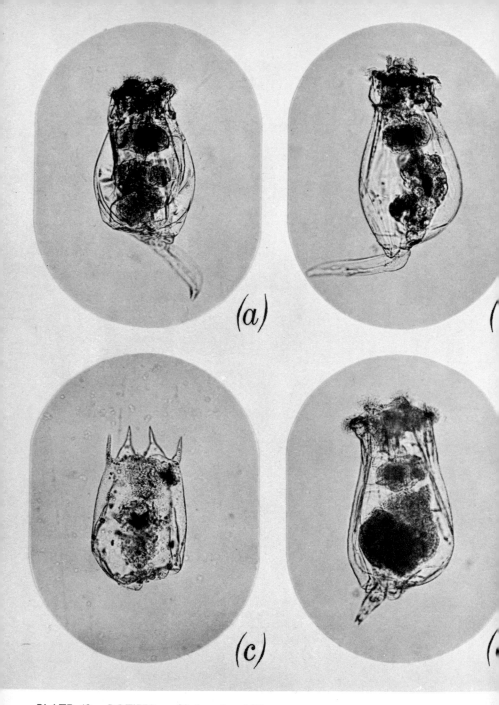

PLATE 48.   ROTIFER, × 20 (total × 160)

This series of photomicrographs clearly illustrates the effect a narcotizing agent has on a subje

(a) Live specimen lying in water in hollow slide.
(b) Narcotized with aspirin.
(c) Dead.
(d) Narcotized with amidopyrine.

Miscroscope: Zeiss.   Camera: Macca ½ ×.   Objective: 16 mm.   Eyepiece: × 2.   Substage: comp
Tube length: 170 mm.   Emulsion: P.300.   Filter: nil.   Illumination: transmitted.   Exposure: 1/50 second

(a) (b) (c) (d)

E 49.   AIRBORNE FUNGI

se photographs were obtained by exposing on the bench open Petri dishes containing Sabourand's
gar, for 30 minutes.   The plates were incubated at room temperature and slides for photographing
stained and mounted in lactophenol cotton blue (Amann's medium).

) *Aspergillus* sp.;   (b) *Aspergillus* sp. head with mass of spores;   (c) *Penicillium* sp.;
                              (d) "*Penicillus*" head with spores.

nification: (a) × 240 (total × 400) (b) × 700 (total × 1,000), (c) × 500, (d) × 700 (total × 1,000).
cope: Leitz.   Camera: Watson.   Eyepiece: 22 mm.   × 11 mm.   Substage: complete.   Tube length:
m.   Illumination: transmitted.   Objective: (a) 8 mm. N.A. 0·65, (b) 4 mm. N.A. 0·75, (c) 4 mm. N.A.
d) 4 mm.   Bellows length: (a) 10 in., (b) 14 in., (c) 7 in., (d) 14 in.   Emulsion: (a and b) O.250, (c)
, (d) chromatic.   Filter: (a) green and orange, (b) blue, (c) green and yellow, (d) green.   Exposure:
econds, (b) 15 seconds, (c) 2 minutes, (d) 24 seconds.

PLATE 50.   TABLET STABILITY TESTS

(*top left*) Tablets fully exposed at 20° C for 4 months (actual size).

(*top right*) Tablets showing discoloration and salicylic acid crystal growth after having been stored fully exposed at 40° C, 80% R.H. for 4 months (actual size).

(*centre left*) Tablets showing surface structure after having been stored fully exposed at 20° C for 4 months ($\times$ 4).

(*centre right*) Tablets showing surface structure after having been fully exposed at 40° C, 80% R.H. for 4 months ($\times$ 4).

(*lower*) Section of tablets as they lay in the test dish, showing salicylic acid crystals growing from tablets ($\times$ 10).   (See also Plate 24.)
This sample was taken from a tablet which was exposed at 40° C, 80% R.H. for four months.

The photomacrographs were photographed with a 4-in. R.R. lens, using the bellows length to assist in making the magnification.   Critical focusing, plus the correct strength of illumination and its direction, and, of course, processing the plate, are the key points.   When making prints it is advisable to have a tablet to hand, making the prints tone with them.   Remember the shadows help to give a three-dimensional effect, at the same time keep shadows soft.   Emulsion: O.250.

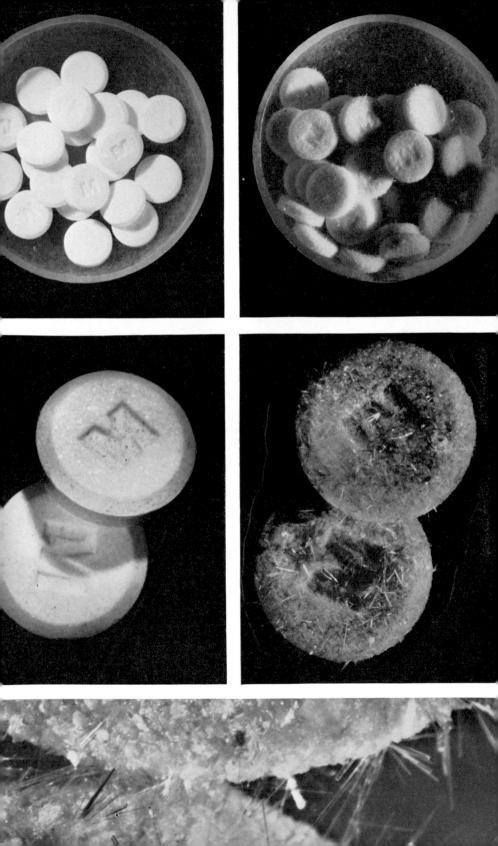

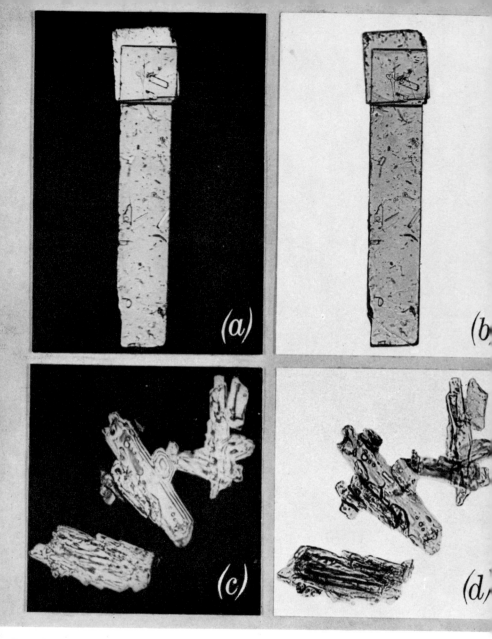

(*a* and *b*) ACETYLSALICYLIC ACID CRYSTAL, × 40 (total × 120)

Unmounted specimen. Not every subject lends itself to dark-ground illumination. In this case the dark-ground plate (*a*) does not show up any more detail than the plate taken with transmitted light.

Microscope: Zeiss. Camera: Macca ½ ×. Objective: 16 mm. Eyepiece: × 10. Substage: comp *Tube length: 170 mm. Emulsion: P.300. Filter: (a) nil, (b) green. Illumination: (a) dark-ground, transmitted. Exposure: (a) 30 seconds, (b) 3 seconds.*

(*c* and *d*) NITRO-ACETIC ACID CRYSTALS, × 40 (total × 120)

Crystals mounted in paraffin. The structural details are given by both methods of illumination. T crystals are very difficult to photograph when using normal transmitted light.

Microscope: Zeiss. Camera: Macca ½ ×. Objective: 16 mm. Eyepiece: × 10. Substage: comp *Tube length: 170 mm. Emulsion: process pan. Filter: (c) Wratten F, (d) Wratten B. Illumination: polarized light, (d) transmitted. Exposure: (c) 1 minute, (d) 20 seconds.*

PLATE 51

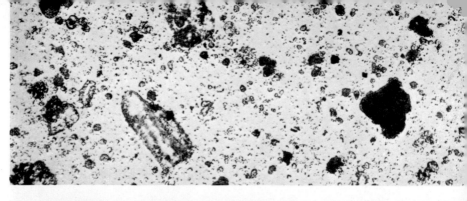

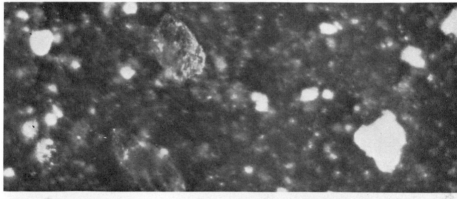

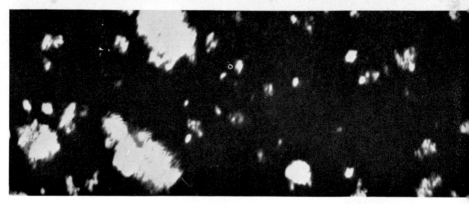

PLATE 52. MEDICAL POWDER MIXTURE, × 85 (total × 300)

(*upper*) The powder was mounted in Detel—the only medium to give an even dispersion of the crystals, enabling large and small to be clearly seen. The crystals seen in the photomicrograph are sodium carbonate, magnesium carbonate, calcium carbonate and bismuth carbonate.

(*centre*) The same field has been photographed by top oblique illumination. The magnesium carbonate (black in upper picture) now reproduces as a clear white, while sodium carbonate and calcium carbonate crystals are glass-like and grey. Bismuth is not seen.

(*lower*) The same field illuminated by polarized light. It will be noted that only the sodium carbonate crystals appear.

Microscope: Leitz. Camera: Watson. Objective: 25 mm. N.A. 0·30. Eyepiece: 22 mm. × 6 Substage: top lens removed. Tube length: 170 mm. Bellows length: 21 in. Emulsion: Ilford Special Rapid. Filter: Wratten B. Illumination: transmitted. Exposure: 4 seconds.

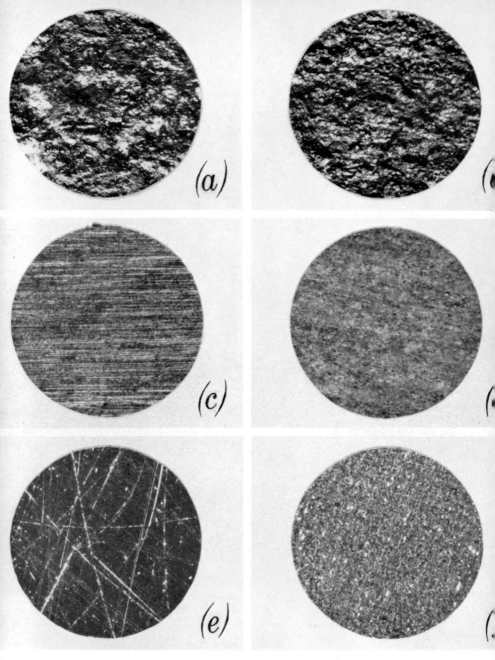

PLATE 53. METAL SURFACES, × 30

(a) Steel surface coated with rust.
(b) Rusted surface after treatment with Deran.
(c) Normal surface of aluminium sheet.
(d) Surface of aluminium sheet after treatment with chromate-oxidation process.
(e) Steel surface free from oxidation.
(f) Steel surface protected with a phosphate coating.

*Microscope: Watson.   Camera: Una ¼-plate.   Objective: 25 mm. N.A. 0·30.   Eyepiece: 45 mm. × 6
Substage: nil.   Tube length: 160 mm.   Bellows length: 8½ in.   Emulsion: 0.250.   Illumination: oblique
Exposure: 10 seconds.*

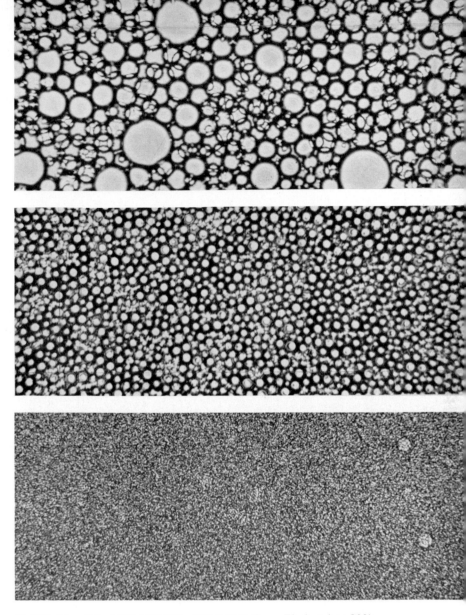

PLATE 54. OIL-AND-WATER EMULSIONS, × 70 (total × 300)

These photomicrographs were taken to illustrate the size and distribution of the globules, which can be seen in optical plane, made possible by the 'hanging drop' method of mounting (Fig. 112). Top shows the product of the *old* formuia and *old* emulsifying procedure. Globules produced by the *old* emulsifying procedure and *new* formula are seen centre, and the bottom photomicrograph shows granular structure produced by *new* emulsifying procedure and *new* formula.

When producing photomicrographs for this purpose, it is necessary to show a large coverage of field, making possible a true average size and distribution.

Microscope: Leitz. Camera: Watson. Objective: 16 mm. N.A. 30. Eyepiece: 22 mm. × 6. Substage: complete. Tube length: 170 mm. Bellows length: 12 in. Emulsion: 0.250. Filter: blue. Illumination: transmitted. Exposure: 2 seconds.

PLATE 55

(a) CRYSTALLIZED LIPSTICK, × 250 (total × 400)

Photomicrographs of this everyday subject are surprisingly rare. This record was obtained from a smear on the slide.

Microscope: Watson. Camera: Watson. Objective: 4 mm. N.A. 0·66. Eyepiece: 22 mm. × 11. Substage: complete. Tube length: 160 mm. Emulsion: O.250. Filter: Wratten B. Illumination: Beck Intensity. Exposure: 2½ seconds.

(b) FUNGI ON ORANGE PEEL, × 250 (total × 400)

The field photographed clearly shows two planes—in focus and out of focus.
The critical point of focus illustrates the importance of this, permitting one plane to be followed without becoming confused with other planes. The specimen was dry mounted.

Microscope: Watson. Camera: Watson. Objective: 4 mm. N.A. 0·66. Eyepiece: 22 mm. × 11. Substage: nil. Tube length: 160 mm. Emulsion: O.250. Filter: Wratten B. Illumination: Top oblique. Exposure: 20 seconds.

(c) TRANSVERSE SECTION OF HUMAN HAIR, × 35 (total × 150)

Hair unstained and mounted in Detel. Note the split hairs.

Microscope: Watson. Camera: Watson ¼-plate. Objective: 16 mm. N.A. 0·30. Eyepiece: × 6. Substage: top lens removed. Tube length: 170 mm. Bellows length: nil. Emulsion: H.P.3. Filter: Orange. Illumination: transmitted. Exposure: 1 second.

(d) TARTARIC ACID, × 70 (total × 200)

Specimen heated at 100° C. and exposed to 75% RH for 4 days. Note how the crystal has grown needles.

Microscope: Watson. Camera: Macca ½ ×. Objective: 8 mm. N.A. 0·65. Eyepiece: × 6. Substage: complete. Tube length: 160 mm. Emulsion: O.250. Filter: Wratten B. Illumination: transmitted. Exposure: 6 seconds.

(e) CRYSTALS OF SHAVING SOAP CREAM, × 950 (total × 1,750)

Oil immersion dark-ground illumination was used because no other means of illumination produced results.

Microscope: Leitz. Camera: Macca ½ ×. Objective: 2 mm. N.A. 1·37 oil immersion. Eyepiece: × 10. Substage: Leitz dark-ground, oil immersion. Tube length: 170 mm. Emulsion: O.250. Illumination: dark-ground. Exposure: 4 seconds.

(f) TARTARIC ACID, × 70 (total × 200)

This dry mounted crystal was an attractive subject for polarized light. The photomicrograph shows the development of growth fronts in closed loops, growth of the higher face being greater than those neighbouring low-index faces. Data as for (d).

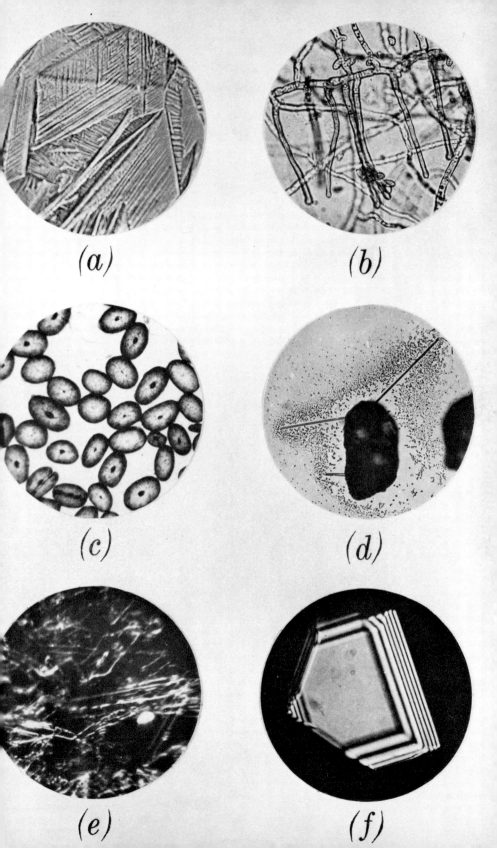

(a)

(b)

(c)

(d)

(e)

(f)

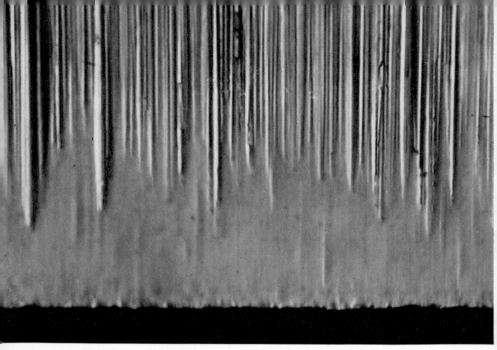
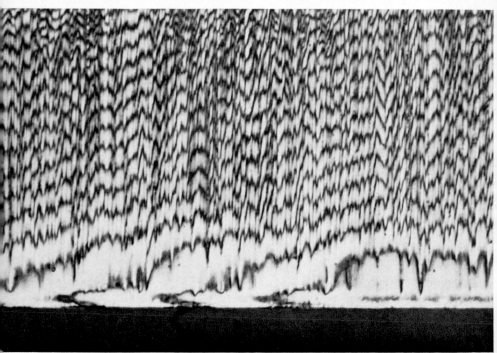

PLATE 56.   EDGE OF SAFETY RAZOR BLADE

(*upper*) The illuminator converging lens was offset 5 mm.   The combination of filters passes a band around 5400 Å.

(*lower*) The interference fringes of a razor-blade edge provided a means of determining its sharpness.   The filters used isolated the yellow mercury lines (5770-5798 Å).

Magnification: (upper) × 1,000, (total × 1,500), (lower) × 300, (total × 450). *Microscope and Camera:* (upper) Bausch & Lomb Metallograph, (lower) Vickers projection. *Objective:* (upper) × 50, (lower) 16 mm. *Eyepiece:* (upper) × 10 amplifier, (lower) × 10. *Substage: complete. Bellows length:* (upper) 37 cm., (lower) nil. *Emulsion:* (upper and lower) O.250. *Filter:* (upper) green and yellow, (lower) Ilford 202 and 404. *Ilumination:* (upper) incident, 100-watt ribbon filament, (lower) incident, 80-watt mercury vapour lamp. *Exposure:* (upper) 3 seconds, (lower) 60 seconds.

(Courtesy of I. Ferdinand Kayser)

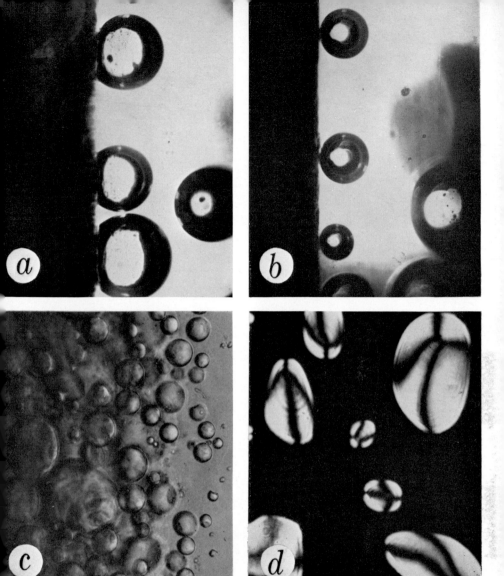

a) HYDROPHOBIC SURFACE SHOWING AIR BUBBLES, × 48
Both microscope and camera were in the horizontal. There was very little time in which
to take the photomicrographs as the air bubbles quickly became dislodged from the dirty glass
surface and floated on the top (see Fig. 46).

b) HYDROPHILIC SURFACE SHOWING BUBBLES, × 48
Air bubbles on the side of clean glass surface. Greater depth of focus was necessary.

c) STRUCTURE OF OIL EMULSION, × 400 (total × 600)
The hanging-drop method was used to obtain this photomicrograph (see Fig. 112).

d) STARCH GRAINS FROM POTATO, × 200 (total × 450)
Microscope: (a, b and c) Leitz, (d) Zeiss. Camera: (a and b) Watson ¼-plate, (c) Watson, (d)
acca ½ ×. Objective: (a and b) I in., (c) L6 × 45, 3·5 mm., (d) 4 mm. Eyepiece: (a and b) 45 mm.
6, (c) 22 mm. × II, (d) 22 mm. × II. Substage: (a and b) nil, (c) complete with bull's eye con-
denser, (d) complete. Tube length: (a and b) 170 mm., (c and d) 160 mm. Bellows length: (a
and b) 13 in. (c) 7 in, (d) nil. Emulsion: (a and b) process, (c) P.1200, (d) process pan. Filter:
(a and b) Wratten G, (c) Wratten C5, (d) nil. Illumination: (a, b and c) transmitted, (d) polarized
light. Exposure: (a and b) 2 seconds, (c) 30 seconds, (d) I minute.

PLATE 57

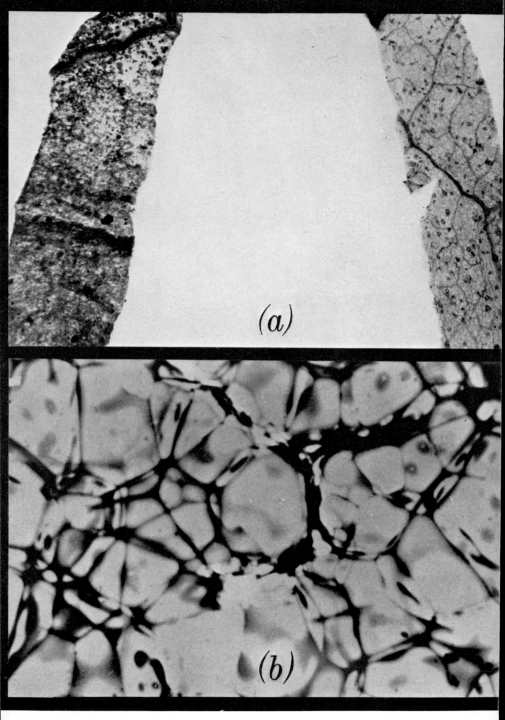

PLATE 58. X-RAY PHOTOMICROGRAPHS

    (a) Tobacco shreds, from a smoked cigarette (left) and from a cigarette prior to smoking, × 50.

    (b) Aluminium tin alloy, 0·020 in. thick, used in aircraft industry. Shows large crystals of alumin
and interfaces filled with tin, × 100.

(Courtesy of General Electric X-ray Corp., Milwa

of course, at an angle to the axis of the condenser, as already mentioned. The angle of the pencil rays of light which strike the specimen is controlled by the positioning of the stop. The nearer the stop is to the centre of the substage condenser, the more vertical is the angle of the pencil rays of light. When two apertures are used

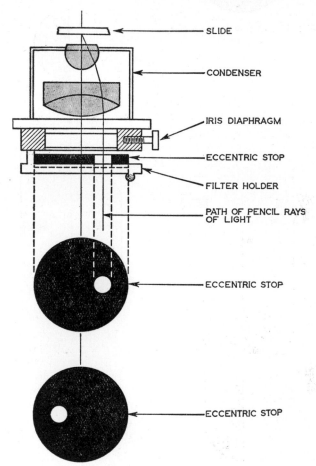

Fig. 99. Eccentric stop as used with substage condenser

the two images can be exposed on the same negative, whereas when one aperture is used, images are made on separate plates.

Another means of producing stereo-photomicrographs of small subjects is to take two photographs from positions equally spaced from the perpendicular and to make two exposures as in other

Fig. 100. Eccentric stop for objective

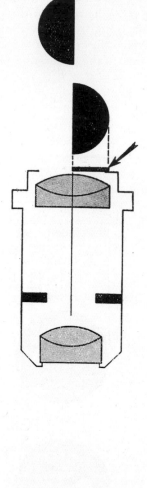

Fig. 101 (right). Half-lens (top) method of making stereo-pairs

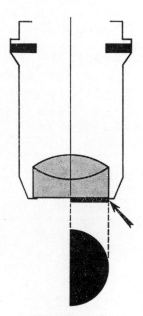

Fig. 102 (left). Half-lens (lower) method of making stereo-pairs

cases; for this method, however, it is advisable to use a ½-plate if two images cannot be accommodated on a ¼-plate. This procedure is quite simple. A line is drawn across the centre of the ground-glass screen and at equal distances on either side another mark is made, the overall distance being 2½ in. or 6 cm. This method cannot be employed unless the whole of the plate can be illuminated by the eyepiece, since two images must be made on the plate.

Many subjects do not lend themselves to this method, as the area illuminated by the projected light of the eyepiece allows for only one exposure in the centre of the plate. It is sometimes necessary to remove the eyepiece, and even the draw tube, to enable a wider field of projected light to fill the plate. When one is ready to make an exposure, the centre of the subject is placed to coincide with one line—say the right-hand—the exposure is made and the image moved to the left side, giving the same exposure as for the first (Plate 60(*upper*)). The plate is then processed in the normal manner and prints reversed when mounting takes place.

When loading the ½-plate into the carrier it is advisable to mask one half so that this does not receive stray light when making the first exposure. The same applies when making the second exposure; the exposed half is then covered up. If the illumination covers a sufficiently wide field there will be no need to make any adjustment when taking the second shot. Any alterations of the lighting arrangement between exposures may, of course, ruin the stereo-pair of photomicrographs. It is assumed that a mechanical stage is used for this method to ensure that the subject is moved along the same line. If the quality of the objective is poor, it may not cover a wide area on the plate, and may fail to produce a sharp image other than in the centre of the plate. It has been stated, however, that a stereoscopic effect is seen when the subject is shifted only ½ mm. each side of the central line on the ground glass.

Another method of obtaining stereo-pairs of photomicrographs is to move the objective from side to side as indicated by A. C. Banfield (*Journal of the Queckett Microscopical Club* (1909) pp. 459–64, and *J. Roy. Micr. Soc.* (1910), p. 233). In many respects the method is limited and few will find it rewarding.

The moving-objective method is not as satisfactory as the following two methods. An objective stop similar to that used with the condenser may be employed to direct a pencil beam of light after it leaves the objective. The eccentric stop (Fig. 100) must be small, approximately $2\frac{1}{2}$ mm., and fit over the back lens of the objective not farther than 1 mm. from the lens. This provides a small circular aperture and ensures a pencil beam of light. The inner edge of the aperture should be as near as possible to the centre of the objective, which will, of course, ensure the sharpness of the image. As applied to the substage eccentric stop, this too is turned 180° after making the first exposure (Plate 59(*lower*)). With this method it is not easy to turn the stop exactly 180°, in which case the stereoscopic effect is not secured.

The half-lens method is based upon the Whenham system of stereos, using a D-shaped disc placed behind the top of an objective (Fig. 101), or, in the case of a single-lens objective such as a 3-in., a disc can be placed in front of the lens (Fig. 102). As can be seen from the diagram, only half of the optical system is used, but nevertheless with great effect. The advantage in this method is the fact that no extra equipment is required, an ordinary microscope being utilized. As a precautionary measure the straight side of the D-stop should run across the centre of the lens at points equidistant from the intersection of the horizontal with the vertical bisector.

By removing the eyepiece and looking down the tube, it will clearly be seen whether or not the mask is in position. As in the previous method the mask must be moved to cover the other half of the lens before the second exposure is made. Attention must be paid to several points when this is done, such as taking care not to move the specimen when removing and replacing the objective, and also guarding against accidentally moving the illuminant. The third point to remember is to make sure that the focusing is carried out on the same plane as the first exposure. To ensure the correct rotation of the mask it is recommended that the metal surround of the front or back lens be marked lightly in quadrants, in white ink, for example.

In all these methods involving two exposures it is advisable to make a test negative to find the correct exposure, so that both negatives will be of the same density (Plate 59(*upper*)).

13

PHOTOMICROGRAPHY
BY FLASHLIGHT

RAPIDLY moving objects have always caused some anxiety to the photomicrographer, and before the technique of flashlight was introduced the results were often unpredictable. The problems which have faced the photomicrographer have been far too many to surmount without the aid of an electronic or the normal synchronized flash outfits. These flash outfits give brief exposures, ranging from hundredths to thousandths of a second. This means of illumination must not be confused with that of the electron microscope which permits only the study of dry subjects. In view of this, flash microscopy has an advantage inasmuch as the motion of creatures swimming in their free state can be arrested. Another important point in favour of the flash illumination is that it enables Brownian motion to be arrested (i.e. the movement of microscopic particles in fluids, emulsions, etc.). When this occurs, and an instantaneous exposure cannot be given, long delays are experienced until such movements cease. The electron microscope does, however, have two big advantages over flash microscopy: the resolution is considerably higher ($0\cdot002\,\mu$ against $0\cdot2\,\mu$) and there is also a considerable increase in the depth of field.

In the past it was presumed that the specimen to be photographed had been rendered immobile by narcotization, or perhaps was a prepared slide. It was unusual to photograph an animal in its free-moving state because of the comparatively long exposure which, of course, caused image movement on the plate. Daphnia, rotifer, cyclops, vorticella and many other creatures of the pond can easily be photographed with normal lighting by giving a fairly short exposure, e.g. 1/50th of a second. In these cases all movement has been arrested, but there are many subjects which are more rapid in their movements; no exposure longer than 1/1,000th to 1/3,000th of a second will stop such movement.

The electronic-flash outfit is composed of two principal parts, the gas-filled tube which produces the flash and the power pack. The latter builds up the high-voltage charge of electricity in a capacitor reservoir. The gas usually used in the flash tubes is xenon, and this produces a blue-white light similar to daylight. Xenon gas is obtained by the distillation of liquid air. The proportion of xenon in the air is in the region of one part in twenty million. The high-intensity light is caused by the sudden discharge of energy; the higher the amount of energy the greater the brilliance of the flash. The energy is measured in watt-seconds or joules. The output of electronic-flash outfits is rated in so many joules, equivalent to the amount of energy suddenly discharged into the gas tube.

The tube most suited to this particular branch of photography is, of course, very small and gives out only a very narrow beam of light. The xenon tube contains, as a rule, a coiled spiral, or a U-shaped filament. On the other hand, Langham Photographic Instruments Ltd. use the linear type of tube in one of their lamps. They also have an efficient electronic-flash ring illuminator suitable for macro work. The stored electricity is suddenly discharged and passed to the electrodes at the ends of the tube. The light-output can be increased or decreased according to the type of reflector. In view of this, the design and size of the reflector in microscopy must be such that the whole light-output is fully utilized and directed into the narrow optical system, via the substage condenser.

Electronic flash is particularly suited to colour photomicrography, as its colour temperature is approximately that of daylight. An ultra-violet filter can be used to improve the colour balance. This in no way alters the flash factor; it simply corrects the colour balance.

When the contents of a drop of pond water are examined

under the microscope, many specimens are seen to move very rapidly, while others pass slowly across the field of view. Often these creatures have rapidly moving cilia, which rotate through the water at terrific speeds, producing only a blurred image on the film by exposures not made with an electronic flash. With free-swimming subjects there is always the danger of camera or microscope vibration, caused, say, by movement of the body, or somebody walking in an adjacent room, or perhaps a passing train or traffic. With flash technique such worries disappear.

The flash technique has come to stay and much is being learnt from the photographs obtained. For instance, limbs in action can now be recorded; fast-moving cilia can be frozen; swimmerets which propel the creatures along can be arrested; digestive organs can be seen operating; breeding can be seen taking place; and a host of other phenomena, hitherto unstudied, can now be recorded. Such information has in the past come from visual observations translated on to paper with pen and pencil. With the flash technique of today, naturalists are able to study every movement from 'living' photographs, thereby dispensing to a large degree with narcotized and dead, stained specimens. Often it is impossible to narcotize a creature without causing distortion, which leads to an untrue picture.

Some photomicrographers using this means of illumination have devised their own technique. In many instances a unique microscope photographic-flash outfit has developed from the original crude apparatus. With the electronic flash-tubes of 80 to 160 and up to 240 joules now available, it is possible to incorporate these with the microscope, but before this can be done there must be some experimental work.

EQUIPMENT

The equipment needed for this specialized branch of photomicrography consists of the normal microscope fitted with an observation or viewing eyepiece to enable the specimen to be watched right up to the time of the exposure. Watching or viewing eyepieces give two images of the object, one projecting an image on to the photographic material and the other image being viewed from the side; the adjustment of both images is synchronized. As the animals are moving rapidly they quickly disappear out of the field of view, but with the aid of the viewing eyepiece they can be followed by means of a rotating stage or movement of the mechanical stage. Furthermore, the creature's up-and-down movements make focusing difficult. While these small animals move about they can be illuminated by a secondary built-in light-source, which is sufficient to allow them to be seen and followed and the necessary adjustments made (centring and focusing) before the flash is fired. Since both hands are fully occupied when arranging the picture, it is advisable to have some form of foot-switch to fire the flash and automatically operate the camera shutter. An enlarger foot-switch is ideal.

Having a light burning for such a long time obviously builds up a considerable amount of heat. Therefore, it is recommended that a piece of heat-resisting glass be used between the secondary source of light and the substage. In addition, a sheet of stout ground glass should be used to assist in giving a greater spread and even light. Because a fairly strong secondary light is used, the open-shutter technique cannot be introduced. This light would be sufficient to cause a secondary image, or images, before the flash is fired, and after, if the shutter is not quickly closed. In view of this, the camera shutter must be accurately synchronized so that it is wide open during the flash. With such a strong light as the flash, it is not necessary to switch off the secondary light, the shutter speed being far too short to cause a secondary image. The illumination from the mirror to the substage condenser must be carefully adjusted, and may best be done first with an auxiliary lamp in the place which will be occupied by the flash tube. Owing to the intense light one is tempted to operate the substage with a smaller aperture than is normally used, which will, of course, give a greater depth of field, but this may result in a loss in definition.

A means of illumination by electronic flash has also been introduced by Leitz for use with their microscope and is now fitted to the Ortholux, seen in Plate 11. This flash apparatus is not made by the makers of this famous microscope, but has been perfected by Multiblitz. The flash tube is housed in a special metal case from which is emitted a light beam just under 6 mm. in width, having an energy rating of either 150 joules at 1/1,000th of a second, or 300 joules at 1/500th of a second. This attachment takes 1–2 minutes as opposed to the usual charging time. It is housed directly beneath the substage condenser, thus ensuring that an accurately adjusted beam of intense light passes through the optical path of the microscope to the photographic emulsion. The flash tube is so arranged that the ordinary microscope illumination can pass through it as secondary illumination, thus the alignment does not cause any undue difficulties. An arrangement for dimming the secondary light is a great advantage when one is about to make an exposure. The neatly constructed capacitor and control panel can clearly be seen in Plate 11. Further information on flash as a means of illumination is given in Chapter 6.

14

PHOTOMICROGRAPHY
IN COLOUR

TODAY colour photography is practised, written and talked about more than ever. It is amazing the effect colour has on a picture. For instance, black and white prints are seen to some disadvantage when placed alongside a correct colour print; this may leave the worker with the feeling that monochrome photomicrographs are not the best reproduction.

Records show that colour photography was written about more than a hundred years ago. Fox Talbot produced colour pictures in the 1840s, but unfortunately these had no lasting properties. Half a century passed before colour photography was further developed by Gabriel Lippmann, some of whose work can now be seen in the Science Museum, London. Some years later a Frenchman, Louis Ducos du Hauron, produced colour photographs and also wrote extensively about his experiences in this field. In the early 1900s colour photography was taken up in the U.S.A., where an American, F. E. Ives, contributed to its advancement.

There were many inventions and discoveries up to the year 1906, when colour photographic plates were marketed. These plates, known as the Lumière Autochrome colour plates, were quite small, 9 × 12 cm., and were invented by Lumière. A screen process of starch grains comprising red, green and blue, was mixed and spread over the plate surface. The Finlay plate made an appearance a few years before World War I. At the same time Louis Dufay also put a colour-screen process on the market, this being one of the forerunners of the Johnson colour-screen process. During the Lumière–Dufay period Eastman Kodak produced the colour film known as Kodacolor, but this was a far different process from the Kodacolor of the present time.

After World War I there was a temporary lull in the colour field, until the 1930s, when Kodachrome was introduced as the result of many years' research. About the same time Agfacolor became available, together with a process known as Ansco Color. At the time of writing there are many colour processes to choose from: Ektachrome, Ansco Color, Kodachrome, Gevacolor, Ilford Colour, Pakolor, Ferraniacolor and others. It is somewhat difficult to give an up-to-date list of colour materials on the market, as the colour market changes from day to day, new products being introduced and others withdrawn.

As soon as colour photography is embarked upon it is discovered that images are more difficult to record in colour than in monochrome. There are several difficulties to overcome and the first is exposure; one soon becomes aware of the limited latitude in exposure times as compared with black and white. An exposure meter will give a reading in the region of the correct exposure, but it is also essential to exercise a little judgement. Furthermore, the degree of success is coupled with the knowledge of the changes which take place at the light-source. Colours change according to the temperature of the source. Another governing factor when exposing is the actual colour of the preparation, its colour brightness. Sometimes a subject is far too bright to be accurately recorded on a film; for instance, when it has a lower-sensitivity colour range.

PRINCIPLES AND TECHNIQUE

To enable the beginner to have a greater realization of colour and the effect the light-source has on the finished product, it is necessary to go right back to the first principles of light. White light is a combination of colours, and when passed through a prism is resolved or split into various colours. This range of colours is known as the visible spectrum. Blue, green and red are known as the primary colours; white light is merely the result of the superposition of the three primary colours (Fig. 103). A prism does not produce them, it only separates the beams. The mixing of red and green light gives yellow light, red and blue light make magenta light, blue and green light make cyan (the photographic term for blue-green light). If any of the primary colours is taken from white light, for instance blue, we are left with a mixture of red and green, this again giving yellow.

Colour temperature is measured in degrees Kelvin and is referred to as ° K (see page 66). A 75-watt gas-filled tungsten lamp is in the region of 2,750° K, whereas the colour temperature of the sun is approximately twice this figure. On a cloudless day, when a 'hedge-sparrow blue' is our overall ceiling, the figure rises to between 18,000 and 24,000° K. It might be doubted whether

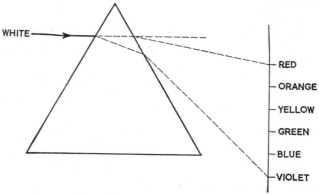

Fig. 103. Dispersion by refraction

the colour temperature of the sun is less than that of a clear blue sky, but it must be remembered that colour temperature is a measure of the proportions of different colours in the light.

There is very little difference in the colour temperature of normal household bulbs of varying wattages. But each colour film has its own particular colour temperature, and each is best suited to a certain colour temperature. Therefore, only the illuminant for which the film was designed will give true colour renderings of the original subject. Kodak Ltd., however, manufacture a number of colour correction filters as listed in Table 8. If a film such as Ektachrome, Type B (for artificial light), is exposed to daylight without a correction filter, the final transparency will have an overall strong blue tint. Another example can be given by quoting just the reverse, namely, a colour film which, balanced for daylight, is exposed to tungsten light. This will result in an overall yellowish tint. Ektachrome Type B used here was illuminated with the Pointolite which has a colour temperature comparable with that for which this film is balanced, this being 3,100–3,200° K.

When making a transparency it is essential to see that the correct exposure is given; error either way produces a slight change in the colours recorded on the film. It is, however, difficult to produce a true colour. The higher the magnification of a photomicrograph the less saturated becomes the colour; the original specimen will, therefore, appear to be much brighter.

TABLE 8. CONVERSION OF COLOUR TEMPERATURE TO 3,400° K

Colour Temperature of Source in ° K	Wratten Filters Required	Exposure Increase in Stops
2610	82C + 82C	$1\frac{1}{3}$
2700	82C + 82B	$1\frac{1}{3}$
2780	82C + 82A	1
2870	22C + 82	1
2950	82C	$\frac{2}{3}$
3060	82B	$\frac{2}{3}$
3180	82A	$\frac{1}{3}$
3290	82	$\frac{1}{3}$
3510	81	$\frac{1}{3}$

There are three types of emulsion in use:

(a) that balanced for daylight use, known as daylight type;

(b) that balanced for tungsten light of colour temperature 3,300 to 3,400° K, such as Kodachrome Type A;

(c) that balanced for clear flashlamps of colour temperature 3,800° K.

In some negative–positive colour photographic systems, such as Kodacolor, the compensation for illuminant colour can be made at the printing stage; this also applies to I.C.I. Colour.

The type of illuminant controls the colour reproduction as does the exposure. In no case should the type of lighting be mixed; daylight and artificial illuminants should never be used together. As the tungsten bulb increases in age, so the colour temperature changes, and this is more noticeable when the light-source consists of a single lamp. Most makers of colour photographic material recommend a correction filter to be used with their emulsion when using ribbon-filament bulbs (Table 8). If, however, the colour temperature of a tungsten bulb is higher than that intended (for which the film is balanced), the final result will be unsatisfactory, resulting in an overall blue tint, lacking yellow. The reverse effect is evident when the colour temperature is too low.

The subject-matter for colour photomicrography is restricted. Stained subjects do, however, suit most colour photographic materials and specimens which lend themselves to being illuminated by polarized light look very attractive.

No change is necessary in the equipment for this type of photomicrography. If separation negatives are to be made, great care must be taken to ensure that the camera is static; all plates must be exposed in exactly the same place. Otherwise the three colours will not register as one.

A means of photographing living yeast cells in colour has been reported by J. D. Levi (*Nature, Lond.* (1957), **179**, 494), and in so doing the true internal structure of the cells has been captured. As already mentioned, when some specimens are stained the structure is broken down and the true record does not exist. Interference microscopy enables minute cells, such as yeast, to be recorded in their true state. When an interference system is not available, this means of illumination answers the purpose. Owing to the size of the cells, objectives of 2 and 4 mm. must be used. In conjunction with these, two filters of contrasting colours were placed side by side with their adjacent edges in contact. They were placed directly in the beam of light between the source and the substage condenser. The 1½-in. square Wratten filters were so arranged that the two colours, red and green, each filled half of the illuminated field, when low-power was used. When the high-power objective was brought into operation, a double colour effect was obtained, one colour overlapping the other. This means of illuminating the specimen introduces an interference: two beams each having a different wave-length, therefore creating a double-image effect. Levi also states that a variety of effects can be obtained by making small lateral movements of the filters, and these ranged from one background colour with contrasting cells to the opposite colour combination.

It is recommended that a colourless medium, such as methyl methacrylate or polystyrene (in place of Canada balsam), be used for mounting specimens to be photographed in colour; colourless oil for immersion purposes can be used in place of cedarwood oil.

Colour balance is an important factor in photographing double- or treble-stained specimens, or subjects illuminated by polarized light. One colour or more can be held back, or emphasized, whichever is required. For instance, a blue-yellow filter will bring about a complete change in the colour rendering of a given subject. Sometimes a second filter is necessary as, for instance, when the defect in colour balance is in the primary colours. Messrs. Helios Ltd. have produced a colour temperature meter which consists of a photo-electric cell fitted with two rotating filters. These meters are best suited for pictorial and outdoor colour photography, but in addition can be used for photomicrography.

TYPES OF COLOUR PROCESS

Pakolor.—These colour films can be processed at home by the amateur and professional alike, the makers supplying a special processing kit for film and paper. Both film and paper are composed of four layers of coating, one upon the other. Three of these are emulsions, which form the colour-image; the fourth acts as a filter screen, with the two layers beneath forming the blue light. Here again, the colour process is built upon the governing colour principles, this particular emulsion being known as Monopack. As this is a negative–positive process, the negative is reversed in the same manner as a monochrome negative; light and shade values are reversed, as are the colour values; red appears as its complementary, cyan; blue-violet as yellow; and yellow-green as magenta. A print, similar to the original, is made from these colour negatives on Pakolor Type FC paper, which does not contain a filter layer. Instead the makers have increased the speed between the top emulsion and the other two emulsions, thus ensuring an evenly colour-balanced print. Pakolor film is made as daylight-balanced and artificial light types; the former is known as Type PK 24 and the latter as Type A. The artificial type has a colour balance of 3,000° K, and this is stepped up to 3,800° K for use with a flashbulb. As with all other colour films the exposure must be accurate to give correct colour balance; if the light-source is other than 3,000° to 3,400° K, correction filters should be used.

Ansco Color.—At the time of writing this colour film is not officially obtainable in this country, although a certain amount is finding its way over the counter to be trade processed. Ansco Color is manufactured in the U.S.A., and is sold in many sizes of roll film and cut films, which produce delightful positive colour transparencies through the three separate emulsion layers. The 35-mm. film is packed in red cassettes, or in small containers holding three refills. This film is marked 234 for tungsten light and 235 for daylight. The film recommended for artificial light is particularly suited to a tungsten ribbon filament, 18-amp, 6-volt bulb, or a white-flame carbon arc with a colour temperature of 3,200° K. Ansco artificial-light stock is now balanced to suit Photoflood lighting which is in common use today. If the colour temperature does not coincide with this, colour correction filters should be used.

As for other processes, some test exposures are necessary before the perfect transparent positive is produced. As this film is a reversal process the colours are formed in each layer of emulsion when processed in a colour developer. If neither of the recommended illuminants is used, some experiments with correction filters are absolutely essential before the light can be balanced to the film. Finding the correct exposure for oblique illumination is a somewhat more complex problem than finding that for transmitted light, and this applies to all colour processes. Colour films can be processed at home; for this purpose developing outfits can, of course, be purchased. The Ansco Color film, by the way, is no more difficult to develop than a monochrome film. The worker who processes his own black and white film will not find any more difficulties with this colour film, provided the instructions are followed accurately.

Pleasing colour prints can be made from Ansco Color transparencies. The Ansco Color Printon is one of the simplest methods which permits both contact prints and enlargement prints to be made. Prints are made by a single exposure, after which the print goes through the reversal process, thus producing a delightful colour positive print from a well-balanced positive transparency.

Ferraniacolor.—This is one of the latest types of colour film and yields beautiful colour transparencies which can also be processed in the home. It is a subtractive, integral tripack type of reversal film and is listed as having a speed of 25° Scheiner. These films are sold in 35-mm. and 120, 127 and 620 roll film. The 35-mm. film has 20 exposures per cassette and refills can be purchased without the cassette. These films can be processed in the normal developing tanks and the instructions should, of course, be followed closely.

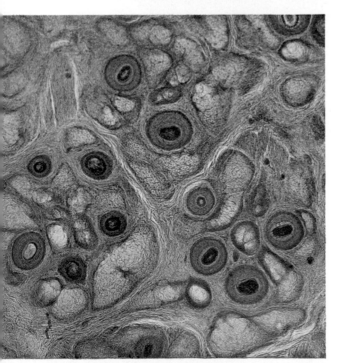

TRANSVERSE SECTION
OF HUMAN SCALP, × 100

Objective: 16 mm. Eye-
piece: × 6. Tube length:
160 mm. Bellows length: 8
in. Substage: complete.
Emulsion: Ektachrome B.

(Colour photomicrographs by
the author)

GUINEA-PIG SPERMATOZOA, × 6

In the photomicrograph on the
guinea-pig spermatozoa are fluoresci
ultra-violet radiation after treat
with acridine orange. They were ph
graphed soon after collection.

RAT SPERMATOZOA, × 660

This photomicrograph illustrates the
different fluorescence exhibited by
living (yellow) and dead (blue) rat
spermatozoa when treated with a
mixture of primulin and rhodamin B
and examined in ultra-violet radiation.

*(Fluorescence photomicrographs by
courtesy of M. R. Young and the editor,
"Endeavour" (Imperial Chemical Industries Ltd.))*

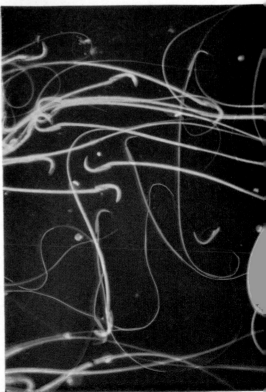

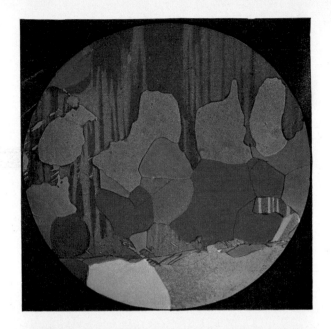

ROTATION OF ELECTROPOLISHED BISMUTH UNDER CROSSED POLARIZERS WITH A SENSITIVE TINT-PLATE INSERTED

The development of new techniques and improvements to existing methods of examining opaque objects have resulted in considerable progress in the determination of the surface structure of metals. The photomicrographs illustrate results which have been obtained by the use of polarized light. A Bausch and Lomb metallograph was used with an additional fitting, the Foster calcite prism reflector. This has resulted in the efficiency of the apparatus being increased by 45–50 per cent. The figures show colour-changes in an electrolytically polished specimen of bismuth when rotated. The plane of the central violet grain, which remains the same colour throughout rotation of the stage, must be perpendicular to the optical axis.

(Photomicrographs by courtesy of the editor, "Endeavour" (Imperial Chemical Industries Ltd.))

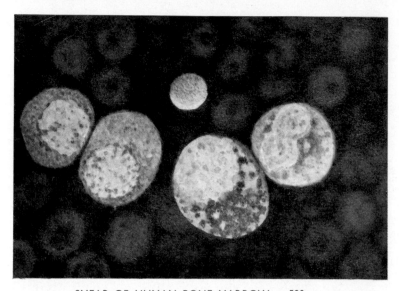

SMEAR OF HUMAN BONE MARROW, × 500

Stained with combined movin-thiazin red fluorochrome according to Fellinger-Pakesch.

RAT JOINT, × 500

After experimental formalin arthritis. Stained with thioflavin according to Haitinger. Both photomicrographs were taken on the Reichert Fluorescence microscope and camera with a × 60 achromat in use.

(Photomicrographs by courtesy of C. Reichert A.G., Vienna)

The colours of this film are formed in each layer of emulsion when developed in (colour) developer. Special processing kits are available at low prices. These kits, in Parts I and II, can be handled by those with comparatively little knowledge of colour processing. Careful attention should be given to the processing times and temperatures of the various solutions. Variation of colour strength depends upon the development time of the second (colour) development. It is advisable to use fresh developers. Used Ferraniacolor developers will not keep, as some do, but the hardener, bleach and fixer can be used more than once, the life of these solutions being longer if the films are adequately washed before transferring from one to another. The temperature of the developers should be 65° F; if possible the washing water should be the same temperature. To ensure this it is advisable to have both hot and cold taps connected to a master tap, thus allowing the temperature of the running water to be controlled through the master tap. A thermometer can quite easily be fitted.

The following are the official processing formulae for processing Ferraniacolor reversal film:

FIRST DEVELOPMENT (RC 109):

Calgon	1 gm.
Sodium sulphite anhydrous	50 gm.
Amidol	5 gm.
Potassium bromide	1 gm.
Water to	1 l.

HARDENER (VC 207):

Sodium acetate anhydrous	56 gm.
Boric acid	5 gm.
Potassium alum	30 gm.
Water to	1 l.

COLOUR DEVELOPER (RC 103):
Solution A

Hydroxylamine hydrochloride	1 gm.
Activol H	2·8 gm.
(Diethyl-p-phenylene diamine hydrochloride)	
Water to	500 c.c.

T.P.—14

Solution B

Calgon	2 gm.
Sodium carbonate anhydrous	65 gm.
Sodium sulphite anhydrous	2·5 gm.
Sodium hydroxide	1 gm.
Potassium bromide	1·2 gm.
Water to	500 c.c.

Prepare Solutions A and B separately; then add Solution A to Solution B slowly, while stirring.

BLEACH HARDENER (VC 212):

Potassium ferricyanide	50 gm.
Potassium bromide	25 gm.
Sodium acetate anhydrous	37 gm.
Boric acid	5 gm.
Potassium alum	30 gm.
Water to	1 l.

FIXER (FC 200):

Sodium thiosulphate (hypo) crystals	200 gm.
anhydrous	125 gm.
Water to	1 l.

Dissolve the chemicals in the order given, using about ¾ of the final volume of water. Use cold or slightly warm water, not hot. Solutions should stand for about 30 minutes and be filtered before using.

Neither the first developer nor the colour developer keeps well. These must not be stored for longer than 48 hours after use, but if unused will keep for about a week in full, stoppered bottles. The other solutions will keep in good condition for several months provided that they are stored in airtight bottles. The bleach hardener must also be protected from strong light; if possible, store in a brown glass bottle. Should the solutions become discoloured, it does not indicate that they have deteriorated; this is quite normal. Filter before use.

PROCESSING

1. First development	65° F	14 minutes
2. Wash	65° F	5 minutes
3. Hardening	65° F	5–8 minutes
4. Wash	65° F	5 minutes

Second Exposure

Remove film from spiral and expose each side for approximately 1½ minutes at a distance of 1 ft. from a 100-watt lamp.

5. Colour development   8 minutes
   In soft-water districts 3 minutes in a bath of 2 per cent magnesium sulphate crystals is recommended immediately after colour development.
6. Wash   15 minutes
7. Bleach hardening   10 minutes
8. Wash   5 minutes
9. Fixing   8–10 minutes
10. Wash   15 minutes

Stages 1–4 must be carried out in total darkness; all subsequent stages may be carried out in normal light.

Kodachrome.—Two types of Kodachrome film are available, one for daylight and the other for artificial light, including flash. Owing to the rather complex nature of this colour process, all Kodachrome films must be returned to the manufacturer for processing and the colour transparencies are attractively mounted in neat slides for easy viewing.

The question of ascertaining the correct exposure is always a problem and only by experience coupled with the use of an exposure meter can it be determined. When using a photometer, a reading should be taken of the brightest section of the field. This may appear somewhat confusing, owing to the fact that for normal black-and-white work a reading is taken from the less bright field. Kodachrome film coated for daylight gives correct colour balance for a light of 6,000° K. This, of course, corresponds to the sun at its brightest. There is a great difference in the colour temperature of the artificial-light type (Type A) which is adjusted to 3,300–3,400° K.

A careful test of the final colour balance of the illumination should be made before an exposure is made. The illumination qualities at the specimen are somewhat different from those at the source, since the light has passed through several lenses. It must be remembered that it is the final colour balance which governs the exposure; therefore, a number of exposures may be necessary before the correct exposure is found. The photometer will, of course, give some guide. Kodachrome film has the normal three coatings of light-sensitive emulsions, namely red, green and blue. The red layer is attached to the base of the film; above the red layer is the green layer; and above this a yellow filter material which cuts out all blue light from reaching these two colour-sensitive layers. The top layer is an emulsion which records blue light. After exposure, this film is processed in a similar manner to a monochrome film, developing only the silver grains in each of the three layers.

During the second process of development, the film is passed through a colour developer and coupler. The bottom layer of emulsion is now a cyan positive. After a brief exposure to blue light the top layer becomes a yellow positive. Both outer layers of emulsion are then developed and are in positive colours. This leaves the middle layer, which is developed, and after this all exposed silver is removed by a bleaching bath.

Kodacolor.—Perfected during the last war, Kodacolor is another product of the Kodak Company. The film is now available in many roll sizes and processed to a complementary negative, from which beautiful positive prints are made, both by contact and enlargement. Instead of having couplers in the developers to produce the colour, as with the Kodachrome method, this film has the couplers dispersed in each of the three emulsion layers. When Kodacolor film has been developed the bottom layer has a cyan image, the top layer a yellow and the middle layer a magenta image. After development, this film also passes through a bleaching bath which removes developed silver grains from the three emulsions. This leaves the film as a colour negative from which positive prints are made.

Ektachrome.—This can be processed in the home; it is available in various sizes of sheet film and roll films. Ektachrome produces excellent photomicrographs ranging from a single colour to a multi-coloured subject. Like many other colour films, this has three layers of emulsion, each with its own particular coupler dispersed therein. The film is first processed in a normal developer, which gives a monochrome negative; it is then exposed to white light, this being the second exposure, as for the processes already mentioned. The film is then re-developed in colour developer, which gives the colour positive transparency. The processing is very much the same as for other reversal processes. Due care must be given to the temperatures of the solutions to ensure the best results.

To produce colour prints, separation negatives must be made. These separations are made either from colour transparencies, or from a colour negative. Bromide prints are made from the separation negatives through the Carbro process. This process enables the three colour layers (cyan, magenta and yellow) to produce their own images, which, when superimposed together, make one colour print. Prints can also be made by the dye-transfer process, which is long and complicated, the print going through many stages before the final print is produced. Ektachrome film will give a correctly colour-balanced transparency when exposed to light having a colour temperature of 3,100° to 3,200° K. It must be handled in total darkness as it is sensitive to all colours of the visible spectrum.

Ilford Colour Film.—This is available in 35-mm. size, and in two types—Type D for daylight, and Type F for clear flashbulbs. The recommended meter settings for the daylight type film are ASA and Weston Master III 10, BS 1 21° and DIN 11°. For use with tungsten light, the Type F film is recommended with an Ilford Filter No. 172 over the camera lens or light-source. Under these conditions the speed of the film is the same as that of Type D used in daylight. This film is described as a subtractive integral tripack film and, like some of these colour films, gives a colour transparency processed by the reversal method, having the following three colour-sensitive emulsions: a yellow dye image in the blue-sensitive emulsion; a magenta in the green; and a cyan image in the red. This film has dye deposits with a very fine grain and is highly transparent, which allows for high magnifications when it is projected on a screen. These films are packed in cassettes, giving twenty or thirty-six exposures.

Agfacolor.—This is available as a negative material which is processed to complementary colours from which colour prints may then be made. It is available in sizes 35 mm., roll film and standard dimensions of cut film. Agfacolor film Type CN 17 is a universal material for exposure in daylight or artificial light. Filters need not be used when exposing this material. In addition to the negative colour film, a reversal colour material CK is available of 17° DIN sensitivity as well as CT 18 daylight material of 18°DIN. Unless exposure is correct, colour falsifications will occur and correct colour prints cannot be made. There is very little grain to the negative film. When a correctly exposed negative is produced there is every reason to expect a good colour print, whether it be by contact or enlargement. It is very difficult to produce a colour print with finely divided colour separation between two hues such as red and orange, but owing to recent advances in the sensitivity separation of Agfacolor film, colour fidelity of a very high order can be achieved. In addition, owing to the use of recently introduced colour couplers and colour developing agents, greatly improved reds are obtained, but should it be desired to improve these even further, dyes may be applied to colour prints, which will further increase the brightness of these.

Gevacolor.—Gevacolor Type R 5 gives direct positive transparencies and Type N 5 complementary colour negatives, both yielding beautifully natural colours. The Gevacolor reversal material is obtainable in roll and in miniature films.

Raycolor.—One of the most recent colour processes is Raycolor, which is a welcome addition to the many others already in use. This is available in three reversal and two negative types. Each of these can be processed by the amateur; processing kits are available in several sizes. The film is marketed in 120 and 620 roll-films and 35 mm. The films are rated at 12–24 Weston. For artificial light Type A is, of course, a little slower. The processing is straightforward and the directions should naturally be followed.

15

PROCESSING PLATE
AND PAPER

THE darkroom must be properly equipped if a success is to be made of photomicrography; it is a waste of time taking all possible care with the microscope if darkroom essentials have been ignored. The darkroom, in which many hours are spent, should be spacious and well ventilated, the walls light in colour and the room completely light-tight when doors and windows are closed. The sink should be of the square type, so that the dishes rest on the flat bottom instead of rocking about, as is so often the case with normal domestic sinks. Lead sinks are, of course, the best, but this type is not always available. A porcelain sink will, however, serve the purpose. A well-equipped sink is one which has hot and cold running water and is fitted with a good waste-pipe and an adequate overflow-pipe. The latter is essential, as the waste can quite easily become blocked if cotton-wool or a print is sucked over the waste hole. It is advisable to make some modifications in connection with the waste. The author has made a perforated funnel stop, which allows the water to flow away from the bottom of the sink at a rate equal to that of the in-flow. Syphon washing-tanks are excellent for print washing, etc. This type of tank can be left in the sink with the plug out, without fear of an overflow.

Safelights should be well arranged to give good service within a safe illuminating distance of the sink where processing takes place. When processing fast panchromatic plates, try to work without a safelight which, however carefully it is used, is likely to fog a fast panchromatic emulsion. If such an emulsion must be inspected, do it after it has had several minutes' development; there will then be less likelihood of fogging. Safelight switches should be of the pull-switch type to eliminate the possibility of an electric shock. Good cupboards and shelves are, of course, always very convenient and assist in keeping the room tidy, as do racks for housing various sizes of developing dish. Storage cupboards for photographic materials and microscope accessories should be in a dry, cool place and all opened packages of paper and plates should be stowed in light-tight drawers, or similar containers.

It is advisable to keep chemicals away from sensitive materials, perhaps on the floor, as a safety measure against accidents. If bottles containing acids and developers must be stored in cupboards, attention should be given to the type of material stowed beneath them.

When weighing-up chemicals, do so in a place away from all sensitive materials, taking great care not to blow or drop chemicals where any part of the microscope or similar instrument is likely to be. When the enlarger is in the same room as the sink it ought to be well away from the taps so that it is beyond the reach of splashing when the tap is left running. On no account should the microscope be where there is running water, or in a damp room, if corrosion of the metalwork is to be avoided. Always clean up after a day's or evening's work; cleanliness is one of the first and foremost attributes of good photography.

PHOTOGRAPHIC PLATES AND FILMS

The coating on a plate or film is known as the emulsion. This gelatine film holds in suspension several sensitive silver salts. These salts can be silver bromide, silver chloride or silver iodide. They are formed by the combination of silver and one of a group of elements known as halogens. These compounds are termed halides; the most sensitive of these is silver bromide.

When a plate or film has been exposed in a camera there is no visible change in the emulsion, but because further treatment with a developing agent will eventually make a change at this stage it is called the latent image. The action of the developer converts the invisible image into a visible image. The plate or film is now referred to as a negative, because the light and dark areas of the image are the reverse of those of the actual specimen. The exposure has changed the silver bromide so that the bromide can be removed from the emulsion, leaving the black metallic silver behind in the gelatine, the metallic silver being the areas which have been affected by light from the brightest parts of the subject. From this it can be seen that the darkening of the silver halides takes place on exposure to light.

Sunlight is a white light which, on passing through a prism, is seen to comprise a number of colours. It has already been said that these colours (violet, blue, green, yellow, orange and red) are known as the visible spectrum.

When the silver halide is exposed to white light, the red part of the spectrum has less effect than the blue, which has affected the silver halide, producing a darkened area. Beyond this range of blue there is the ultra-violet, which is not visible, but does, however, affect the silver halide and also has a darkening effect. From this it can be seen that certain coloured filters and coloured stains have a greater use than others, especially when photographing treble-stained specimens. When staining specimens it is advisable to bear in mind the type of plate to be used, different colours having different effects on various plates; red has the least effect on orthochromatic material. Other colours have effect in ascending order of the spectrum up to blue and violet. For this reason it can be seen that orthochromatic plates do not cover the complete colour range, as do the panchromatic plates or films. This type of emulsion is often referred to as the red-sensitive emulsion. The Ilford chromatic plate is, on the other hand, sensitive only to green. This extremely useful plate gives fine grain.

DEVELOPER

Types and Use.—Developers—chemical agents which render the latent image visible—can be divided into two groups: the chemical developers and physical developers, which work in a different manner.

The chemical developer is capable of reducing the soluble and insoluble silver compounds into the metallic state after exposure. Physical developers can act only in reducing soluble silver compounds. The developer must contain an element which will readily combine with the bromide in the exposed silver salts without having any effect on the unexposed salts.

The developing agents most commonly used are hydroquinone, pyrogallol, amidol, metol and sodium hydroxide. A developing agent is completely useless on its own, therefore other chemicals are added to form a complete working formula. The action of the developing agent is to change or reduce the metallic salts into the metallic state. The developing agent would take a long time to develop the plate or film on its own, so to decrease this developing time a chemical such as sodium carbonate is added; this is known as an accelerator. The development time has thus, it is true, been accelerated, but these two chemicals quickly cause the solution to become oxidized, and to prevent this another chemical, sodium sulphite, is added. This acts as a preservative. Amidol does not last for more than a few hours because of the lack of a preservative in the solution.

The formula thus far comprises the developing agent proper, the accelerator and preservative; if these are used together they are liable to develop some of the unaffected silver bromide; to overcome this yet another chemical, potassium bromide, is added, which restrains the action of the solution and thus reduces the possibility of development fog. Lastly, the solvent (water) is added proportionately. When the sodium sulphite is omitted from a developer, it is made up in two solutions, Parts I and II, to prevent oxidation.

The most commonly used developer has been chosen to illustrate the working action of a developer, but it must not be taken for granted that all developers work on these lines, many formulae being long and varied. It will be seen, therefore, that basically a developer comprises the following:

1. The developing agent—M.Q., metol, pyro, etc.
2. The accelerator—generally sodium carbonate, or borax, but there are others.
3. The preservative—generally sodium sulphite, but metabisulphite can be used.
4. The restrainer—potassium bromide.
5. The solvent—water.

For those who suffer from metol poisoning there is a special developer packed by Ilfords and known as Phenidone. This will not trouble the skin as does a M.Q. developer.

During development the silver bromide grains which have been affected by light are reduced to black metallic silver. As soon as an exposed plate is immersed in a developer each grain of silver bromide is gradually reduced by the solvent until complete development has taken place, by which time the areas which have received the most light are black. Another area which has received only half the light of that of the first area is grey when completely developed, while yet another area which has not received any light at all is still transparent on completion of development, and the grains remain unchanged. If development is carried on to excess, development fog becomes evident, this being due to a thin layer of silver forming in the negative through the long action of the developer. Chemical fog also takes place in the areas which have not been affected by exposure. This type of fog will occur more easily with fast panchromatic plates than with orthochromatic material. Stale plates or films, whether fast or slow, will produce a veil of fog over the whole area of the emulsion when developed.

Dichroic fog is yet another form of fogging and is caused by the developer creating a veil over the emulsion. This veil appears red when the film or plate is viewed by transmitted light and green when viewed by reflected light. One of the most common causes of dichroic fog is the presence of hypo (sodium thiosulphate) in the developer or the transferring of plate or film straight from developer to hypo bath without a rinse. When this fog appears it can be removed by a weak solution of Howard Farmer's reducer, after which the plate should be refixed.

Should an emulsion be over-exposed, and the existence of this fault be known before development, extra potassium bromide may be added to the developer, thus retarding the action of the solvent and allowing the lower tones to become developed in relation to the highlights.

The main agent in the rarely used metallic chemical developer is ferrous oxalate, forming the double salt, ferrous potassium oxalate. This reduces the exposed silver grains to metallic silver, as do the other developers.

The rate at which the silver grains develop depends upon the number of grains which are undeveloped. As these grains are unexposed, the emulsion remains unchanged. When development is complete, some areas will be black, some less dense, others light grey, and so on, until clear emulsion is reached.

When forcing the development in an effort to increase the density of the light areas, an unlimited amount of fog may occur.

Contrast increases as the development time increases, but a film which has received an even overall exposure of a subject ranging from black to white will produce a negative contrast in relation to the original, unless, of course, colours are present in the original and a coloured filter is used. The amount of contrast needed in a negative solely depends upon the purpose for which it is required. In other words, when a negative is made the worker should have in mind the type of print he hopes to achieve.

The activity of the developer increases with an increase of temperature. At the other extreme, a cold developer will take far longer to develop an emulsion than a warm one. From this it can be seen that a warm developer will take less time to act on the exposed silver salts. If, however, the developer is too warm it may cause the gelatine to melt. The ideal temperature is 65° F. If the temperature of the developer is in excess of 75° F, it will be found that the emulsion swells and becomes very soft, which makes handling difficult, as the emulsion is very easily damaged. When conditions are such that the developer must be used at a temperature above 70° F, a hardening bath should be used before developing takes place, since damage cannot be rectified after development. The pre-hardening solution is made up in a fairly large dish to allow plenty of room for soaking. The film or plate is placed first in this solution, and is soaked for approximately 3 minutes, after which it is rinsed in running water. The pre-hardening bath can be made up of either sodium sulphate or tropical hardener (Ilford).

Should the washing water be warm, and it be feared that the emulsion may become damaged, the use of a hypo-eliminator should be introduced to reduce the washing time. When the film has had ample fixing it should be given a brief rinse for 3 or 4 minutes and then immersed in the hypo-eliminator for double the rinsing time, constant agitation being carried out at the same time. After a final rinse of 4 minutes, followed by light wiping, the film should be hung to dry.

If the temperature of the developing agent is constant, the developing time automatically becomes the same. To produce good negatives there must be some form of standardization of processing technique. The person who is always changing from one developer to another, and also varying the emulsion speeds, has less chance of turning out a good negative; and no doubt he sometimes wonders why the results vary.

Fine Grain.—In the early days of the miniature camera, when film manufacturers had not produced a fast film which, coupled with a fine-grain developer, would give a fine-grain negative, there was always the problem of large-grain size, but over the past years there have been rapid advances in the field of films and fine-grain developers. When these developers are used intelligently they will give all that is desired in the way of fine grain, but even so, one still sees grainy prints. Unless the worker knows how to use fine-grain developers, coarse-grained negatives may still result. In general, the slowest emulsions give the finest grain, even when developed in a simple M.Q. developer, but unfortunately such films need long exposures.

The reason why slow and medium films need more exposure than, say, Pan X or Super XX, is the very fact that the small grains of silver are less sensitive to light than the large ones. An emulsion consists of a coating of gelatine on a cellulose nitrate base and in this gelatine are suspended grains of silver halide. After exposure, and during development, a reaction takes place, as a result of which the emulsion becomes soft and the silver grains become metallic silver. If an inherently fine-grained film is over-developed, some of the tiny grains of silver may coalesce, giving rise to coarse grains.

Exposure plays its part in contributing to the grain size, and an over-exposed film developed for the normal time will be both dense and grainy. If an over-exposed film or plate is deliberately under-developed, the result will be a flat, granular negative. On the other hand, known under-exposure may lead to an attempt at correction by over-development. This can result in lack of detail and excessive grain.

Here a simple test will satisfy any doubt on these points. Expose a roll of film, giving some correct exposure, some over- and some under-exposure. After the film has been processed make a print from each negative at, say, ten times enlarged, and compare the grain size. Scattering of light is likely to take place in the emulsion of over-exposed negatives; this introduces poor resolution, and is every bit as bad as coarse grain. The resolving power of an emulsion increases to a maximum when correctly exposed and developed, with a fair latitude before the resolution is lost.

Another contributing factor to coarse grain in a film is a variation in the temperatures of the different solutions used. For ideal processing a constant temperature of developer, rinsing water and hypo must be maintained. If the developer is at a high temperature the development time should be considerably reduced, thus helping to keep the grain size down. If normal development time is given under such conditions, large grains will appear and the negative will also be over-developed. The making of really fine-grained negatives is also dependent upon the developer being used at the temperature recommended by the makers.

If a well-known formula, say D 76, is examined, it can be seen that the sodium sulphite content is higher than that of a normal quick-acting developer, such as M.Q. In general it is accepted that grain size is less when the concentration of sulphite is high. In addition to this, potassium bromide and thiocyanate also help to reduce the grain size, but these unfortunately have a slowing effect on the emulsion.

Rinsing.—After development it is essential to give the plate or film a thorough rinse before transferring it to a fixing bath. In the case of a film being attached to a developing machine, it is suggested that the film be passed from one spool to the other at least twice; this should be done slowly in running water.

FIXING

Although fixing is a simple operation, some films and plates develop stains when being transferred from the rinse to the fixing bath, whilst others stain during fixing. To render the film or plate permanent, and to enable it to be handled freely, it must be completely fixed. During the fixing operation the silver salts which have not been reduced by the developer must be removed. The fixing solution is sodium thiosulphate. If the solution has been extensively used, a greater proportion of the solution, in which is dissolved silver, will be deficient in hypo. When this happens it is not possible to remove all the unexposed silver in an emulsion; thus, the need for a new bath is indicated. When the fixing solution takes twice as long to fix a plate as it did when first made up, this is yet another sign that the solution needs to be replaced. Films should be constantly agitated from the time they are immersed until the milky appearance has disappeared from the back of the negative. After this the emulsion should be left for at least twice the time it took to clear.

The final washing is often regarded as not so important; the film is hurriedly washed, and stains and crystals on the emulsion become evident some months later. Plates and films need at least

30 minutes in running water to ensure proper washing. If it is not possible to use running water, many changes of water should be made before finally accepting the film as completely washed.

Owing to the use of a plain fixing solution, and perhaps hard water, films sometimes develop a heavy scum. To remove this it is necessary to rinse the affected emulsion through a weak chrome alum bath, after which the film should be rewashed. In practice it should take only a few minutes to clear the scum from the film or plate.

REDUCTION

When a negative has been over-exposed and fully developed, it produces a dense image, the light areas of the subject becoming heavy and the dark areas having a light film of fog over them. It would be impossible to make a satisfactory print from such a negative, however soft the printing paper might be. Therefore, to make a printable negative, it must be reduced by either the popular Howard Farmer's reducer (which is made up of potassium ferricyanide and hypo), or an ammonium persulphate reducer. Unfortunately, the chemical action of the former, when a negative is immersed in the solution, attacks the lower densities first before any change can be seen on the higher densities. It can thus be seen that reduction on such negatives is uneven. The reason for the delay in the attack on the dense areas is because there is more silver to be removed from the well-packed silver image, the removed silver becoming silver ferrocyanide.

Howard Farmer's reducer is the best suited to a negative of a line drawing, or one of clear crystals and similar substances, as it gives the negative far more contrast. On the other hand, the ammonium persulphate attacks a negative at a more even rate, reducing the dark and light areas at a proportionately even rate, the silver being removed in this case as silver sulphate. Strange as it may seem, there is one disadvantage to this particular reducer in that on occasions, for no apparent reason, it refuses to be effective on some negatives. An ammonium persulphate reducer must be used when freshly made up because it quickly decomposes.

INTENSIFICATION

When a negative lacks contrast, intensification is carried out to increase the density. The chromium intensifier is the most popular, but before a negative can be intensified it must first be reduced or bleached in a solution of potassium bichromate and hydrochloric acid, when the silver image changes to silver chloride. When the negative changes to a milky brown it is washed thoroughly, after which it is redeveloped; the negative image then quickly re-appears.

REVERSAL PROCESS

Dark-ground effects are often simulated by simply reversing a negative (Plate 44), thus making it a positive, and then using it to make a print. The positive then has a black background, as for dark-ground illumination. The print is not, however, truly dark-ground, and cannot show all the information of a true dark-ground image. Reversing the negative can be carried out by two methods, either by the reversal process or by making a positive transparency from the original negative. There is little to choose between the final results of these two processes, but the reversal takes longer.

The positive can be made by enlargement or by contact. The transparency should be contrasty and bold. The reversal process is as follows: the first development may be carried out in D 168, the negative is then washed for 5 minutes, after which bleaching takes place in R 21A for 5 minutes. The plate is then washed for a further 5 minutes and cleared in 21B for 2 minutes. The rinse follows for 2 minutes and redevelopment takes place in D 158.

REVERSAL PROCESS

Development	6 minutes at 65° F in D 19
Wash	4 minutes
Reverse	6 minutes at 65° F (1 oz. potassium bichromate and 1 oz. sulphuric acid in 80 oz. water)
Wash	6 minutes
Whitening	5 minutes at 65° F (4 oz. sodium sulphite in 80 oz. water)
Wash	2 minutes
Second exposure	$1\frac{1}{2}$ minutes to 500-watt bulb, 6 ft. from film
Development	3 minutes at 65° F in first developer
Wash	2 minutes
Fix	4 minutes at 65° F in acid fixer
Wash	30 minutes
Dry	

)RAMINIFERA FROM THE CARIBBEAN SEA, × 100

This stereo-pair was taken with the top lens of the objective half covered by a stop as
1strated in Fig. 101.   One lamp was placed twice as far from the subject as the other.
Microscope: Leitz.   Camera: Macca ½×.   Objective: 25 mm.   Eyepiece: nil.   Substage:
▸ Tube length: nil.   Bellows length: nil.   Emulsion: O.250.   Filter: nil.   Illumination: two
oblique lamps.   Exposure: 15 seconds each.

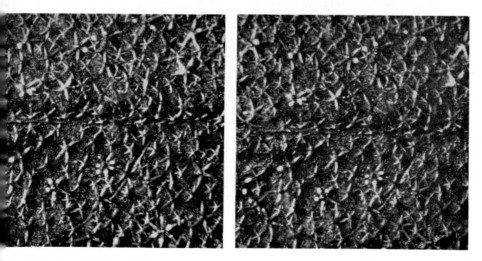

▸P SIDE OF SCABIA LEAF, × 40

he eccentric stop for the objective was used as illustrated in Fig. 99.   The exposure was, of
rse, very long.   Both plates were processed together, ensuring that both were of equal
sity.
Microscope: Leitz.   Camera: Watson.   Objective: 25 mm.   Bellows length: 8 in.   Emulsion:
50.   Illumination: top oblique, one lamp.   Exposure: 1 minute each.

PLATE 59

EGGS OF STONE-FLY, × 40

This stereo pair was made by moving the subject as described in Chapter 12.

Microscope: Leitz. Camera: E.C.2. Objective: 3 in. Eyepiece: nil. Substage: nil. Tube length: nil. Bellows length: nil. Emulsion: P.1200. Filter: nil. Illumination: top oblique, one lamp. Exposure: 3 seconds.

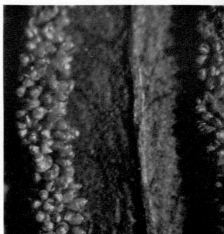

BACK OF FERN LEAF, SHOWING SPORES, × 100

The tilting stage method (Fig. 97) was used to produce this pair. Illumination and focus remained unaltered for both exposures.

Microscope: Leitz. Camera: Golder Microflex. Objective: 25 mm. Eyepiece: × 6. Substage: nil. Tube length: 170 mm. Camera length: 8 in. Emulsion: Ilford Special Rapid. Filter: nil. Illumination: top oblique, one lamp. Exposure: 20 seconds.

PLATE 60

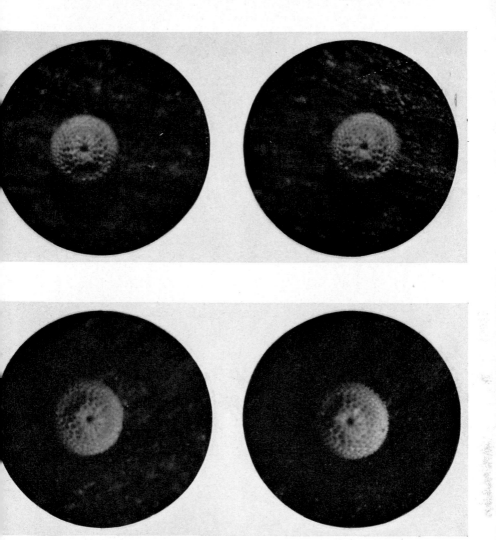

PLATE 61. EGG OF BROWN HAIRSTREAK BUTTERFLY, *Thecla betulae*, × 30

The upper stereo-pair was produced by the tilting stage method (see page 174), two negatives being exposed. The lower pair was taken on one plate, half of which was masked during exposure. The method used was that illustrated in Fig. 97.

Microscope: Leitz. Camera: Watson. Objective: (upper) 1 in., (lower) 3 in. Eyepiece: (upper) × 6, (lower) nil. Substage: nil. Tube length: (upper) 160 mm., (lower) nil. Bellows length: (upper) 10 in., (lower) 20 in. Emulsion: (upper) 0.250, ¼-plate, (lower) Ilford Special Rapid ½-plate. Filter: nil. Illumination: top oblique. Exposure: (upper) 5 seconds, (lower) 14 seconds.

PLATE 62. OIL-AND-WATER EMULSION. DIFFRACTION RINGS, × 200 (total × 450)

Diffraction rings are caused by the inability of a lens to produce a clear, defined image of a minute object. Instead, numerous rings of various density (and on various planes) are formed around the image proper. The rings around the image are referred to as 'circles of confusion' and are often called the Airy Disc or anti-point (see (c)). This effect can be caused by misusing the substage iris diaphragm: reducing the aperture to excess immediately reduces the angular aperture and resolving power of an objective, and the change in wave-length automatically alters the resolving power and numerical aperture.

The 'correct' setting of the iris diaphragm in photographing an oil-and-water emulsion is illustrated in (a). Not more than one-third of the substage light should be included from the back lens of the objective in use. Upon looking down the microscope tube to the objective one should see a clear image of the substage iris. With this setting the back lens should appear four-fifths filled with light.

The centre photomicrograph is of the same field, but this time the iris diaphragm has decreased by half the aperture of that of (a). The effect of this over-stopping is evident and the dark mass in the centre becomes obtrusive. Here more than one-third of the back lens of the objective was blotted out.

Results of excessive stopping down of the substage iris diaphragm are shown in (c). Stopping down beyond a certain point alters the numerical aperture of the optical system and this in turn affects the resolution of the lenses. When adjusting the iris diaphragm it is advisable to remove the eyepiece to allow one to look down the microscope tube to view the back lens of the objective, and care must be taken to prevent the specimen from becoming flooded with light. The introduction of too small an aperture automatically introduces a strong secondary field, as illustrated here.

Microscope: Leitz. Camera: Golden Microflex. Objective: 4 mm. Eyepiece: × 10. Substage: complete. Tube length: 160 mm. Emulsion: 0.250. Illumination: transmitted. Exposure: (a) 4 seconds, (b) 9 seconds, (c) 35 seconds.

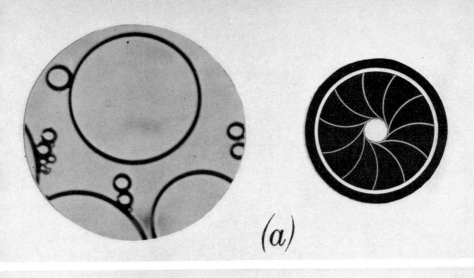

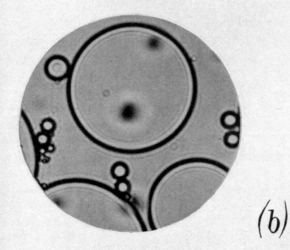

(b)

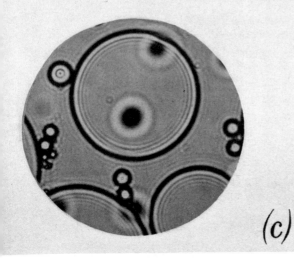

(c)

PLATE 62.

PLATE 63

(a) EMPTY FORAMINIFERA SHELLS, × 35 (total × 140)

Sample from the Adriatic Sea. The globigerina ooze which covers a large part of the ocean floor is composed chiefly of these minute shells.

Microscope: Leitz. Camera: Una ¼-plate. Objective: 25 mm. Eyepiece: 45 mm. × 8. Tube length: 170 mm. Bellows length: 10 in. Emulsion: P.1200. Illumination: reflected. Exposure: 13 seconds.

(b) EGGS OF PARASITE OF WILLOW WARBLER, × 10 (total × 40)

Flood light controlled in tapering tube 13 inches in length. These eggs were left on the feather on which they were found and were photographed with one light and a reflector.

Microscope: Leitz. Camera: box. Objective: 25 mm. Emulsion: Ortho film. Filter: yellow. Illumination: reflected 1/500 watt. Exposure: ⅕ second.

(c) WING SCALES OF PAINTED LADY BUTTERFLY, × 45 (total × 70)

It took a long time to find the correct angle of tilt which would give the correct lighting of the tips, showing them up against a background which was difficult to control.

Microscope: Reichert. Camera: Watson. Objective: 16 mm. Eyepiece: 22 mm. × 11. Substage: nil. Tube length: 160 mm. Emulsion: Special Rapid. Filter: nil. Illumination: oblique. Exposure: 3 seconds.

(d) SKIN OF SOLE FISH, × 45

Tube length plays no part in forming the image when the eyepiece is removed. The filter was used to reduce glare in places. The near-gold spikes and scales are only seen when the oblique lighting is in a certain position.

Microscope: Leitz. Camera: Una ¼-plate. Objective: 25 mm. Bellows length: 12 in. Emulsion: H.P.3. Filter: pale green Wratten 66. Illumination: reflected. Exposure: 5 seconds.

(e) LOBES OF PROBOSCIS OF BLOWFLY, × 555 (total × 600)

The strange looking spring-like structures are in fact food channels which pass on food particles of 0·002—0·003 mm. There are some thirty-five on each side of the tongue.

Microscope: Leitz. Camera: Watson. Objective: 4 mm. N.A. 0·75. Eyepiece: 22 mm. × 11. Substage: complete with bull's eye condenser. Tube length: 160 mm. Bellows length: 13 in. Emulsion: O.250. Filter: diffuser and copper sulphate liquid filter. Illumination: transmitted. Exposure: 30 seconds.

(f) RADIOLARIAN OOZE, × 150 (total × 400)

Two lamps were used to illuminate the specimen, thus preventing hard shadows. Sample from Barbados. Sea beds of the Pacific and Indian Oceans are covered with similar protozoan skeletons which form radiolarian ooze.

Microscope: Leitz. Camera: Una ¼-plate. Objective: 16 mm. N.A. 0·30. Eyepiece: 22 mm. × 11. Substage: nil. Tube length: 170 mm. Bellows length: 15 in. Emulsion: P.1500. Filter: diffuser only. Illumination: reflected. Exposure: 4 seconds.

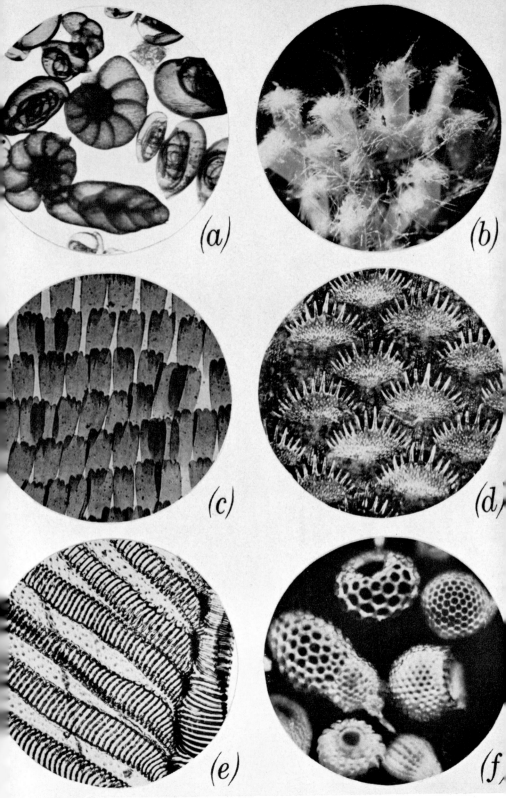

PLATE 63

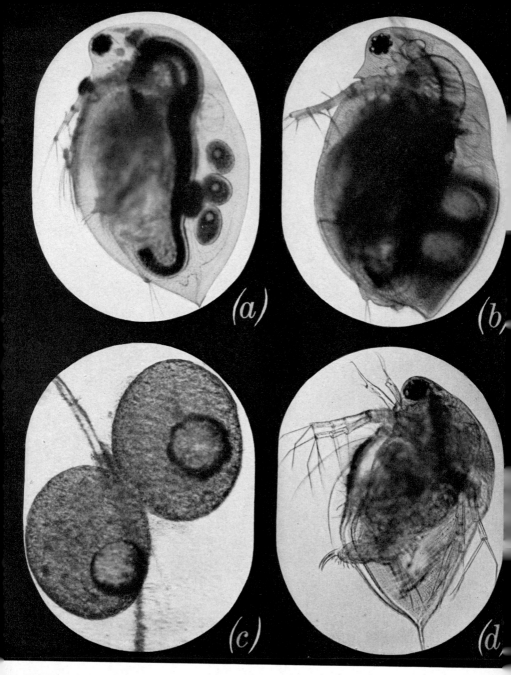

PLATE 64.   DAPHNIA, × 50 (total × 60)

(a) Daphnia with three-day summer eggs in brood sac.   The heart can be seen just above the top

(b) Daphnia with winter eggs in their final stage about to break away from the carapace.

(c) First-day summer eggs of *Daphnia pulex*, × 500.   Photographed as they lay in the brood sac.

(d) Male daphnia.   This is believed to be the first published photomicrograph of a male, whic extremely rare.

All specimens were photographed in their free swimming state.

Microscope: Leitz.   Camera: Watson.   Objective: 25 mm. N.A. 30.   Eyepiece: 45 mm. × 6.   Substage: bull's eye condenser.   Tube length: 160 mm.   Bellows length: 13½ in.   Emulsion: Ilford Special Rapid.   Fi daylight blue.   Illumination: transmitted.   Exposure: 1/25 second.

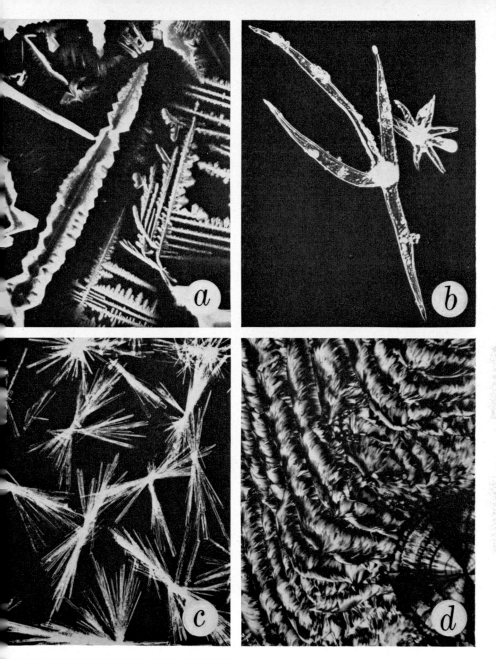

) POTASSIUM FERRICYANIDE CRYSTALS, × 40

Subject recrystallized on microscope slide, producing an attractive pattern.

) MALTOSE CRYSTALS, × 110

Found on stem of ivy bud; floated off on to the microscope slide and photographed wet.

CRYSTALLINE CALCIUM SALT OF URIC ACID, × 50

SALACIN CRYSTALS, × 75

Microscope: Leitz. Camera: Watson. Objective: (a) 2 in. (b) 16 mm. (c and d) 25 mm.
piece: (a) × 8, (b, c and d) × 6. Substage: (a) nil, (b, c and d) less top condenser. Tube
gth: (a) 160 mm., (b, c and d) 170 mm. Bellows length: (a) 16 in., (b and d) 20 in., (c) 13 in.
ulsion: (a and c) B.40, (b and d) N. 40. Illumination: (a and b) transmitted dark-ground, (c)
nsmitted, (d) polarized.

PLATE 65

Plate Emulsion
Speed 31° Scheiner

Developed in Promicrol
at 68°, × 35

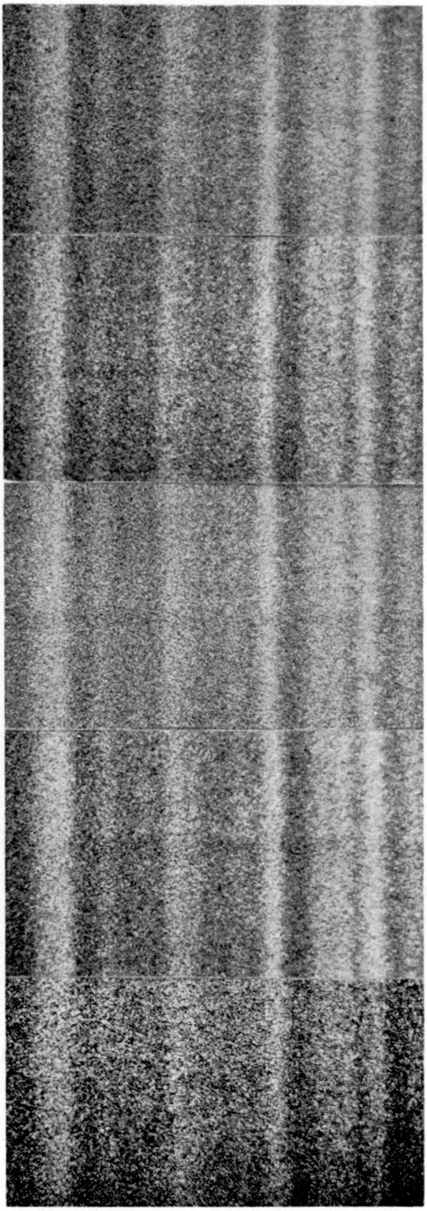

9 minutes' development time

9½ minutes' development time

11 minutes' development time

13 minutes' development time

15 minutes' development time

PLATE 66. DEMONSTRATING EFFECT OF DEVELOPMENT TIMES WITH PR
MICROL DEVELOPER, SHOWING GRAIN SIZE, × 35

Developing Agent   H.P.3. Plate, × 35

M. Q.
4 minutes' development
68°

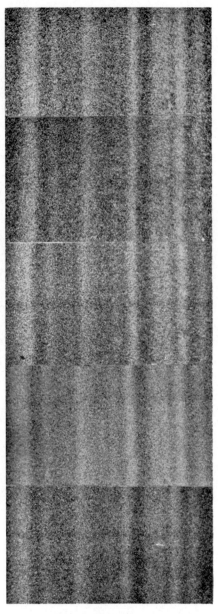

I. D. 48
11 minutes'
68°

Promicrol
10 minutes'
68°

D. 76
9 minutes'
68°

Microdol
13 minutes'
68°

PLATE 67.   DEMONSTRATING EFFECT ON AN EMULSION OF VARIOUS
DEVELOPING AGENTS, SHOWING GRAIN SIZE, × 35

Plates developed in
M. Q. at 68°, × 35

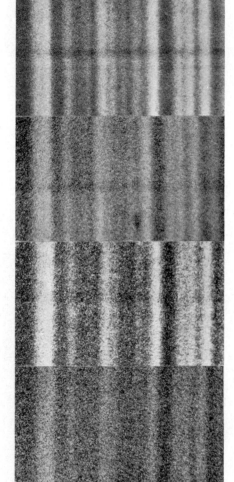

Process, 15° Scheiner

Rapid Ortho, 20° Scheiner

Soft gradation pan, 20° Scheiner

Pan, 25° Scheiner

Pan, 31° Scheiner

PLATE 68. DEMONSTRATING EFFECT ON VARIOUS EMULSIONS OF ONE
DEVELOPING AGENT, SHOWING GRAIN SIZE, × 35

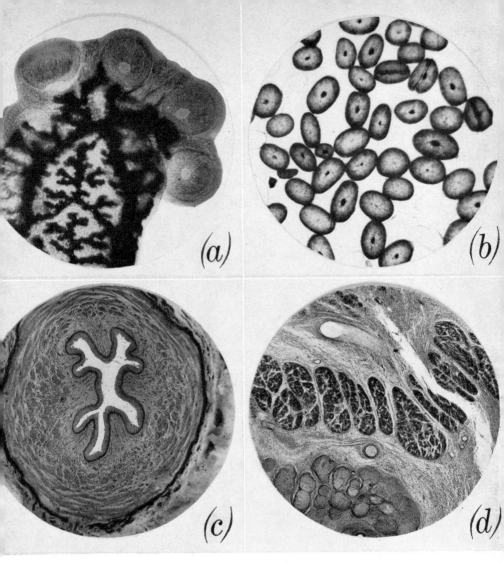

(a) "HEAD" OF *POLYSTOMUM INTEGERRIMUM*, × 10 (total × 45)
   Subject taken from the bladder of a frog, mounted and unstained.

(b) TRANSVERSE SECTIONS OF HUMAN HAIR, × 35 (total × 150)
   These sections cut with microtome and mounted in Detel.

(c) TRANSVERSE SECTION OF HUMAN URETER, × 20 (total × 25)
   Photographed from a permanent slide.

(d) MEIBOMIAN GLANDS OF HUMAN EYE-LID, × 40
   Section stained and mounted.

Microscope: Leitz. Camera: Watson. Objective: 25 mm. Eyepiece: × 6. Substage: (a) nil, (b and d) complete. (c) less top condenser. Tube length: 170 mm. Bellows Length: (a and b) 10 in., (c) 6 in., (d) 9 in. Emulsion: (a) H.P.3., (b and c) O.250, (d) Special Rapid. Filter: (a) light green, (c) light blue, (b and d) nil. Illumination: transmitted.

PLATE 69

PLATE 70. BACTERIA, × 2,000

(a) *Neisseria pharyngis* var. *flavus.* Gram-negative diplococcus.

(b) *Staphylococcus aureus.* Gram-positive coccus.

(c) *Streptococcus viridans.* Gram-positive coccus. Grown on agar.

(d) *Streptococcus pyogenes.* Gram-positive coccus. Grown on broth.

(e) *Pasteurella pseudotuberculosis.* Gram-negative coccobacillus.

(f) *Bacillus subtilis.* Gram-positive bacillus.

The objective was used at N.A. 1·37. Non-drying immersion oil with a refractive index = 1·524 at 20° C. was used between substage condenser and underside of slide and between objective and top of slide.

There are many basic aniline stains, of which the following are the most commonly used:

Violet stains—methyl-violet; Hoffmann's violet; gentian-violet.

Blue stains—methylene-blue; thionin-blue.

Red stains—basic fuchsin; basic rubin; magenta.

Brown stains—Bismarck brown; vesuvin; phenylene-brown.

Microscope: Watson. Camera: Watson. Objective: 2 mm. apochromatic. N.A. 1·37. Eyepiece: 22 mm. × 11. Substage: complete. Tube length: 160 mm. Bellows length: 17 in. Emulsion: chromatic. Filter: green. Illumination: transmitted by intensity lamp. Exposure: 2 seconds.

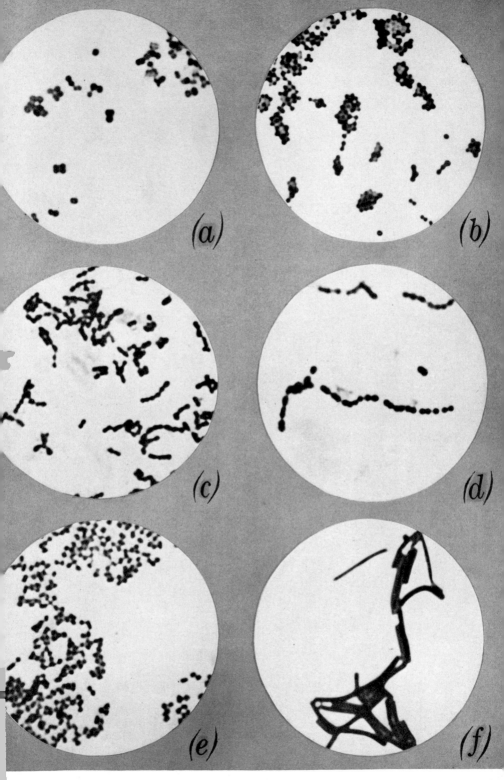

(a)

(b)

(c)

(d)

(e)

(f)

PLATE 70

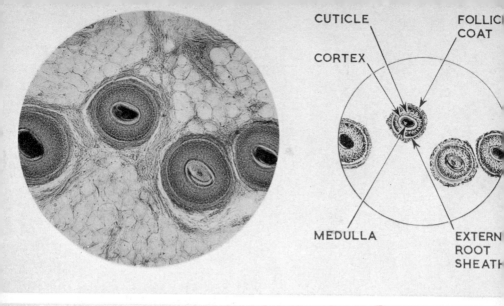

CUTICLE   FOLLIC
COAT

CORTEX

MEDULLA

EXTERN
ROOT
SHEATH

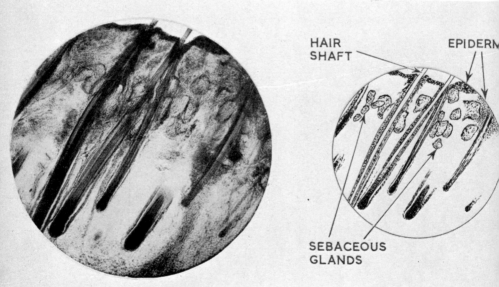

HAIR
SHAFT   EPIDERM

SEBACEOUS
GLANDS

PLATE 71. SECTIONS OF HUMAN SCALP

The form and structure of human hair are clearly shown by these photomicrographs, the upper of which is a transverse section of human scalp, and the lower a longitudinal section.

An easy method of producing a true-to-scale drawing of a photomicrograph is to make a print, draw with indian black ink (waterproof) over the subject, allow to dry, bleach the print in potassium ferricyanide. Wash, dry and copy on process emulsion.

Magnification: (upper) × 60, (lower) × 20. Microscope: Leitz. Camera: Linhof ¼-plate. Objective: (upper) 25 mm. (lower) 2 in. Eyepiece: × 8. Substage: (upper) complete with top condenser, (lower) less top condenser. Tube length: 170 mm. Bellows length: (upper) 12 in: (lower) 8 in. Emulsion: O.250. Filter: light blue. Illumination: transmitted.

PRINTING

Although the various types of printing papers are numerous, the question of the most suitable type for the reproduction of a picture of a microscopic specimen need not cause anxiety; this is decided for us, as will be seen.

Papers vary in grain size, as do photographic plates, and in a way can help to control the final graininess of the picture. The glossy paper is devoid of grain; at least it is not visible to the naked eye. Semi-matt papers show a little grain, but not so much as matt papers, which are very rough. The final choice of paper is dependent upon the effect the worker is trying to achieve. In addition to this, the rough-grained paper does help to camouflage a negative which is not quite as sharp as it ought to be, whereas if the same negative were printed on a glossy paper the defect would be seen at its worst at once. Some pictorial workers like a 'fussy' print, whereas scientific workers must produce a print which is clear, sharp and full of detail. The recommended paper for scientific work, such as photomicrography, is undoubtedly glossy, with matt as second choice. If the utmost care has been taken to produce a sharp grainless negative with fine definition, it leaves no choice but to use glossy paper if these finer points are to be seen to the best advantage.

Papers are, as a rule, made in three or four grades—soft, normal, contrasty and extra hard. The soft bromide papers will show a wide range of tones, from white to black. This paper has also a considerable latitude in exposure, but does not have the same latitude in development times as does a photographic plate. Normal paper gives less grey tones between white and full black, whereas a high-contrast paper shows very few grey tones between black and white.

The final photomicrograph should show nearly all the detail as seen on the photographic plate. This can be ensured only by printing on the correct grade of paper. Test strips should be printed on the various grades of paper and finally placed side by side to assist the user in deciding which is the best, but without having too soft a picture or one that is too contrasty. The final print should have in it all the tones shown in the negative, ranging from a pure white to a dead black (neither a greyish-white nor a greenish-black).

Lantern Slides.—The treatment of lantern slides is very similar to the process of printing, the only difference being that lantern slides are transparent. When such slides are being made the image should not be made too big, and it should be borne in mind that the subject is highly magnified when seen on the screen.

EXHIBITION PRINTS

The number of photomicrographs exhibited at photographic exhibitions is declining, owing to several possible factors. One may be the lengthy period entailed in collecting, staining and mounting the subjects beforehand and finally photographing them. Another reason for the lack of exhibition prints in this field may be the shortage of judges, which the author has himself experienced a number of times, when pictures have been returned for this reason. This strange situation is, to say the least of it, more than disappointing to the exhibitor. Another point is that a judge of this type of work needs a comprehensive knowledge of photomicrographic subjects, which does not appear to be a common attainment. It is the wish of the author to see more photomicrographs being entered in photographic exhibitions, thereby regaining the place they once held in the photographic world. Photomicrography is not exactly easy, and the number of subjects suitable for exhibition work is limited. All the photomacrographs and photomicrographs by the author, illustrated in this book, have, however, been exhibited at the British International Exhibitions.

The exhibitor should pay particular attention to presentation, thus showing his work to best advantage. The prints need not be very large; 3×3 in. is quite sufficient, with possibly whole plate or 15×12 in. as the limit, although on rare occasions it is possible to make a 16×16-in. print. It is not possible in this field of photography to fill the whole mount; small prints submitted should, therefore, be mounted in some order of tonal values, the light prints at the top and the darker prints at the bottom. Twelve 3×3-in. prints fit nicely on a 20×16-in. mount and can be made to look very attractive. The top outside prints look best with subjects pointing inwards, and with a light background if possible. The bottom three prints should be the darkest and have a dark background. The centre three prints are best displayed if the image is upright.

The annotating should be done carefully and be consistent throughout. Presenting the scientific print in an attractive manner plays an important part in gaining the verdict 'in'. The print ought not to be retouched or defaced in any way. If it is, it is not a true record of the subject and ceases to be of scientific value. When a photomicrographic negative has fine lines very close together it is possible to make an enlargement from it, thereby giving greater visible detail in a higher magnification of the overall area. There is, however, a danger of making a print too large. Any details already clearly visible on the negative do not need further enlarging, as this only results in empty magnifications. Often a negative reveals such fine detail where two lines are so close together that it is necessary to enlarge to separate the lines on the print. This, then, is not a case where it can be said that an enlargement produces empty magnifications.

16

MOUNTING AND STAINING

THE only way to improve one's knowledge of microscopy is to acquire facility in the preparation and mounting of specimens. Prepared slides, expertly cut, stained and mounted, can be purchased. Slides of this type are invaluable to the newcomer to photomicrography, since any defects in the final photograph may be associated with an error in microscope technique rather than in the preparation of the specimen. Apart, however, from the satisfaction which results from the production of good-quality slides, it is often necessary for the working photomicrographer to be able to prepare suitable specimens.

FIXING AND HARDENING

The nature of the specimen and the observations required must decide the type of slide to be prepared. Small animals and other objects are sometimes mounted whole. Fluids such as blood may simply be smeared on to a slide. When the contents of a cell are to be studied and the structure of the cell is unimportant, the specimen may simply be squashed under a cover glass. But the majority of specimens which require examination by transmitted light are so thick that they must be cut into thin sections. This must not distort the structure and it is also often necessary to stain the section selectively to render structural details visible.

The majority of tissues, such as wood, skin, hair, leaf and stem, are usually examined in this way. Most of these tissues are too soft to be cut without introducing distortion. Such tissues must, therefore, be fixed. In this operation the aim is to kill and harden the tissue without damaging or distorting it in any way. These twin objectives are not easily realized. There are several fixatives, each with its own characteristics. The most commonly used fixative is 70 per cent alcohol, but care is necessary in its use since it causes shrinkage of fine cell structures. Acetic acid is also used for fixing specimens, and it is more rapid than alcohol. In general, however, it does not harden as well as the 70 per cent alcohol. However, a mixture of 99 per cent of the 70 per cent alcohol with 1 per cent of glacial acetic acid is a very efficient fixative, especially for nuclei and chromosomes. Ethyl alcohol is most suited to animal and plant tissues and will fix in a comparatively short time, 2–3 hours.

Chromic acid is suitable for fixing plant and animal tissues and algae. The subject-matter must be small, as this medium does not penetrate as quickly as others and is also very slow, requiring 18–24 hours. However, tissues stain very well after being fixed with this reagent.

Formaldehyde is one of the most popular fixatives and is used for this purpose in most laboratories. Unfortunately, it is very slow and requires a fixing time of about 48 hours. It is used mainly for animal and histological material, and is not suitable for use with water, chromic acid or potassium dichromate. If used carefully it produces very little shrinkage in the tissue. If subsequent staining is to be conducted with haematoxylin, very good results are obtained with a formaldehyde fixative.

A solution of 70 per cent alcohol and 30 per cent formalin (itself a 40 per cent solution of formaldehyde) is a very good general fixative for plant and histological sections, which it is capable of fixing within 15 minutes.

Tenker-formol is a very good fixative for vertebrate specimens. It contains a mixture of potassium dichromate and formaldehyde. Fixing time is in the region of 24 hours and an equal time of washing follows, after which a rinse in mercuric chloride is necessary.

After fixing, tissues must be thoroughly washed in order to remove all trace of the fixative. Failing this the section may not stain evenly and there is also the possibility that reagents left in the section may later crystallize out. When alcohol is used as a fixative no after-washing is necessary, but when the alcohol–acetic method is used the specimen should be washed out with a 70 per cent solution of alcohol.

If mercuric chloride has been used it is necessary to wash the specimen thoroughly in water and then soak it in an aqueous iodine solution followed by further soaking in 70 per cent alcohol. Failure to observe this washing procedure may result in the development of crystals in the finished slide.

For preserving purposes tissues may be bottled in 70 per cent alcohol or formaldehyde. If they are to be stored in the latter, make sure the section is thoroughly washed, or staining may appear.

A simple fixing procedure may be summarized as follows:

Animal Tissue*.—(a) For very rapid fixation of small pieces of fresh tissue, where some degree of damage is acceptable:
(1) Drop into hot water at 90° C for 1 minute.
(2) Transfer to a solution of 70 per cent alcohol for 1 minute.

(b) For general use:
(1) Cut tissue into pieces not larger than 1 × 1 × ½ cm.
(2) Transfer to formol–saline (strong)† for 24 hours.
(3) Transfer to alcohol (50, 70 or 90 per cent), avoid water.

Plant Tissue*.—(a) For rapid fixation of small pieces or sections of fresh tissue and algae:
(1) Formalin–alcohol‡ for 15 minutes.
(2) Alcohol (70 per cent) for 2 minutes.

(b) For general use:
(1) Cut tissue into pieces not larger than 1 × 1 × ½ cm.
(2) Soak in chrome–acetic for 24 hours.
(3) Wash in running water for 12 hours.

SECTIONING

Sectioning is best done with a microtome, but reasonably thin and uniform sections can be prepared free-hand with a razor blade, or even with dissecting scissors.

Thin sections can be cut from a variety of subjects, such as hair,

* H. Alan Peacock.
† To make 'strong formol–saline' use sodium chloride solution (0·9 per cent aq.) as the diluent for formaldehyde (10 per cent).
‡ Alcohol (70 per cent), 100 c.c.; formaldehyde (40 per cent): 6 c.c.

fibre, biological preparations, textiles, animal and human tissues and botanical material.

A section must be very thin, but more particularly it must be of uniform thickness. The cutting action must therefore be smooth with a very sharp knife. For ease and facility in the preparation of specimens a microtome is necessary. Essentially it consists of a rigid frame supporting both knife and specimen, with means for traversing the knife across the specimen together with a device for advancing the specimen as required. It is usually necessary to provide a supporting material, even with fixed and hardened specimens. A very simple method which can be employed with durable specimens is to freeze them. The Reichert O.M.P. microtome is adapted for this purpose: a jet of carbon dioxide is directed on to the specimen to freeze it, and this usually suffices to hold the specimen to the stage as well. More delicate material must be embedded in a suitable supporting medium, such as paraffin wax. The Reichert O.M.E. is an excellent example of a modern microtome suitable for handling embedded specimens. When the irregular surface material has been removed, either the O.M.P. or O.M.E. permits the production of a succession of slices with a minimum thickness of some 20 microns (1 micron $= 10^{-3}$ mm.).

Many workers have made their own microtomes, using one of the old 'cut-throat' type of razor. Provided that the specimen and blade are rigidly supported and the razor is very sharp, extremely thin sections can be cut from a wide range of materials. Any unevenness in the thickness of the specimen will lead to difficulties later on, since staining will give a deeper coloration in the thick regions and the variation in surface height may result in out-of-focus bands across the field of view. Thus, in making a microtome, rigidity and smooth movement of the knife must be ensured.

The majority of soft specimens can be supported in paraffin wax, tallow, lard or some similar material, but there is much to be said for the freezing method. This may be used not only to make the specimen rigid but also to freeze it to the specimen support. If carbon dioxide is sprayed on the specimen it will quickly become covered with a thin film of ice. This treatment can be repeated should the specimen show any signs of thawing out. Alternatively, a block of solid carbon dioxide may be placed on the stage, to which it will freeze; the top may then be levelled off to take the specimen. With this latter method there is the

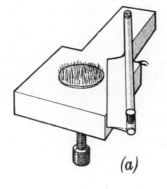

(a)

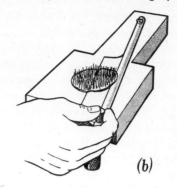

(b)

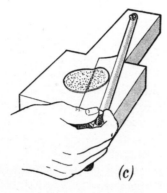

(c)

Fig. 104. Microtome
(a) hair or fibre before
initial cut; (b) levelling the
subject which can be supported
in wax or firm substance; (c)
making the thin section

disadvantage that the specimen is supported by a block of carbon dioxide and there is some loss of rigidity.

If the specimen is to be frozen to the stage it may be washed in water after being soaked in 70 per cent alcohol. Should the specimen require embedding in wax, it must first be dehydrated in 95 per cent alcohol and then cleared of alcohol in a medium such as xylene. Fig. 104 illustrates the home-made microtome used by the author. This instrument is easy to make and very easy to manipulate, and produces thin sections which can be cut from objects frozen to the stage or held in wax, etc. The various parts of the microtome are shown in Fig. 105. A is made from a piece of hardwood, 1 in. in thickness. A hardwood is necessary to resist wear and distortion and be easy to clean. The microtome is fixed to a table or bench top L by a clamp K which is fixed to A by two or more screws N. The inner cylinder B fits tightly into the hole B_1, the top of the cylinder being fixed $\frac{1}{2}$ in. below the top surface of A. The cylinder B is tapped to receive a fine-threaded screw F

passing through it, with a knurled head at D. The other end of the thread has a conical retaining spigot E on which the stage E_1 is free to rotate. The specimen may be supported on the stage and advanced enough for each section by rotation of D. The blade M is fastened by a small screw G through the hole G_1 and a small grip H fastened at H_1 enables the blade to be swung to and fro. Fig. 104 illustrates the microtome in use: (a) showing the subject immediately after mounting; (b) illustrating the initial cut which leaves a flat even surface; and (c) showing the first thin slice being cut. Immediately the required slice has been cut it should be placed in a beaker of water, from which it may be floated on to a slide.

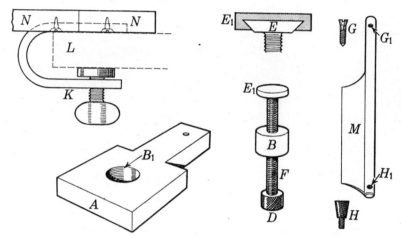

Fig. 105. Component parts of microtome

Larger sections may require preliminary dissection, so that, in addition to a microtome, dissecting scissors are invaluable. A large range of suitable instruments is available from W. Watson & Sons Ltd., in fact a complete set of dissecting instruments can be purchased from them, consisting of: microtome razor; diamond pencil; scalpels of various blade sizes; Borrodaile's needle; scissors, straight and curved; forceps, straight, blunt and sharp; forceps, curved; cornet forceps; needles, straight and curved in handles; seeker, straight and curved; blow-pipe; and section lifter. Both Beck's and Watson's supply dissecting microscopes and dissecting arms. The design and construction of these instruments give perfect stability, together with ample access for the hands and support for the wrists and arms. The lenses are carried on a swinging arm which is focused by the usual rack-and-pinion movement providing a vertical travel of 3 in. A plane mirror and opal glass disc are provided, and the instruments are well finished and easily cleaned.

STAINING

In order to differentiate between the various components of a thin section it is usually necessary to stain the specimen. Some of the staining procedures are highly complex and their discussion would be out of place in this book. It is therefore suggested that *Elementary Microtechnique* by H. Alan Peacock and *Biology Staining Schedules* by R. R. Fowell be to hand. A list of the stains commonly employed is given in Tables 9 and 10.

TABLE 9. BOTANICAL STAINS

Stain	Solvent	Staining Reactions	
Aniline hydrochloride	Water	Yellow	—
Bismarck brown	70 per cent alcohol	—	Brown
Delafield's haematoxylin	Weak alcohol	Yellow	Purple-blue
Erythrosine	Lactophenol	Yellow-Orange — (dense protoplasmic structures stain red)	
Gentian violet	Water or 20 per cent alcohol	Violet	—
*Iodine	Water	Deep yellow	Pale yellow
	Starch	Oxford Blue	—
Light green	Clove oil	—	Green
Phloroglucinol	95 per cent alcohol	Red	—
Safranin	50 per cent alcohol	Red	—
Schulze's soln.	Water	Yellow	Violet

* This must first be dissolved in a small quantity of strong potassium iodide solution.

TABLE 10. ZOOLOGICAL STAINS

Stain	Solvent	Staining Reactions	
Borax carmine	50 per cent alcohol	Red	—
Ehrlich's haematoxylin	70 per cent alcohol	Purple	Pink
Eosin	90 per cent alcohol	—	—
Leishman's stain	Methyl alcohol	Purple-blue (oxyphil granules red)	Pale blue
Methyl green	Water	Deep green	Pale green

If the specimen to be stained was embedded in wax for sectioning, the wax must be removed with a solvent such as xylene, which must then be removed with alcohol. The specimen must then be washed with water if the subsequent stain is a water-soluble type.

When the section has been satisfactorily stained, all water must be removed before the section can be infiltrated and mounted with Canada balsam or any similar medium. If ethyl alcohol is used, a series of solutions of increasing strength will minimize the risk of damage by diffusion currents. Cellosolve is an efficient and rapid dehydrating agent which will displace the water from an average section in approximately 1 minute.

The dehydrating agent must then be removed by a clearing agent such as benzene, cedarwood oil, clove oil or xylene; this process will also render the section transparent. The whole series of operations may readily be conducted in a line of watch glasses, so that the section is simply moved along in a steady and logical sequence.

MOUNTING

The purpose of mounting the specimen is to enable it to be handled for examination and photography. Such mounts may be either temporary or permanent. Saline solution, glycerine and distilled water are suitable for mounting tissues in a temporary manner. There is a large range of mounting media suitable for the preparation of permanent mounts; this includes Hydrax, Naphrax, Pleurax, lactophenol, gum styrax, realgar, clarite,

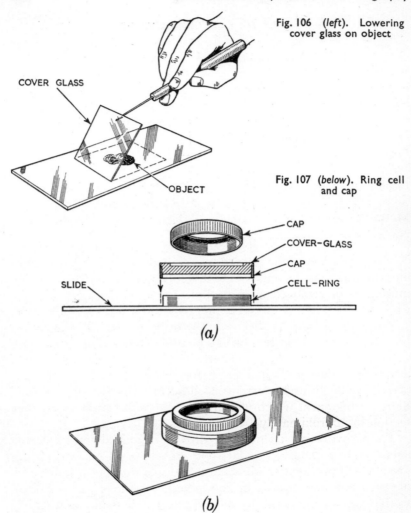

Fig. 106 (*left*). Lowering cover glass on object

COVER GLASS

OBJECT

Fig. 107 (*below*). Ring cell and cap

CAP

COVER-GLASS

CAP

CELL-RING

SLIDE

(a)

(b)

Canada balsam, Euparal, Diaphane and glycerine jelly. There are many variations in the technique of preparing permanent mounts, and it is possible to give only a brief general account in this book.

Manipulative technique and cleanliness are very important in the preparation of mounted sections. In particular, dust and fibres from cleaning materials must not be allowed to spoil the specimen. The slides generally used are 3 × 1 in. and the object is, as a rule, placed in the centre. The cover glass rests on the mounting medium, which is allowed to spread out to the edge of the cover glass and set (Fig. 106). On occasions it is necessary to rest the cover glass on a ring, owing to the thickness of the object (Fig. 107(*a*) and (*b*)). Cover glasses are made round, square and rectangular, and are manufactured in several thicknesses, as mentioned earlier in this book. Thick cover glasses, made from crown glass, are used for low-power and visual work, but for high-power photomicrography unannealed glass is the best. These cover glasses vary in thickness; they are also brittle and must be handled with care.

First, dust both slide and specimen with a camel-hair brush; then place a drop of mountant on the clean slide and by means of

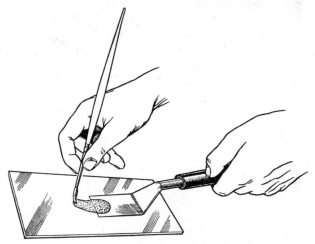

Fig. 108. Transferring very thin section to slide

a flat spoon and camel-hair brush (Fig. 108) or by holding one corner with tweezers place the specimen in position. Place a cover glass on one edge and gently lower it by means of a mounted needle as shown in Fig. 106 and allow it to settle. Do not press it down. If this operation is hurried, air bubbles may be trapped beneath the cover slip and subsequent attempts at remounting may harm the specimen. If the slide is gently warmed over a small flame, the bubbles are more rapidly dispersed. The mounting medium may take several days to set, and if there is a small area near the edge of the cover glass into which the mounting medium has not penetrated, this can be filled later on. When the edges are finally dry the slide can be ringed with gold size and finished

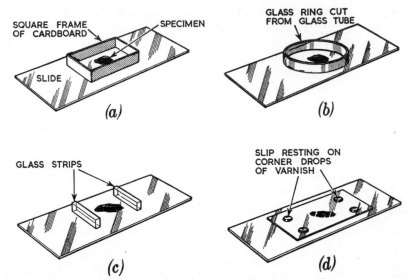

Fig. 109. Various methods of raising cover glass above thick specimen or opaque object

off. If it is not absolutely dry when the gold size is applied, the slide is almost certain to be spoilt by the later development of bubbles within the mounting medium.

If the specimen is thick it is advisable to introduce a built-up cell on which to rest the cover glass. There are several ways of doing this as shown in Fig. 109. Square frames can be cut from millboard, as shown in Fig. 109(a), but there is always the possibility of difficulty if the mounting medium is absorbed by the millboard. Thin strips cut from cover glasses can be used to support the cover glass as shown in Fig. 109(c) to permit a thick layer of mounting medium to be placed on the slide, in order to make the final mount air-tight. Aluminium cell rings are available in three diameters, $\frac{5}{8}$, $\frac{3}{4}$ and $\frac{7}{8}$ in., and of thickness $\frac{1}{16}$, $\frac{1}{24}$ and $\frac{1}{32}$ in., from Messrs. Watson & Sons Ltd.

When prepared cells are not to hand, several layers of varnish laid successively in rings around the specimen may be used to support the cover glass. Alternatively, a short length of glass tube may be used as shown in Fig. 109(b). Such rings, however, are not easily prepared.

The 'corner post' method shown in Fig. 109(d) is sometimes used. Drops of varnish are placed on the slide where they will support the cover glass. However, it is difficult to arrange for all the blobs to be of equal height, and this may result in a crack in the cover glass. The crack will probably run over the area occupied by the specimen.

Fresh algae, which is easily damaged by the pressure of a cover glass, is usually mounted within a cell in glycerine jelly. Such cells are ringed with a cap and sealed off as a permanent slide. Care must be taken when the cover glass is sealed to the top of the cell wall. Any trace of glycerine or water at the top edge of the cell wall will later result in a leak. Varnish is probably better than gold size for making this type of seal.

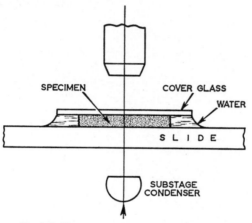

Fig. 110. Temporary wet mounted specimen

There are many subjects which, by virtue of their nature, are mounted in a fluid medium. It is then necessary to run a ring of cement round the specimen. The following are very good cements:

(1) One part Canada balsam, one part paraffin wax. Melt and warm gently together until golden, apply warm.

(2) Tolu balsam cement. Two parts tolu balsam, one part Canada balsam, two parts shellac, and chloroform to bring to a syrupy consistency.

Most commercially prepared slides are ringed to provide an attractive finish and a more lasting slide. In addition to the cements mentioned above, Brunswick black is very good, in both its application and appearance. If large numbers of slides are to be ringed, it is advisable to do so with a turntable made for the purpose. Such turntables are available from Messrs. Watson and other firms.

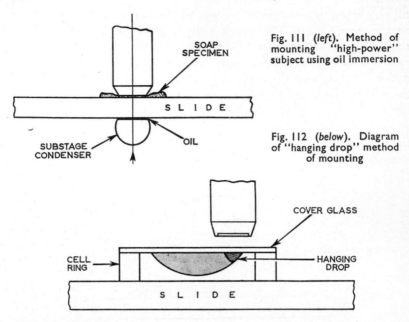

Fig. 111 (*left*). Method of mounting "high-power" subject using oil immersion

SOAP SPECIMEN

S L I D E

SUBSTAGE CONDENSER

OIL

Fig. 112 (*below*). Diagram of "hanging drop" method of mounting

COVER GLASS

CELL RING

HANGING DROP

S L I D E

It is not always necessary to make a permanent and mounted slide, especially as it is now possible to obtain a photographic record. In a way, the negative may replace the slide and it is always to hand for inspection and the production of prints. The preparation of temporary mounts is therefore increasing in the laboratory. If the specimen cannot easily be handled (a section of pickled cauliflower, for example), a very good method is to mount it in water and place a cover glass over the top, as shown in Fig. 110. It is advisable to see that the specimen is well covered, so that there is no possibility of spurious reflections or rapid drying out.

Considerable difficulty often arises when trying to find a suitable mounting medium; this was the case when trying to photograph the shaving-soap cream shown in Plate 55(*e*). Various media and mixtures were used and finally a mixture of equal parts by volume of diethylene glycol mono-ethyl-ether and ethylene glycol mono-ethyl-ether having a refractive index of 1·42 at 18° C was found to give the best differentiation in crystal structure. With oil-immersion technique, the oil is sandwiched between the lower lens of the objective and the top of the cover glass, and between the substage lens and the slide (Fig. 111).

The 'hanging drop' method shown in Fig. 112 is particularly useful when photographing emulsions; this makes the study and recording of the globular structure possible, and comparisons can be made as shown in Plate 54. Bacteria can also be photographed in this manner. This method is a temporary one, and if the subject is left any length of time during photography, evaporation takes place around the edges. The method adopted is quite

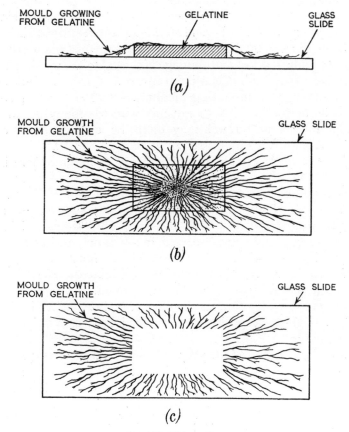

Fig. 113. Slide culture

simple and yet efficient. A thin glass rod is placed in a bottle of the emulsion, withdrawn and allowed to drain, leaving just enough to make a drop on a cover glass. This is then turned upside down and placed on a cell ring as shown in Fig. 112.

Moulds can be grown on slide cultures as shown in Fig. 113,

enabling photomicrographs to be obtained. Mould spores can be collected in most places where there are foodstuffs; a simple method of collecting the airborne spores is to expose a slide containing agar–czapek medium in a suitable position in store or larder for approximately 30 minutes. The mould spores will come into contact with the tacky surface of the medium, from which they will grow as shown in Fig. 113(*a*) and (*b*) if maintained at a temperature of approximately 25° C for about 3 days. When the growth is at its peak, carefully remove the agar, leaving the fungus growth as in Fig. 113(*c*). Permanent stained slides can also be made, and these give greater contrast when photographed, but some realism is lost and damage is caused to the sporing heads.

Detel, a product used as a paint ingredient, can also be used in the laboratory as a mounting medium. There are some powders (Plates 34 and 52) which do not mix with the many known and popular media, and Detel may often be used in such cases. Detel also has a very useful refractive index of 1·510.

Opaque objects are comparatively easy to mount, there being very little preparative work, and such subjects, if semi-permanent, can be mounted in Canada balsam to prevent slipping. Moth and butterfly eggs (Plates 20 and 26) and many such subjects can easily be transferred on a leaf and fixed on a slide, and in this manner successfully photographed many times during a period of days. Plate 26 of the ladybird's eggs clearly illustrates this point.

Some subjects, e.g. blood cells, do not lend themselves to the same treatment as tissues already mentioned. In such cases it is usual to make a very thin smear along the slide, as in Fig. 114(*a*) and (*b*). High-power objectives are used and, as a rule, counts must be made.

W. Watson & Sons Ltd. prepare a wide range of eyepiece and slide graticules; 40 divisions on the graticule equal 0·2 mm. on the stage micrometer; the value of each division on the graticule is then 0·2/40 = 0·005 mm. (5 microns).

After the specimen is mounted it should be labelled before storing in the slide cabinet. The labels should be small and the data clearly written—all pertinent information about the subject, method of fixation, stain, date of preparation and the maker's name. How interesting it is to purchase an old prepared slide from a shop and find the above information thereon. It is often startling to find that the slide may be well over sixty years old and still as good as the day it was mounted.

SOME USEFUL MOUNTING MEDIA

Canada Balsam.—A yellowish resin, obtained from Canadian fir and known to all who work with a microscope. Rarely do air bubbles appear in this medium, as they are automatically absorbed by the balsam.

Euparal.—A very useful mounting medium for stained blood-smears, starches and insect sections. It is said by the makers that this colourless medium adds to the green of haematoxylin stain. Particularly suitable for use with high-power objectives. It is a mixture of menthol, camphor, oil of eucalyptus, salol, paraldehyde and gum sandarac. Alcohol should not be mixed with or allowed to come into contact with Euparal, since it may cause bleaching. Dry within 2 or 3 days, when a covering of shellac can be applied.

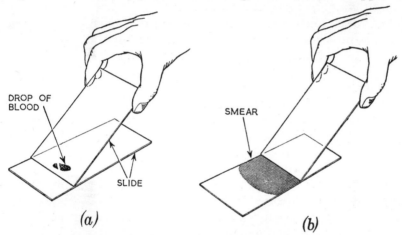

Fig. 114. Making a blood smear

Hydrax.—This originated in the United States and requires more time and technique in mounting. After a liberal drop of Hydrax has been placed on the slide it should be left for 3–4 hours to allow evaporation to take place. During final mounting, the slide must be maintained at a constant temperature of 100° C, and should remain at this temperature for nearly 1 hour after mounting is complete. This is rather a drawback, but otherwise the medium suffers a reduction in its refractive index. When dry, the slide is treated in the normal manner.

Methylene Iodide.—This is a very useful mounting medium to have to hand in the laboratory. It is most suitable for mounting semi-permanent preparations.

Pleurax.—This stands high on the list of mounting media, and is very useful in research and industry, since a great deal of time is saved when mounting specimens. These can be transferred direct from a 95 per cent solution of alcohol to Pleurax. Its usefulness also lies in its high refractive index.

Diaphane.—With its comparatively low refractive index, Diaphane is suitable for stained sections, insects and stained bloodsmears, and can be used directly after alcohol without any intermediate treatment. This quick-drying mountant can be used with nearly all stains with great success.

Glycerine Jelly.—Gelatine 1 part (by weight) and distilled water 6 parts (by weight) are left to digest for over 2 hours, after which 7 parts (by weight) glycerine are added and thereafter 1 gm. of pure thymol to every 100 gm. of mixture. Warm, filter through filter paper, and store. Research laboratories make particular use of this medium in mounting drugs. The slide is warmed, the object placed in position and the jelly applied last. The keeping properties of this medium are equal to those of Canada balsam.

Detel.—This is a paint product and has many uses in the laboratory. It has a good dispersive quality and a useful refractive index (1·510). It is a useful mounting medium for starches, crystals, pollen grains and powders. It is colourless and takes 2–3 days to set.

A.L.P. 1. Immersion Oil.—This is a non-drying mountant particularly useful for slides of the hanging-drop type, when bacteria can be photographed alive. It is a transparent medium of refractive index 1·524 at 20° C. It is available from Messrs. Cooke Troughton and Simms.

Realgar.—This very useful mountant is unequalled for mounting finely marked diatoms, revealing far more detail than any other medium. It is not easy to handle as a mounting medium. The dry specimen is placed on the slide with a piece of clean realgar alongside it. The slide is gradually heated until the realgar melts, when a cover glass is applied. When dry, the usual after-treatment can be carried out.

Green Damar.—Although by no means universally popular, this mountant is preferred by some to the more common Canada balsam. Most stained preparations mount and keep well in this translucent medium. The gum is dissolved in chemically pure benzene, after which it is diluted in resin.

Henry Green Method.—Green damar plays an important part in this method. It is mixed with cumar gum to make a really good dispersing medium.

Xylol.—This has its place in photomicrography as a solvent and clearing agent.

ADDITIONAL STAINS AND ROUTINE METHODS

Bismarck Brown (Aqueous).—Stain for ½–1 minute in a 0·5 per cent solution of Bismarck brown in distilled water, rinse and dry.

Ehrlich's Haematoxylin.—Stain for 20 minutes and wash in running water until the tissues appear blue. Counter-stain for ½–1 minute in eosin (yellow) and rinse in distilled water, passing quickly through the alcohol baths. Alternatively one may counter-stain for ½ minute in 0·5 per cent aqueous Biebrick scarlet, wash quickly with 95 per cent alcohol and finally pass on to absolute alcohol and into xylene, resulting in blue nuclei and yellowish-pink cytoplasm.

Van Gieson's Stain.—This method enables rapid differentiation to be achieved between muscle and collagen. Stain for a period of 4 minutes, rinse in running water and pass straight on to the alcohols. Collagen fibres stain red; muscle and epithelia, yellow.

Masson's Trichrome Method.—This brilliant technique, though not as simple as the Van Gieson method, can be relied upon once the technique has been mastered. Histological and micro-anatomical sections 5–6 microns in thickness respond best. I. R. Baker has modified this stain as follows. Soak for 1 hour in 4 per cent aqueous iron alum. Stain for 1 hour in Heidenhain's haematoxylin and differentiate in alcoholic picric acid until collagen fibres and cytoplasm are completely decolorized, while nuclei still retain the stain. Wash for 5 minutes in running water. Stain the muscle and cytoplasm of the epithelial cells pink in xylidine ponceau and rinse in distilled water. The specimen is now placed in 1 per cent aqueous phosphomolybdic acid and rinsed; the collagen fibres are stained in light green which occupies about 2 minutes, during which time the tissues are rinsed in distilled water for short periods and examined under the microscope. When staining is complete, pass the tissue quickly through an alcohol bath and then into xylene. The final section should give blackish nuclei, green collagen fibres, and the muscle and cytoplasm of the epithelial cells, etc., pink.

HISTOLOGICAL, PATHOLOGICAL AND ZOOLOGICAL METHOD

Volkensky's method is perhaps a little complicated, but nevertheless gives a brilliant tricolour finish. The chromatin is a different colour to the mitochondria and cytoplasm. Fix the section in

Mercuric chloride	5 gm.
Potassium dichromate	2·5 gm.
Sodium sulphate	1 gm.
Distilled water	100 ml.

for 6 hours and when ready for use add 1 ml. of formaldehyde solution (approximately 40 per cent) to each 20 ml. of this fluid. Postchrome for 2 days in a saturated aqueous solution of potassium dichromate at 30° C and wash overnight in slowly running water. Section should be cut 3 or 4 microns in thickness. Place the section on a slide with water, dry off around all edges and flood with a 6 per cent solution of acid fuchsin in aniline water. Place on a hot plate for 3 minutes, after which the slide should be left to cool for about 5 minutes. Lightly wash excess stain off with distilled water and differentiate with aurantia, 0·25 per cent in 70 per cent alcohol, until the cytoplasm is pale yellow while the mitochondria are still bright red. Rinse and pass on into 1 per cent aqueous phosphomolybdic acid for 4 minutes, rinse and stain for 4 minutes in Volkensky's methylene violet. Differentiate in tannin orange until only nuclei are blue and cytoplasm is yellow. Follow by a rinse in distilled water and lightly blot. Dip momentarily in 90 per cent alcohol and transfer to absolute alcohol for 1 minute. Pass section through xylene and finally into the mounting medium, Canada balsam. The final effect is:

Mitochondria,	red;
Chromatin,	blue;
Cytoplasm,	yellow.

Blood Staining.—Prepare a smear in the usual way, allow to dry, fix in solvent methyl alcohol, B.D.H. Stain smears with Jenner's stain (Jenner's stain powder 0·5 gm., solvent methyl alcohol 100 ml.) for 3 minutes in a moist Petri dish. Wash off with distilled water until pink.

Janus Green.—A 0·01 per cent solution should be used for mitochondria (and lepidosomes). At extreme dilutions (0·002 per cent) it is specific for mitochondria.

METHODS FOR PLANT CHROMOSOMES

Navashin's Fluid and Iron Haematoxylin.—Fix for 1–2 days in Navashin's fluid (chromic acid, 1 per cent aqueous solution 15 ml.; glacial acetic acid 1 ml.); immediately before use add 0·25 ml. of a 40 per cent solution of formaldehyde. Wash overnight in slowly running water and stain paraffin sections with iron haematoxylin, as follows: flood the slide with water and soak for 1 hour in 4 per cent iron alum, rinse in water, and stain in Heidenhain's haematoxylin (dissolve 0·5 gm. haematoxylin in 10 ml. of 96 per cent alcohol and add 90 ml. distilled water), rinse and differentiate in 2·5 per cent iron alum solution until only the chromosomes are stained. Wash for five minutes in running water and pass through alcohols and xylene and mount in Canada balsam.

Aceto-carmine.—This is most suitable for the preparation of non-permanent preparations of chromosomes. Simply dip the section in a drop of aceto-carmine,* lay on a slide and cover with a slip. Chromosomes are stained red.

Some of these staining methods are described in a very useful booklet specially prepared for microscopical use by The British Drug Houses, Ltd., Chemicals Group. All these methods have been used by the author and found to be most satisfactory.

FLUOROCHROMES

The fundamental work on fluorochromes was carried out by Dr. H. C. Max Haitinger, of Vienna, who has also introduced many new stains and increased the staining intensity of the existing fluorochromes. These stains, which cover a wide range of colours, provide a means of differentiating tissues as well as detecting tiny quantities of infiltrations or deposit. Furthermore, fluorochromes can be used for histological and bacteriological examination.

NARCOTIZING

It is often necessary to arrest all movement when photographing fast-swimming pond creatures, without disturbing them in any way. The following has been proved to be very useful in this respect:

2 per cent solution hydrochlorate of cocaine	3 parts
Alcohol	1 part
Water , ...	6 parts

* Saturate boiling 45 per cent acetic acid with carmine, cool, then filter.

GLOSSARY OF TERMS

ABBE TEST PLATE. A test slide with a regular array of intersecting lines ruled through a very thin layer of silver, protected by a cover glass. The lines are used in the determination of spherical and chromatic aberrations present in an objective.

ABERRATION, CHROMATIC. The inability of a lens to bring light of different colours to a common focus.

ABERRATION, SPHERICAL. The inability of a lens to bring the marginal and central rays to a common focus.

ACHROMATIC. Partially corrected for chromatic and spherical aberrations.

ACHROMATIC OBJECTIVE. An objective corrected for chromatic aberration in two colours (yellow-green) and for spherical aberration in one colour.

APERTOMETER. A device for determining the numerical aperture of objectives.

APERTURE, ANGULAR. The angle of the cone of light accepted by the objective from a point source. Increasing the angular aperture of an objective automatically increases the amount of light being accepted by the lens, thus increasing the resolving power.

APERTURE, NUMERICAL. The product of the refractive index of the medium between objective and specimen, and the sine of half the angular aperture of the objective. The higher the N.A. the greater the resolving power of the objective.

APLANATIC. A term used to describe a substage condenser corrected for spherical aberration.

APOCHROMATIC OBJECTIVE. An objective which is corrected for chromatic aberration in three colours and for spherical aberration in two colours. These objectives are required for the most exacting work.

APOCHROMATS, SEMI-. Lenses having one or more fluorite components and having correction between that of the achromat and the more expensive apochromat.

ASPHERIC. A term applied to a lens which forms an image in a parabolic surface rather than in a spherical surface. This reduction in spherical aberration is achieved by grinding the margin of one lens surface more than the centre.

BODY TUBE. The tube which carries the draw tube at its upper end and the objective, or objective-holder, at its lower end. The focusing is accomplished by moving this tube up and down with fine and coarse adjustments.

BULL'S EYE. An auxiliary planoconvex condensing lens.

COARSE ADJUSTMENT. The adjustment which moves the body or stage of a microscope relatively large distances.

COMPOUND MICROSCOPE. An instrument with more than one lens system, such as an objective and an eyepiece.

CONDENSER. The condenser focuses the light from the source on to the specimen.

CONDENSER, SUBSTAGE. Directs the light on to the specimen and into the objective. Many types are available, from the

simple Abbe to the complex aplanatic–achromatic suitable for work at the highest magnification.

CORRECTION COLLAR. A collar fitted to an objective whereby the optimum cover-glass thickness may be varied.

COVER GLASS. A very thin glass plate, cut in circles, squares or rectangles, used to cover the specimen, and made in various thicknesses. Thick cover glasses are suitable only for low-power work; the usual thickness for work at high powers is 0·12 mm.

CRITICAL ANGLE. The angle of incidence beyond which light will not pass into a medium of lower optical density.

DEPTH OF FOCUS. The axial distance through an object which may simultaneously be brought into focus in the image. In microscopy it is usually very small; the depth of focus of an objective decreases with increasing N.A. For an objective of $\frac{1}{2}$ in. focal length it is approximately 0·0008 in.

DIAPHRAGM, IRIS. A circular opening of variable aperture.

DIFFRACTION. Interaction between minute structural detail in the specimen and the wave-fronts of the incident light produces diffraction phenomena. If the substage iris diaphragm is not opened sufficiently, spurious diffraction phenomena appear in and around the image.

DISPERSION. The separation of light of different colours on passing from one medium into another of different optical density.

DRAW TUBE. Adjustable tube situated in the top of the body tube.

EYEPIECE. An optical system which magnifies the primary image of the objective forming a virtual image at a distance of 10 in. from the eye.

FIELD. The area of the specimen which is in view at one time.

FILTER. A transparent sheet of colour material which absorbs some part or parts of the spectrum and transmits others.

FINE ADJUSTMENT. The fine-focusing mechanism of the microscope, enabling small adjusting movements to be made.

FOCAL LENGTH. When a parallel beam of light is brought to a focus, the distance of the image from the nearest focal plane within the lens is the focal length of the lens.

HOLOSCOPIC EYEPIECE. An eyepiece manufactured by Messrs. Watson & Sons and suitable for achromatic and apochromatic objectives.

HOMAL EYEPIECE. A compensating eyepiece made by Zeiss; it provides a wide flat field.

HUYGHENIAN EYEPIECE. Consists of two plano-convex lenses with a diaphragm between them.

ILLUMINATION, CRITICAL. An image of the source is focused on the subject.

ILLUMINATION, DARK-GROUND. A means of illumination whereby the specimen is made to stand out as a brightly lit body against a black background. No direct light can enter objective.

ILLUMINATION, KÖHLER. An image of the light-source is formed at the substage condenser iris.

IMMERSION OBJECTIVE. An objective computed to operate with a thin film of oil or water between the front lens and specimen or cover glass. As a rule cedarwood oil is used because its refractive index is similar to that of the crown glass commonly used. An oil-immersion system is sometimes called a homogeneous system.

MECHANICAL STAGE. A microscope stage or attachment which enables controlled traversing of a slide to be accomplished in two directions at right angles to each other.

MECHANICAL TUBE-LENGTH. The length of the body tube from the lower flange of the thread which houses the objective to the upper end of the draw tube. Usually 160, 170 or 180 mm.

MENISCUS LENS. A concavo-convex lens, such as a spectacle lens, can be used as a supplementary lens in ordinary photography.

MICROGRAPH. A free-hand drawing of the image seen through the microscope.

MICROMETER EYEPIECE. An eyepiece fitted with a graticule in the plane of the field diaphragm. The graticule is usually divided into 100 equal divisions.

MICROMETER, STAGE. A microscope slide 3 × 1 in., bearing a 1 or 2 mm. scale divided into 0·01 mm. spaces. Used to determine magnification.

MICROPHOTOGRAPH. A minute image of a large object.

MICROSCOPE. *See* Compound Microscope.

MICROSCOPE, SIMPLE. A single magnifying glass mounted in a simple stand. When placed close to the eye a magnified virtual image is seen.

MONOCHROMATIC LIGHT. Light of one colour, incorporating a narrow band of the spectrum.

NOSEPIECE. A fitting attached to the lower end of the microscope body tube to carry from two to five interchangeable objectives.

NUMERICAL APERTURE. *See* Aperture, Numerical.

OBJECTIVE. The lens system used to form the primary image.

OBLIQUE LIGHT. A narrow beam of light directed at the specimen at an angle to the optical axis. This method, particularly with transmitted light, must be used with care.

OIL IMMERSION. *See* Immersion Objective.

OPTICAL AXIS. The principal axis of a lens or lens system, through the centres of curvature of the faces.

OPTICAL BENCH. A bench (usually of metal) upon which optical components can be moved without disturbing the alignment of the optical axis. Some

microscopes are built upon an optical bench.

PARABOLOID CONDENSER. A condenser specially made for darkground work, having a parabolic reflecting surface.

PARFOCAL. When objectives may be interchanged without altering the focus of the image they are said to be parfocal.

PERIPLANATIC EYEPIECE. An eyepiece which produces a wide flat image. It is fitted with a doublet eye-lens.

PHASE CONTRAST. A discovery of F. Zernike which enables slight differences in optical density or path length to be seen as differences of contrast.

PHOTOMACROGRAPH. An enlarged image of an object, produced without the aid of the microscope.

PHOTOMICROGRAPH. An enlarged image of a minute object photographed through a microscope.

RAMSDEN EYEPIECE. An eyepiece consisting of two plano-convex lenses with their flat sides nearest the objective. This system is known as the positive type because the focal plane is outside the system.

REFRACTION. A beam of light passing through an interface between media of differing refractive indices suffers a change of direction, or refraction.

REFRACTIVE INDEX. The ratio of the sine of the angle of incidence and the sine of the angle of refraction when a beam of white light passes from air into a given transparent medium.

RESOLVING POWER. The ability of a lens to separate the images of closely spaced lines. It is directly proportional to the N.A. of the objective and increases with a decrease in the wave-length of the light used.

SLIDE, MICROSCOPE. The slide of white glass measuring 3 × 1 in. used for mounting the specimen.

SPECTRUM. The radiation over a given range of wave-lengths.

STAGE MICROMETER. See Micrometer, Stage.

STAGE, MICROSCOPE. The platform upon which the microscope slide is placed for inspection. See Mechanical Stage.

SUPPLEMENTARY LENS. A lens of meniscus type, often placed in front of a camera lens to reduce its effective focal length and produce a larger image of the subject. Used in photomacrography.

TUBE-LENGTH, OPTICAL. The distance from the upper focal plane of the objective to the lower focal plane of the eyepiece.

WIDE-FIELD EYEPIECE. An eyepiece fitted with an achromatic doublet eye-lens having the plane side of the lower lens nearest to the objective.

WORKING DISTANCE. The distance between the front lens of an objective and the upper surface of the cover glass when focused on the specimen.

VERTICAL INCIDENT ILLUMINATION. A system of illumination in which the light is projected down through the objective in use on to the specimen and reflected back.

VERTICAL TRANSMITTED ILLUMINATION. A system of illumination in which the light is projected through the specimen from a substage condenser.

BIBLIOGRAPHY

GENERAL

NICHOLLS, J. *Microscopic Photography: Its Art and Mystery*. (F. Cox, London, 1860.)

BANFIELD, A. C. "On a Method of Preparing Stereophotomicrographs." *J. Queckett. Mic. Club* (1909) **10,** 459–464.

HIND, H. L., and RANDLES, W. B. *Handbook of Photomicrography*. (Routledge and Kegan Paul, London, 2nd Ed., 1927.)

LAWRIE, L. G. *Textile Microscopy*. (Benn, London, 1928.)

GARNER, W. *Industrial Microscopy*. (Pitman and Sons, London, 1932.)

BARNARD, J. E., and WELCH, F. V. *Practical Photo-Micrography*. (E. Arnold and Co., London, 3rd Ed., 1936.)

TOBIAS, J. C. *Student's Manual of Microscopic Technique*. (American Photographic Publishing Co., Boston, 1936.)

GATENBY, J. B. *Biological Laboratory Technique*. (J. and A. Churchill, Ltd., London, 1937.)

PEACOCK, H. A. *Elementary Microtechnique*. (Edward Arnold and Co., London, 2nd Ed., 1940.)

STRONG, J., and Others. *Modern Physical Laboratory Practice*. (Blackie and Sons, London, 1940.)

Photomicrography. (Eastman Kodak Co., New York, 14th Ed., 1944.)

SHILLABER, C. P. *Photomicrography in Theory and Practice*. (John Wiley, New York, 1944.)

BAUD, C. A. "Inframicroscopy." *C. R. Acad. Sci.* (1947), **225,** 590–592.

MERTON, T. "Increasing Contrast in Microscopy." *Proc. Roy. Soc.* A (1947), **189,** 309–313.

BAILY, R. "Infra-red Microscopy." *Science* (1948), **108,** 143.

JACKSON, A. *Amateur Photomicrography*. (Focal Press, London and New York, 7th Ed., 1958.)

MILLER, R. F. E. *Practical Photomicrography*. (Percival Marshall, London, 1948.)

DONALDSON, J. C., and SNOOK, T. "Direct Projection of Microscopic Sections in a Modern Lantern." *J. Biol. Photogr. Assoc.* (1950), **18**, 178–179.

GREAVES, R. H., and WRIGHTON, H. *Practical Microscopical Metallography*. (Chapman and Hall, London, Rev. Ed., 1950.)

HEGRE, E. S. "An Embryo Reconstructed from Block-Surface Photomicrographs." *Anat. Rec.* (1950), **106**, 304.

RICHARDS, O. W. "Stereo Photomicrography." *J. Biol. Photogr. Assoc.* (1951), **19**, 7–15.

SANO, M. E., GAULT, E. S., and HENNY, G. S. "Motion Tissue Culture." *J. Biol. Photogr. Assoc.* (1951), **19**, 62–65.

STEVENSON, D. G. "Histological Photomicrography." *J. Sci. Instrum.* (1951), **28**, 275.

JOHNSTONE, G. R. "Absolute Magnification." *J. Biol. Photogr. Assoc.* (1952), **20**, 21–23.

LARUE, M. W. "Cine-Photomicrography." *J. Biol. Photogr. Assoc.* (1952), **20**, 65–71.

LINSSEN, E. F. *Entomological Photography in Practice*. (Fountain Press, London, 1953.)

SCHAEFFER, H. F. *Microscopy for Chemists*. (D. Van Nostrand and Co., New York, 1953.)

WALSH, J. W. T. *Photometry*. (Constable and Co., 2nd Ed., 1953.)

GIBSON, H. L. "Photomacrography of Insects." *J. Biol. Photogr. Assoc.* (1954), **22**, 93–110.

HARKER, A. *Petrology for Students*. (Macmillan, 8th Ed., 1954.)

HEUNERT, HANS H. *Die Nahaufnahme Leitfaben für die Makrophotographie in Wissenshaff und Technik*. (Springer, Berlin, 1954.)

ALLEN, R. M. *Photomicrography*. (D. Van Nostrand and Co., New York, 2nd Ed., 1958.)

NEEDHAM, G. H. *The Practical Use of the Microscope including Photomicrography*. (Thomas, C. C., Springfield, Illinois, 1958.)

GENERAL PHOTOGRAPHY

JACOBSON, C. I. *All About Filters and Your Camera*. (Focal Press, London, 2nd Ed., 1941.)

COOTE, J. H. *Making Colour Prints*. (Focal Press, London, 4th Ed., 1948.)

GLOVER, B. T. J., and WAKEFIELD, G. L. *Perfect Negatives*. (Fountain Press, London, 8th Ed., 1948.)

GLOVER, B. T. J., and WAKEFIELD, G. L. *Print Perfection*. (Fountain Press, London, 4th Ed., 1950.)

CHESTERMAN, W. D., GLEGG, D. R., PECK, G. T., and MEADOWCROFT, A. J. "High-Speed Flash Photography." *Proc. I.E.E.*, (1951), **98** (2), 619–634.

SPENCER, D. A. *Colour Photography in Practice*. (Pitman, London, 3rd Ed., 1952.)

WAKEFIELD, G. L., and SMITH, N. W. *Synchro-Flash Photography*. (Focal Press, London, 3rd Ed., 1952.)

JACOBSON, C. I., and SMETHURST, P. C. *Enlarging*. (Focal Press, London, 15th Ed., 1954.)

HALL, M. L. *Colour Photography for the Amateur*. (George Newnes Ltd., London, 2nd Ed., 1958.)

HALL, M. L. (Ed.) *Newnes Complete Amateur Photography*. (George Newnes Ltd., London, 1958.)

COLOUR PHOTOMICROGPAPHY

ROYER, G. L., and WISSEMAN, M. E. "Colour Photomicrography of Biological Specimens." *J. Biol. Photogr. Assoc.* (1940), **8**, 115–118.

SCHAUB, B. M. "Photographing Small Minerals in Colour." (Deals with photomacrography.) *Photo Tech.* (1940), **2**, 34–37.

LOVELAND, R. P. "Kodachrome Photomicrography of Stained Slides." *J. Biol. Photogr. Assoc.* (1944), **12**, 143–157.

LOVELAND, R. P. "Metallography in Color." *A. S. T. M. Bull.* (1944), No. 128, 19–29.

LOVELAND, R. P. "Metallography in Color." *Metal Ind.* (1945), **67**, 82–85, 98–100, 119–120.

LOVELAND, R. P. "Colour Photomicrography in the Laboratory." *Brit. J. Photogr.* (1945), **92**, 408–410, 418–419.

LOVELAND, R. P. "Colour Photomicrography in the Laboratory." *Anal. Chem.* (1949), **21**, 467–475.

MILLER, O. E. "Colour Temperature. Its use in Colour Photomicrography." *J. Biol. Photogr. Assoc.* (1950), **18**, 150–158.

LAND, E. H. "Colour with Ultra-Violet." *Med. Biol. Illus.* (1952), **2**, 118–123.

NEUBECKER, R. D. "Technique for taking 35-mm Colour Photomicrographs." *U.S. Armed Forces Med. Jour.* (1952), **3**, 1055–1060.

PERRY, W. E. "High Contrast Colour." *J. Biol. Photogr. Assoc.* (1953), **21**, No. 2, 47–48.

COLE, L. G. "Petrologic Concepts Applied to the Microscopy of Normal and Morbid Tissues." *Med. Radiogr. Photogr.* (1954), **30**, 12–19.

Kodachrome and Ektachrome Exposure in Photomicrography. (Eastman Kodak Co.)

Photomicrography, 14th Ed., Chap. XII. (Eastman Kodak Co.)

ELECTRON MICROSCOPY

ANDERSON, T. F. "Stereoscopic Studies of Cells and Viruses in the Electron Microscope." *Amer. Nat.* (1952), **86**, 91–100.

BIRBECK, M. S. C. "Histological Techniques for the Electron Microscope." *J. Roy. Micr. Soc.* (1952), **71**, 421–428.

ORNSTEIN, D., and POLLISTER, W. "Application of Phase Microscopy in Cytology and Electron Micrography." *Trans. N.Y. Acad. Sci.* (1952), **14**, 194–199.

MARESH, C. "Infra-Photomicrography with the Electron Image Converter Tube." *J. Biol. Photogr. Assoc.* (1953), **21**, (3), 14–23.

EXPOSURE IN PHOTOMICROGRAPHY

LOVELAND, R. P. "Determination of Exposure in Kodachrome Photomicrography." *J. Biol. Photogr. Assoc.* (1944), **13**, 79–97.

WARDLAW, F. "Exposure Meter for use in Photomicrography." *I.B.P. Record* (August, 1950), **29**, 186–187.

"Exposure Photometers for Photomicrography." *J. Biol. Photogr. Assoc.* (1950), **18**, 60–64.

TRONNIER, H., and WAGENER, H. H. "New Photoelectric Intensity Meter for Photomicrography." *Mikroskopie* (1951), **6**, 333–339.

LUCEY, E. "Use of the S.E.1 Exposure Photometer for the Direct Calculation of Exposure in Photomicrography." *Research Film* (1953), No. 2, 27–29.

MINEO, J. E. "Rapid Exposures in Colour Photomicrography." *J. Biol. Photogr. Assoc.* (1953), **21**, No. 2, 45–46.

"Universal Exposure Meter for Photomicrography." *J. Biol. Photogr. Assoc.* (1953), **21**, No. 4, 40.

MACHOWICZ, P., and POWELL, E. W. "A Sensitive Inexpensive Light Meter for Photomicrography." *Science* (1954), **120**, 394–395.

SCHENK, R. "Methods of Determining Exposure Time in Photomicrography." *Röntgen u. Laboratoriums Praxis.* (1955), **8**, 205–211.

INTERFERENCE

FIZEAU, H. *C. R. Acad. Sci.* (1862), **54**, 1237–1239.

FABRY, C., and PEROT, A. *Ann. Chim. Phys.* (1897), **12**, 459–501.

MACLAURIN, C. C. "A Numerical Examination of the Optical Properties of Thin Metallic Plates." *Proc. Roy. Soc.* A (1906), **78**, 296–341.

BENOÎT, J. R., FABRY, C., and PEROT, A. "New Determination of the Relationship of Fundamental Wavelength by means of the Metric System." *Trav. et Mem. Bureau Inter. de Poids et Mesures* (1913), **15**, 1–134.

TWYMAN, F., GREEN, A., and A. HILGER, LTD. "Improvements in Finishing Prisms or Lenses or combinations of same and in Apparatus." B.P. 103832 (1916).

FABRY, C. "Monochromatic Light and its use in the Optical Industry." *Revue d'Optique* (1922), **1**, 445–466.

MACNAIR, W. A. "The Fine Structure of Certain Lines and Energy Levels of Cadmium." *Phil. Mag.* (1926), **2**, 613–621.

BURGER, H. C., and VAN CITTERT, P. H. "The Real and Apparent Widths of Spectral Lines." *Z. Physik.* (1927), **44**, 58–69.

RITSCHL, R. *Z. Physik.* (1931), **69**, 578–585.

BUCKLEY, H. E. "Molecular Configuration and its Relation to Modification of Crystal Growth." *Z. Kristallogr.* (1934), **88**, 381–411.

KAYSER, J. F. "The Microphotography of Diamond and Sapphire Surfaces." *Indust. Diamond Rev.* (1944), **4**, 72–75.

TOLANSKY, S. "New Contributions to Interferometry." *Phil. Mag.* (1944), **35**, 120–136, 179–187.

TOLANSKY, S. "The Topography of Crystal Faces." *Proc. Roy. Soc.* A (1945), **184**, 41 and 63.

TOLANSKY, S. "New Contributions to Interferometry." *Phil. Mag.* (1945), **36**, 225–236.

BROSSEL, T. "Asymmetrical Broadening." *Nature, Lond.* (1946), **157**, 623.

GREENHAM, C. G. "Application of Interferometry to Biological Surfaces." *Aust. J. Sci.* (1946), **9**, 26.

TOLANSKY, S., and KHAMSAVI, A. "Cleavage of Calcite." *Nature, Lond.* (1946), **157**, 661–662. ·

TOLANSKY, S., and WILCOCK, W. L. "Topography of Face of a Diamond Crystal." *Nature, Lond.* (1946), **157,** 583.

TOLANSKY, S. "Further Interferometric Studies with Mica." *Proc. Roy. Soc.* A (1946), **186,** 261–271.

TOLANSKY, S. "Multiple Beam Studies in Mica." *Phil. Mag.* (1946), **37,** 390–398.

MERTON, T. "On Interference Microscopy." *Proc. Roy. Soc.* A (1947), **191,** 1–6.

TOLANSKY, S. *Multiple Beam Interferometry of Surfaces and Films.* (Clarendon Press, Oxford, 1948.)

DYSON, J. "A Transmission-type of Interferometer Microscope." *Nature, Lond.* (1949), **164,** 229.

DYSON, J. "An Interferometer Microscope." *Proc. Roy. Soc.* A (1950), **204,** 170–187.

PHILPOT, J. ST. LEGER. "Improvements relating to Interference Microscopy." B.P. No. 645,464 (1950).

SMITH, F. H. "Improvements relating to Microscopy." B.P. No. 639,014 (1950).

KELLER, E. G. "One-Shot Photomicrographic Camera." *J. Biol. Photogr. Assoc.* (1951), **19,** 138–140.

BARER, R. "Interference Microscopy and Mass Determination." *Nature, Lond.* (1952), **169,** 366–367.

BARER, R. "Interference Microspectroscopy." *Nature, Lond.* (1952), **170,** 29.

BARER, R., and ROSS, K. A. F. "Refractometry of Living Cells." *J. Physiol.* (1952), **118,** 38P.

FRANÇON, M. *Rev. Opt.* (Paris) (1952), **31,** 65–86.

WANG, H., and DOOMAN, J. "A Low-Power Photomicrographic Camera." *J. Biol. Photogr. Assoc.* (1952), **20,** 127–129.

BARER, R., ROSS, K. A. F., and TKACZY, S. "Refractometry of Living Cells." *Nature, Lond.* (1953), **171,** 720–724.

BARER, R. "Determination of Dry Mass . . . Living Cells." *Nature, Lond.* (1953), **172,** 1097.

ZERNIKE, F. "How I Discovered Phase Contrast." *Science* (1955), **121,** 345–349.

HALE, A. J. *The Interference Microscope in Biological Research.* (E. and S. Livingstone Ltd., Edinburgh and London, 1958.)

INTERFERENCE FILTERS

LETZER, E. K., and POWERS, S. A. "Interference Filters for Photographic Densitometry." *J. Opt. Soc. Amer.* (1954), **44,** 870–874.

HEAVENS, O. S. "Multilayer Systems, Anti-Reflecting Systems, High-Reflecting Stacks and Interference Filters." *J. Photogr. Sci.* (1956), **4,** 21–24.

LENSES

JOHNSON, B. K. "An Achromatic Objective for use in Ultra-Violet Microscopy." (Fluorite Objectives.) *Proc. Phys. Soc.* (1939), **51,** 1034–1039.

BARER, R. "The Reflecting Microscope." (Speculum Metal Objective.) *Lancet* (1949), **256,** 533–534.

FOSTER, L. V. "Microscope Optics." *Anal. Chem.* (1949), **21,** 432–436.

WASSERMAN, N. G. D., and WOLF, E. "On the Theory of Aplanatic Aspheric Systems." (Reflecting Objectives.) *Proc. Phys. Soc.* (1949), **62B,** 1–8.

MELLORS, R. J. "The Reflecting Microscope." *Science* (1950), **112,** 381–387.

BARER, R. "The Burch Reflecting Microscope." (Speculum Objectives.) *Microscope* (1951), **8,** 242–243.

BUTTERFIELD, J. V. "New Flat-Field Eyepieces for Photomicrography." *J. Biol. Photogr. Assoc.* (1954), **22,** 145–149.

PHASE CONTRAST

ZERNIKE, F. "Transparent Objects." *Physica* (1942), **9,** 686–693.

RICHARDS, O. W. "Phase Photomicrography." *J. Biol. Photogr. Assoc.* (1947), **16,** 29–38.

BARER, R. "Colour Phase." *Nature, Lond.* (1949), **164,** 1087–1088.

LEWIS, S. R., POMERAT, C. M., and EZELL, D. "Tissue Culture." *Anat. Rec.* (1949), **104,** 487–503.

BARER, R. "Learning About the Invisible, Ultra-Violet and Infra-Red Photomicrograph." *Photogr. J.* (1950), **90B,** 83–91.

BENFORD, J. R., and SEIDENBERG, R. L. "Phase-Contrast Microscopy for Opaque Specimens." *J. Opt. Soc. Amer.* (1950), **40,** 314–316.

GRIGG, F. C. "Colour Phase." *Nature, Lond.* (1950), **165,** 368–369.

PAYNE, B. O. "Variable Amplitude and Phase." *J. Roy. Micr. Soc.* (1950), **70,** 225–231.

SAYLOR, C. P., BRICE, A. T., and ZERNIKE, F. "Colour Phase." *J. Opt. Soc. Amer.* (1950), **40,** 329–334.

SEIDENBERG, R. L., and BENFORD, J. R. "Phase-Contrast Metallography." *Metal Progress* (1950), **58,** 725–728.

TAYLOR, E. W. "Ultra-Violet and Infra-Red Phase." *Proc. Roy. Soc.* B (1950), **137,** 332–339.

BENNET, A. H., and Others. *Phase Microscopy.* (John Wiley and Sons Inc., New York, 1951.)

CLIFFE, P. "Motion Photomicrography." *Med. Biol. Illus.* (1952), **2,** 43–50.

WILSKA, A." Observations with Anoptral Microscope." *Mikroskopie* (1954), **9,** 1–80.

RICHARDS, O. W. "Phase Microscopy, 1954–1956." *Science* (1956), **124,** 810–814.

SPECIAL ILLUMINATION

GRANT, J. "Fluorescence Microscopy." *Microscope* (1940), **4,** 146–155.

LOWENSTEIN, E. "Fluorescence Photomicrography." *J. Biol. Photogr. Assoc.* (1944), **12,** 121–129.

COLE, W. V. "Polarised Light Photomicrography." *J. Biol. Photogr. Assoc.* (1948), **16,** 146–150.

BRAEUTIGAM, F., and GRABNER, A. *Mikroskopie: Beitraege zur Fluoreszene-Mikroskopie.* (George Fromme and Co., Wien, 1949.)

DAVIES, H. G., and WALKER, P. M. B. "Apparatus for Ultra-Violet Microscopy of Living Cells." *Photogr. J.* (1950), **90B,** 92–93.

HARTSHORNE, N. H., and STUART, A. *Crystals and the Polarising Microscope.* (Edward Arnold and Co., London, 2nd Ed., 1950.)

MELLORS, R. C., BERGER, R. E., and STREIM, H. G. "Studies with Reflecting Microscope . . . Ultra-Violet." *Science* (1950), **111,** 627–632.

WEBER, J. "Photomicrography with the Concentrated Arc Lamp." *J. Biol. Photogr. Assoc.* (1950), **18**, 127–138.

HARVEY, E. B., and LAVIN, G. I. "Use of Ultra-Violet, Visible and Infra-Red Light." *Exp. Cell Res.* (1951), **2**, 393–397.

BEVIS, R. E., and HETRICK, W. F. "Flash in Photomicrography." *Science* (1952), **115**, 550.

KING, J. "Simplified Techniques . . . Fluorescence Microscopy." *J. Roy. Micr. Soc.* (1952), **71**, 338–341.

SOARES, J. M. P., and DOS SANTOS, E. C. "The Sabattier Effect in Photomicrography." *Microscope* (1952), **9**, 5–12.

MARTS, R. O. "Wood and Fibre Structure by Incident Fluorescence Microscopy." *J. Biol. Photogr. Assoc.* (1955), **23**, 151–155.

MARTS, R. O. "Fluorescence Microscopy for Measuring Fibral Angles in Pine Tracheids." *Stain Technology* (1955), **30**, 243–248.

SPURR, A. R. "Colour Photomicrography of Fluorescent Plant Material." *J. Biol. Photogr. Assoc.* (1955), **23**, 79–85.

INDEX